Barque Picton Castle

Outward bound on an Epic Circumnavigation of the World in May 2010

The ship and her crew will sail 30,000 miles across the oceans of the world, visiting enchanting islands in the tropics, learning the skills of deepwater mariners and the way of a ship sailing a classic square-rigger in the trade winds in this voyage of a lifetime.

Through the Panama Canal on to the Galapagos, across the South Pacific to Pitcairn Island, Mangareva, Tahiti, Rarotonga, Tonga, Fiji, Espirito Santo, Malekula, Pentecost islands and more, through the Torres Strait to Bali, across the Indian Ocean to South Africa; South Atlantic trade wind passage to the islands of the West Indies, north to Bermuda and homeward bound to Lunenburg, Nova Scotia in just about a year.

(902) 634-9984 ~ www.picton-castle.com

Picton Castle Bosun School

advanced ropework & hawsers I proper bosun chair work I tar & oil mixtures I serving I yards I cotton & dacron sail repair I basic sail making I varnish work I basic carpentry I pitching I small boat building I vessel & boat caulking I wire seizings & wire splicing I rigs & rigging I topmasts I and more

For more information, please visit:

www.picton-castle.com/bosun_school

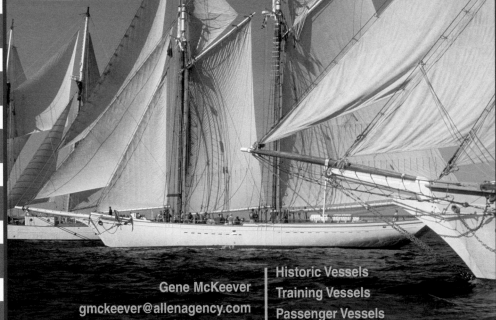

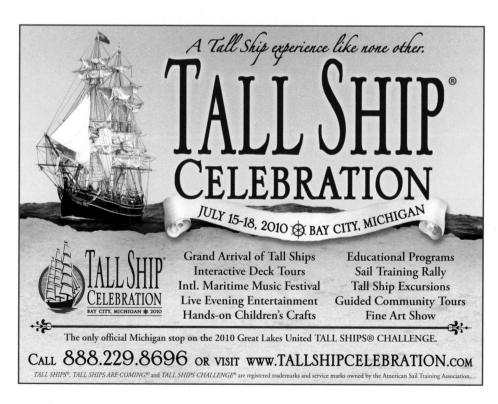

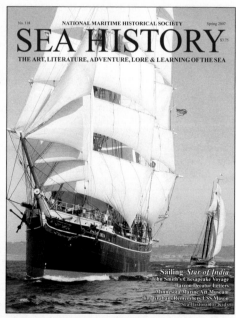

⟨⟩ GREENPORT HARBOR ⟨⟩
LONG ISLAND, NEW YORK

Photo: Gil Amiaga

*An authentic, working deep water port
surrounded by seaside farms & vineyards...*

Official 2004 TALL SHIPS CHALLENGE® Atlantic Coast Port

Tall Ships 2000® Cruise Port

Americas' Sail Host-1995 & 1998

Visit Mitchell Park & Marina.
Deep water dockage, vintage carousel, amphitheater
and boardwalk—all in the heart of the village!
Easy walk to stores, galleries, beach,
hospital & Historic District.

Special arrangements made for visiting tall ships.

Services available include hauling, shipbuilding,
welding, engine repair & hardware.

For more information contact:
Mayor David Nyce, Village of Greenport
236 3rd Street, Greenport, NY 11944
TEL 631-477-0248 • FAX 631-477-1877
or hail the harbormaster on VHF channel 9

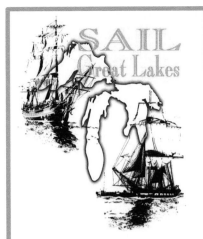

Cruise the Caribbean & Eastern Canada

What passengers are saying...

"We've cruised 2 times now. Caribbean and Newfoundland, and we don't have a favourite! How could we... icebergs, whales and great guests speakers to beautiful beaches, dolphins and amazing snorkeling. One thing is our favourite and it's the sailing. Thanks for life time memories once again." Mike and Sherri C.

"Sailing on the Caledonia was "magical". I can not even begin to tell you how top-notch the crew, the food and the captain were. We were truly pampered!" Susan L.

"This has been such a happy experience - a kind and skillful crew, comfy cabins, fabulous food, fun stuff to do - and a ship with a soul! Thank you!" Bill & Karen M.

Say you saw us here and receive!
$600 off

877-429-9463 / canadiansailingexpeditions.com

American Sail Training Association

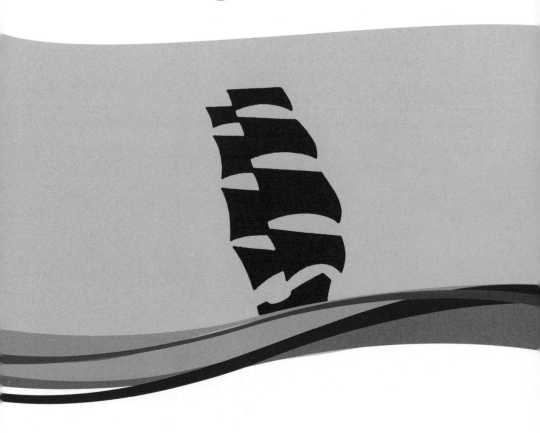

The Mission of the
American Sail Training Association
is to encourage character building
through sail training, promote sail
training to the North American Public,
and support education under sail.

Table of Contents

The mission of the American Sail Training Association is to encourage character building through sail training, promote sail training to the American public, and support education under sail.

American Sail Training Association (ASTA)
PO Box 1459, 240 Thames Street
Newport, RI 02840 USA
Phone: (401) 846-1775 Fax: (401) 849-5400
E-mail: asta@sailtraining.org
Website: www.sailtraining.org

Many of the photographs in this edition of Sail Tall Ships! have been generously donated by:

Thad Koza
Tall Ships Photography
24 Mary St.
Newport, RI 02840 USA
Phone: 401-846-5274
thadkoza@yahoo.com
www.tallshipsinternational.net

MAX
Bywater Lodge-Pierside
Lymington, Hants, ENGLAND
SO41 5SB UK
Phone: + 44-0-1590-672047
max@tallshipstock.com

Matthew Maples
8N246 Cheviot Drive
Bartlett, IL 60103
Phone: 630-707-0632
mfmaples@gmail.com
www.mattmaples.com

Onne van der Wal
Onne van der Wal, Inc.
One Bannister's Wharf
Newport, RI 02840
Phone: 401-849-5556
www.vanderwal.com

The following registered trademarks and service marks are owned by the American Sail Training Association:

Tall Ships®
Tall Ships are Coming!®
TALL SHIPS CHALLENGE®

Sail Tall Ships! A Directory of Sail Training and Adventure at Sea, 18th edition.

Compiled and edited by Lori A. Aguiar, ASTA Director of Operations
Design by Artinium Inc., www.artinium.com
Consulting by Pucino Print Consultants, 631 Fletcher Rd, North Kingstown, RI 02852
Printed in Canada by Dollco Printing, www.dollco.com
ISBN 978 - 0 - 9799878 - 1 - 6
Cover photo: USCGC Barque EAGLE, Photo by Thad Koza

Foreword   By Bert Rogers, ASTA Executive Director

Welcome to the world of seafaring adventure. This book is your portal and your guide to the Age of Sail in the 21st century. You will find within these pages hundreds of sailing ships from North America and the World, each offering its own unique way for you to sign aboard and experience the excitement, the challenge, and the wonder of life at sea.

We call this experience Sail Training, out of respect for the ancient traditions of hands-on learning aboard ship that made able bodied seamen out of landsmen, officers out of seamen, and captains out of officers. Today, when you set sail in an ASTA member vessel, you will indeed *learn* the arts and skills of traditional seamanship, but you will *experience* so much more. In ASTA ships, the voyage is about facing the unknown with courage and confidence, being part of a team that inspires your very best, exploring the vastness and beauty of the ocean world, and living simultaneously with the glory of your sea-borne strength and your inescapable humility at the awesome power of the sea.

These are the core experiences of the ships, people and programs of ASTA. Refreshing indeed, when compared to the noise and distraction that so often dominates contemporary life ashore. Going to sea - whether for a day, a week, a semester or a lifetime - offers a sound alternative, and invaluable life experience in how to find a course and hold it.

So, we hope you will explore these pages with building excitement, until you find the ship and program that best fits your interest, your schedule, and your needs. Then make your voyage, cross your horizons, and take your place among shipmates. Join the unbroken fellowship of seafarers that began with the first reed rafts, and that sails today for people like you.

Bert Rogers, Executive Director
American Sail Training Association

Board of Directors and Staff

Officers
Chairman – Captain Michael J. Rauworth, Esq. – Boston, MA
Vice Chairman – Dr. Eric Shaw, Ph. D. – Newport, RI
Vice Chairman – Mr. Terry Davies – Montreal, Quebec, Canada
Secretary – Captain Christopher Rowsom, Baltimore, MD
Treasurer - Mr. Dexter Donham – Dover, MA
Executive Director - Captain Bert Rogers - Newport, RI

Class of 2011
Captain Les Bolton – Aberdeen, WA
Captain James Gladson – San Pedro, CA
Ms. Susan B. Geiger, Esq. – Washington, DC
Captain Jennifer Haddock - Woods Hole, MA
Mr. Norman Lemley – Arlington, VA
Mr. Paul Madden – Middletown, RI
Dr. David Niebuhr - Yorktown, VA
Mr. Caleb Pifer – Newport, RI
Mr. Barclay "Tim" Warburton IV – Newport, RI

Class of 2010
Mr. Michael Brown – Jamestown, RI
Mr. Robert Frost – White Plains, NY
Captain Deborah Hayes – Newport, RI
Ms. Karen Helmerson – New York, NY
Mr. James Kerr, Esq – New York, NY
Captain Ken Neal – San Francisco, CA
Mr. Dan Stetson – Dana Point, CA
Ms. Alix Thorne – Camden, ME
Mr. F. C. "Bunky" Wichmann – Charleston, SC

Class of 2009
Dr. Raymond Ashley – San Diego, CA
Mr. Daveneet Bakhshi – Boston, MA
Mr. Terry Davies –Montreal, Quebec, Canada
Mr. Kevin Dykema – Bay City, MI
Mr. Richard Hawkins – Hyannis, MA
Mr. James Hiney, Esq. – Middleburg, VA
Mr. John Jamian – Bloomfield Hills, MI
Captain Doug Prothero – Halifax, NS, Canada
Ms. Meghan Wren - Port Norris, NJ

Commodores Council
Mr. Henry H. Anderson, Jr. – Mystic, CT
Mr. Bart Dunbar – Newport, RI
Ms. Nancy H. Richardson – San Pedro, CA
Captain Christopher Rowsom – Baltimore, MD
VADM Thomas R. Weschler, USN (Ret.) – Mystic, CT
CAPT David V. V. Wood, USCG (Ret.) – Newport, RI

National Advisory Board
Captain Richard Bailey – Wellfleet, MA
Mr. Hal Barstow - Anaheim, CA
Ms. Beth Bonds – Mt. Pleasant, SC
Ms. Alice Cochran - San Rafael, CA
Mr. Chuck Fowler – Olympia, WA
Mr. Chris Freeman – Mystic, CT
Mr. Thomas Gochberg – New York, NY
Mr. Andy Hammond - East Boston, MA
Mr. Mike Jehle - Fairfield, CT
Mr. Thad Koza - Newport, RI

Mr. Perry Lewis - Newport, RI
ADM James Lyons - Alexandria, VA
Captain Joe Maggio - Coconut Grove, FL
Mr. Jeff Parker - McLean, VA
Mr. Jed Pearsall - Newport, RI
Mr. Nigel Rowe – Gosport, Hants, UK
Captain Walter Rybka – Erie, PA
CAPT Christopher Sinnett, USCG – Ledyard CT
Mr. Howard Slotnick – Bay Harbor Islands, FL

ASTA Crew
Captain Bert Rogers - Executive Director
Ms. Lori A. Aguiar – Director of Operations
Ms. Jennifer Spring – Operations Coordinator
Ms. Darlene Godin - Office Manager/Bookkeeper
Ms. Patti Lock – TALL SHIPS CHALLENGE® Director
Ms. Erin Short – TALL SHIPS CHALLENGE® Coordinator
Ms. Claudia Bankert – International Ships Liaison

A Brief History of the American Sail Training Association

"This is the Great Purpose of sail training - that the greatest handiwork of man, the sailing ship, shall be borne across the greatest handiwork of God, the sea, to bring together our young people in friendship"

Barclay Warburton III

In the summer of 1972, Barclay Warburton III of Newport, Rhode Island, his two sons, and several friends, sailed his brigantine *Black Pearl* across the Atlantic Ocean to participate in a tall ships race from Cowes on the south coast of England to Malmo in Sweden, organized by what was then known as The Sail Training Association. He was so inspired by the enthusiasm and spirit he saw in that international gathering of tall ships and young people that he set out to create a similar organization in order to bring the same kind of spirit to the United States. Through his efforts, the American Sail Training Association (ASTA) was founded the following year. ASTA soon became the first national association to formally affiliate with what eventually became known as the International Sail Training Association.

The Tall Ships Races in which the *Black Pearl* took part had first been held in 1956, when a London solicitor, Bernard Morgan, had the idea of bringing what he imagined to be the last of the world's great square-riggers together for a race as a last hurrah—a farewell salute—for the Great Age of Sail. A committee was formed, and with the support and assistance of the Portuguese Ambassador in London, a race was organized from Torbay, on England's Cornish coast, to Lisbon, Portugal. Five square-rigged schoolships entered the race: Denmark's *Danmark*, Norway's *Christian Radich* and *Sorlandet*, Belgium's *Mercator*, and Portugal's first *Sagres*. The event proved to be anything but a funeral procession, however, and it has since grown into an annual series that would astonish its original organizers. Today, hundreds of tall ships from around the world come together annually for friendly competition in international and regional Tall Ships Races organized by Sail Training International in Europe and national affiliates such as ASTA. These races, along with waterfront festivals in designated start and finish ports, bring together the ships and young people of most European countries, Russia and the former Soviet states, the Americas, and the Pacific Rim. The key elements uniting these events are an emphasis on youth—from the beginning, tall ship racing rules have required that not less than half those onboard participating vessels be between 15 and 25 years of age— and a formula for rating participating vessels which allows vessels ranging in size from the largest square-riggers down to yachts of 30 or more feet in length.

The American Sail Training Association's efforts in its first decade were primarily focused on organizing tall ships races on the European model, but from the mid-1980s to the mid-1990s, it worked on a multitude of activities broadly aimed at promoting sail training and supporting education under sail in North America. Thus, at the beginning of the 21st century, the American Sail Training Association has evolved into an organizer of tall ships races, a strong industry association for the growing numbers of vessels involved in providing opportunities for people of all ages to take part in deep water sailing experiences, and a public charity which makes sail training more available and affordable for young people.

With an organizational membership of over 200 vessels, the American Sail Training Association serves as a forum for information exchange, professional development, and program standards. Through such initiatives as the Council of Educational Ship Owners, which worked successfully for the passage of the Sailing School Vessels Act of 1982, and the Sailing School Vessels Council founded the following year, ASTA has continued to work with the US Coast Guard and other agencies to create and maintain a friendly regulatory climate for the development of sail training.

Safety at sea has been an enduring emphasis, and in conjunction with the Australian bicentennial gathering of tall ships in Sydney in 1988, a group of ASTA members organized the first international discussion on safety standards and practices, and equipment for sail training programs. Since 1992, ASTA has organized a biennial Safety Forum, which regularly draws professional sail trainers from around the world. Also in the 1980s, ASTA developed the concept of the Sail Training Rally, a competition among crews both at sea and ashore, which provides trainees with an opportunity to demonstrate their seamanship skills in a friendly but competitive format. During shore side events, the general public can observe the sort of teamwork and maritime skills that are learned on board sail training vessels at sea.

Over the years, the American Sail Training Association has undertaken many other projects to meet the needs of a rapidly growing sail training community. These include a variety of publications such as SAIL TALL SHIPS! A Directory of Sail Training and Adventure at Sea, an Annual Conference on Sail Training which attracts international interest and participation, a Billet Bank to assist vessels in finding qualified crewmembers, a growing program of scholarships and grants to support trainees, vessels, and professional crew, and a constantly expanding website. In 2001, building on the spectacular success of Tall Ships 2000®, ASTA launched its most ambitious project to date—the TALL SHIPS CHALLENGE® Series, an annual series of tall ships races and maritime port festivals that informs the general public about tall ships, our maritime heritage, and the incredible power of sail training to change lives.

What Is Sail Training?

In the United States and Canada, there are many sail training vessels which serve as laboratories and classrooms at sea. College and high school students regularly embark on semester-long voyages of offshore discovery while younger children explore local waters on grade school field trips. Water, sediment and biological sampling provide students with tangible lessons in the marine environment as they themselves physically encounter the effect of wind and wave. Formal study aboard a ship is frequently referred to as sea education.

Historic vessels and their reproductions function as interpretive museum exhibits, conducting voyages of outreach to the public. Most North Americans can trace their ancestors' arrival by ship. The last sailing vessel to regularly carry immigrants to America still plies New England waters, now a sailing school vessel, extending her venerable history of more than one hundred years service -- from fishing the Grand Banks to Arctic exploration to African packet. There are reproductions and restorations of ships representative of each of America's naval conflicts. We may board important sailing ships of the American Revolution, the War of 1812, the Civil War and some which played their part in the World Wars. We may experience life at sea aboard Grand Banks fishing schooners, mackerel seiners, oyster boats and whalers, cargo ships, pilot boats, Merchant vessels and immigrant ships. Those pressed into the slave trade. There is not a chapter of our history which does not have a waterborne link. The smell of pine tar and manila, the sounds of a working ship, the view of a whale-spotted horizon from the top of the rig, the motion of a rolling deck -- history is a compelling study of this physical context.

These vessels draw our attention and focus
us on their missions because sailing ships are
powerful icons, symbolizing strength, beauty and
harmony wherever they go.

Other North American ships sail ambassadorial missions for the public they serve, issuing invitations of hospitality and promoting opportunities for economic development. Others sail to save the environment, or to promote international relations through citizen diplomacy, as did a Soviet-American crew sailing past the final sputters of the Cold War. These vessels draw our attention and focus us on their missions because sailing ships are powerful icons, symbolizing strength, beauty and harmony wherever they go. Those who sail know the ocean to be that which connects us to foreign lands -- not a boundary which separates us.

Several American sail training ships serve as treatment centers for adjudicated youth while others provide exclusive corporate team building exercise or offshore adventure travel -- from coastal cruising with gourmet cooking to blue water voyaging. While the clientele could not be more different, these ships are all in the business of enrichment. As diverse an agenda as this may seem at first glance, these ships all provide sail training. The common denominator is that each uses the wind and sea to teach us something else. Sail training, like reading, is not a subject in and of itself. It is a means to an end. A medium. An environment. We at ASTA often say that sail training is not learning to sail, it is learning from sailing. From the ship, from the sea and perhaps most importantly, from yourself.

> Sail training, like reading, is not a subject in and of itself. It is a means to an end. A medium. An environment. We at ASTA often say that sail training is not learning to sail, it is learning from sailing. From the ship, from the sea and perhaps most importantly, from yourself.

A ship at sea has been described as a microcosm of the planet. Resources are finite, waste must be managed responsibly and success depends on one's ability to work as a team. One quickly learns that many hands lighten a load. In a similar way, so do good shipmates -- those who are focused, considerate, and good humored. There is no place on earth which better illuminates leadership qualities, nor marks the path so clearly toward achieving them. The rewards of a smoothly run ship are immediate, obvious and sweetly satisfying. As sailors have said for centuries, take care of your ship and she'll take care of you.

There is no better feeling in the world than coming off an early morning watch having watched the sun rise and helped to scrub everything down for the start of a new day. As you leave the ship in the hands of the next watch you realize how happy you are to see them, and even happier to leave them to it, as you go below for the sort of breakfast you'd never eat ashore and a grateful climb into a narrow berth assuming any angle of heel. Adjusting to sleeping when you can is strangely easy, and you find yourself sleeping easily in your bunk no matter what the time of day or the weather (well, with the occasional notable exception!). You find yourself frequently aware of living completely in the moment, and you take great pride in accomplishing tasks and seeking new challenges for yourself.

Aboard a sail training vessel, as in life, our small piece is a critical part of the whole. The quality of work, and the spirit in which we do it, has a profound effect on the well-being of everyone else aboard. Leadership, paradoxically, is arrived at by learning to take direction, becoming a team player, pulling your share of the load, and being absolutely responsible and dependable. And, learning to depend on the responsibility of others. For no matter what the particular mission of a ship might be, it is essential that she be safely navigated and handsomely attended.

This is true of the larger world, but in the larger world, the quality of our actions are not so immediately apparent. In our day to day lives, most of us do not have at hand accessible evidence of collisions we've safely avoided, environmental conditions we gained advantage from, or courses accurately steered no matter the conditions. Our actions seem at times to be in a vacuum and feedback is often clouded by other issues. It often takes years to measure the efficacy of our navigation and our ability to "hand, reef and steer" our lives. Nor do we often have the simple, yet somehow completely thrilling, affirmation of perfectly set sails in a stiff breeze and a ship "with a bone in her teeth." On a sail training vessel, it's right there. Right now.

For some, sail training offers first time successes. For others, it is a much needed refresher course in life when we find ourselves, for instance, knocking hats off passerby's or staring too long at funeral processions -- which Herman Melville describes as "high time to get to sea" in Moby Dick. For all, sail training offers an absolutely unique experience.

> ASTA member vessels and programs foster opportunities for intensive personal development -- intensive life experience in order to advance leadership development, an utter reverence for nature, a sense of time and place, an appreciation for history, and teamwork ability.

So no, we don't just teach sailing. ASTA member vessels and programs foster opportunities for intensive personal development -- intensive life experience in order to advance leadership development, an utter reverence for nature, a sense of time and place, an appreciation for history, and teamwork ability. Sail training really teaches the qualities of stewardship, resourcefulness, pride, humility, bravery, strength and grace. And we learn to sail, too.

Annual Sail Training Awards

Each year at the Annual Conference on Sail Training and Tall Ships, the American Sail Training Association honors a select group of sail trainers and supporters who have been recognized by their peers and fellow sail trainers for their outstanding contributions to the world of sail training.

The annual award recipients are nominated by the ASTA membership and the final winners selected by the ASTA Board of Directors and staff.

Lifetime Achievement Award

Awarded to an individual who has dedicated his/her life's work to getting people to sea under sail and who has worked to preserve the traditions and skills of sail training.

2007 Lifetime Achievement Award Recipient: Captain Joe Maggio

Captain Joe Maggio has been involved with sail training and the ASTA for over 35 years going as far back as 1976 when he brought his sail training vessel *William H. Albury* to Newport, RI to participate in TALL SHIPS® 1976 - the first Tall Ships® event organized by the newly formed American Sail Training Association. In the years since, Captain Maggio has taken thousands of young people to sea in his "Sea Explorers" program aboard the *William H. Albury* and *Heritage of Miami II*, served many years on the ASTA Board of Directors, and been honored with the ASTA Sail Training program of the Year Award. Captain Maggio currently serves on the ASTA Advisory Council.

2008 Lifetime Achievement Award Recipient: Captain Karl Mehrer

The venue of learning provided by the *Zodiac* has given many students a love and appreciation of not only historic sailing vessels but also an understanding of lifelong learning skills such as teamwork, commitment and cooperation. This would not have happened without the vision, love and dedication of her captain, Karl Mehrer.

Karl is a patient, knowledgeable, and sharing man who knows how to bring out the best in each member of his crew, regardless of their experience and ability. He has inspired many young people to become more involved with sailing, and many have gone on to maritime careers. Karl makes it look easy, bringing together fun and adventure, safety and seamanship, and a joy of sharing the sail training experience.

Lifetime Achievement Award

2008 Lifetime Achievement Award Recipient:
Captain Walter Rybka

A native of Long Island, New York, Captain Rybka developed an early passion for maritime history-a passion he brought to his first post-college job at the South Street Seaport Museum in New York City, where he set about learning seafaring aboard the schooner *Pioneer*. He learned well and became her master before long. In 1977, he joined the project to acquire and restore the barque *Elissa* in Galveston, Texas and in 1979 became Restoration Director, a position he held until 1983. Since those early days, he has exhibited a single-minded passion for preserving, and conveying to future generation, the traditional skills, practices, and techniques of seafaring under sail.

In his own words, he believes that 'the value of preserving anything lies in what it has to teach, and that what ships have to teach is best learned by sailing them,' and he practiced what he preached. In 1991 he was appointed master of the US Brig *Niagara* in Erie, Pennsylvania, and sailed in that capacity until 2001, when he became Director of the Erie Maritime Program at the Pennsylvania Historical and Museum Commission.

Believing that the only way to preserve a historic vessel is to keep her sailing, and recognizing from the outset *Niagara's* safety liabilities, he knew that a strong commitment to sail training was the best way to keep her afloat. As the old saying goes, 'Ships and men rot in port'. He worked single mindedly for nearly fifteen years to change the ship into a better sailing ship, and was the driving force behind converting the vessel into the Coast Guard-certified Sailing School Vessel that she is today, a process that required working to overcome significant bureaucratic and regulatory hurdles. Along the way, he may well have trained more current ASTA skippers and mates in square rig than any other ASTA vessel.

Sail Trainer of the Year

Awarded to an ASTA member whose contribution has been a demonstration of leadership by means of empowerment and inspiration.

2007 Sail Trainer of the Year Award Recipient: Captain Ken Neal

Ken Neal has spent almost twenty years sailing traditional sail-training ships in a variety of rigs, waters, and programs. From a start in sailing the traditional coasting schooners that still ply Maine waters, he moved on to sail training schooners and brigantines, starting a career at the Sea Education Association (S.E.A.) of Woods Hole, Massachusetts where he rose from 3rd mate to Faculty Captain and then Marine Superintendent. During those years, he also worked on other sail training programs and captained the schooners *Californian, Spirit of Massachusetts,* and *Harvey Gamage.* Programs ranged from semester long programs to day sails on the Californian coast, Caribbean waters, and the Eastern Seaboard of the U.S. and Canada.

Eventually Ken worked full-time for S.E.A. as captain of *Westward, Corwith Cramer,* and *Robert C. Seamans.* This position included teaching nautical science courses (accredited through Boston University) in navigation (coastwise and celestial), seamanship, weather, and physics for college students. Ken's last position with S.E.A. was as Port Captain and then Marine Superintendent.

Recognizing the relative lack of sail training opportunities on the West Coast, and particularly Northern California, in 2004 Ken made the commitment to start a new sail training organization based on San Francisco Bay. The result was Call of the Sea, a non-profit educational organization whose mission is "to inspire people of all ages and backgrounds to connect with the sea through educational programs aboard traditional sailing vessels that focus on marine sciences, nautical heritage, the ocean environment and careers in the maritime profession."

Ken has worked tirelessly at the difficult task of building a new sail training organization, and his efforts have been successful. He has assembled a dedicated board of directors and acquired a fine schooner. With Ken at the helm as Executive Director, Call of the Sea now provides seagoing educational experiences to thousands of young people each year, ranging from third-graders teaming up to hoist the mainsail to teenagers making challenging offshore voyages. More information about Call of the Sea and its programs can be found at www.CalloftheSea.org.

Ken's commitment to sail training extends beyond his own organization. He has served ASTA in numerous capacities, with service on its Board and committees, including chairing the Ship Operations and Safety Committee.

Sail Trainer of the Year

2008 Sail Trainer of the Year Award Recipient:
CAPTAIN J. Christopher Sinnett, USCG

As Captain of 'America's Tall Ship', *Eagle*, Chris Sinnett has inspired people of every rank and walk of life, both aboard and ashore. He leads with strength and poise, sharing a sense of awe and respect for the ship and for all who sail her towards her noble mission. Wherever he sails, Chris is the chief ambassador representing excellence in sail training. His welcome of the first group of ASTA Tall Ships® Ambassadors launched a new era in sail training and cooperation with ASTA, ports, youth and the U.S. Coast Guard.

An accomplished seaman with high expectations for all those around him, he's a superb coach and mentor. He delegates without hovering and he reinforces each person's strength. His style develops leadership and followership, resulting in confidence and competence for both individuals and teams.

Chris's goal is clearly to develop qualified successors at every level of the chain of command. He uses every opportunity to encourage progress and recognize achievement. His team management and training skills allow him the satisfaction and reward that is gained from empowering others' success.

Sail Training Program of the Year

Awarded to a current ASTA member program, that significantly contributes to the development of seamanship, navigation skills, teamwork, and leadership skills. The program must be offered aboard a USCG (or national equivalent) inspected vessel, must be offered by certified/qualified personnel, must have clear training goals and curriculum which is compatible to the ASTA sail training logbook and must offer students the opportunity to demonstrate knowledge at sea by participating as active trainees in the running of the vessel.

2007 Sail Training Program of the Year
Award Recipient: *Spirit of Bermuda*

Based on proven world-class Expeditionary Learning methods, *Spirit of Bermuda* takes young Bermudians out of their familiar environments by bringing them aboard ship where they work together to meet specific and very tangible goals. Success in meeting these goals fosters an improved sense of self-worth, and illustrates through self-discovery the importance of leadership and teamwork. Life aboard ship provides the perfect environment for the learning of new personal, social and technical skills.

With a program reflective of Bermuda's make-up by race, gender and private/public school attendance, integrated with formal education and community youth programs and financially self-reliant and fully endowed, *Spirit of Bermuda's* program provides a strong sense of identity for young Bermudians. The ship is a source of pride for the student crew who serve as Bermudian ambassadors in overseas ports.

After just over two years of operation, *Spirit of Bermuda* has provided training for over 700 young people and sailed over 12,000 miles in ten overseas voyages to twelve ports in four countries.

Sail Training Program of the Year

2008 Sail Training Program of the Year
Award Recipient: Privateer *Lynx*

Privateer *Lynx* has successfully completed her 5th annual Pacific sail training voyage to Hawaii from San Francisco. This tall ship voyage is open to young men and women of high school age looking for adventure and the experience of a lifetime. Over 2,100 nautical miles are covered in approximately 16 days. Five students sail with eight professional crew for this incredible sail training experience. This voyage is a fully developed educational program designed to challenge youth and bring them together as a united crew stressing the importance of teamwork and cooperation. As crew in training, students stand watch and learn the many aspects and responsibilities of sailing the vessel and assimilating life aboard the ship. Each trainee aboard is assigned a watch. As a member of that watch, he or she takes part in all aspects of shipboard life: raising, lowering and reefing sails, galley duty, steering, navigating and standing watch.

Log books are issued in which trainees chart their progress through the practical or formal aspects of the training program: rope work and knots, chart work, rules of the road, watch leadership duties, helmsmanship, navigation, theory of sail, history, marine conservation and weather, as well as the progress of the ship and their personal reflections.

Lynx's young crewmembers discover first-hand a rich mix of cultures. They develop leadership skills, confidence, responsibility and personal growth as they respond to unforeseen challenges. Students develop commitment to their small community of co-adventurers while gaining practical understanding of the ethic represented by the ship's motto: "Be excellent to each other and to your ship."

Sea Education Program of the Year

Awarded to a program offered by a current ASTA member which significantly contributed to the educational credibility of programs under sail. The program must be offered in conjunction with a school, school system, school group or other recognized educational institution, must have a clear curriculum of educational goals which are compatible with curriculum goals of traditional schools and must have qualified instructors on a certified vessel.

2007 Sea Education Program of the Year
Award Recipient: Explorer's Program aboard *Alma*

The Explorers Program is a field trip for grades 4-8 that brings students aboard the 117-year-old vessel *Alma* for a four hour sail around San Francisco Bay. Students raise sail under the guidance of the captain and crew, then visit four different education stations. The stations (latitude and longitude, charts of San Francisco Bay, trick at the helm, tools of navigation) are designed to meet California State Standards requirements for Fourth through Seventh Grade curricula, focusing on history, social studies, science, and math.

Accompanying teachers and parents are asked not to interact with the students for the duration of the program. This completely immerses students in the ships' environment and keeps them actively engaged. Students are broken into "crews" at the beginning of the program, giving the students an opportunity to rely on themselves and each other.

Teachers consistently report changes in their classes both during and after the program. Students who don't pay attention in class are alert and active, leaders emerge, and the class has a common experience to which the teacher can repeatedly refer. Explorers is a program that embodies the best traditions of sail training, and gives very young students their first taste of what the sea has to teach us.

Sea Education Program of the Year

2008 Sea Education Program of the Year
Award Recipient: West Island College
International - Class Afloat aboard *Concordia*

A sense of community rests at the heart of all Class Afloat programs; living and working together in pursuit of common goals allows students to develop personal leadership and accountability and to celebrate individual and collective contributions to the school mosaic. With Class Afloat, students are encouraged to stretch themselves outside their comfort zone to embrace global issues and set personal goals, all in a safe and supportive community-oriented environment which inspires both passion and compassion for others and our planet. Class Afloat seeks students who are truly committed to academic excellence, personal integrity and global leadership.

Class Afloat offers challenging academic and experiential programmes which include: High school study at the 10th, 11th and 12th grade levels, Advanced Placement (AP) courses, academic and experiential education with semesters of international travel-study and sail training aboard with the *Concordia*, university academic and travel-study programs through a partnership with Acadia University, academic credit for humanitarian and community service work through partner schools, participation in the prestigious Duke of Edinburgh's Award program and in a myriad of extracurricular activities including athletics, service projects and special interests clubs and individual and group cultural exploration accentuating student travel to more than 20 ports of call worldwide.

All teaching staff are qualified to teach at the secondary or post-secondary level with experience in outdoor experiential education. Professional crew are fully certified and maintain a balance in experience that assures the safe conduct of the vessel.

Volunteer of the Year

Awarded to an ASTA individual member who has significantly advanced ASTA's overall mission.

2007 Volunteer of the Year Award Recipient:
Ron Tasker of Toronto Brigantine, Inc.

Ron Tasker, Vice President (and past President) of Toronto Brigantine, Inc., has worked tirelessly over the past five years to run and rejuvenate the Tall Ship Adventures program at Toronto Brigantines, Inc. Ron, at times single handedly, has taken on trainee bookings, port appearance and group contracts, board meetings, personnel management, banking and a myriad of other tasks. He has motivated the volunteers, and when that didn't work, stepped in and did the job himself. When things seem bleak Ron's typical response is, "Well, we'll just have to do it anyway"! Without exaggeration, Ron Tasker has kept Toronto Brigantine Afloat!

Port City of the Year

Awarded to a city which has demonstrated significant support of ASTA or an ASTA Member Organization and who has furthered public recognition of sail training.

2007 Port City of the Year Award Recipient:
Norfolk, Virginia

2008 Port City of the Year Award Recipient:
Tacoma, Washington

The Perry Bowl

**Awarded to the top finishing ASTA member vessel in the
TALL SHIPS CHALLENGE® Race Series.**

2007 TALL SHIPS CHALLENGE® Atlantic Coast
Perry Bowl Recipient: *Tarangini*

2008 TALL SHIPS CHALLENGE® Pacific Coast
Perry Bowl Recipient: *Lynx*

Special Recognition Award 2007

Captain Joe Davis, Dr. Robin Wallace,
Perry Lewis, Bart Dunbar

For 35 years, the American Sail Training Association has made a difference in young people's lives! Our voyage began in 1973 when Barclay H. Warburton III and a group of Newport, RI maritime leaders founded the American Sail Training Association in the aft cabin of his brigantine *Black Pearl*. What began as a bold vision has evolved into an international force for youth education and character development and the largest Sail Training Association in the world. Aboard traditionally-rigged tall ships, youth of all ages, drawn from every walk of life, are provided sailing adventures to challenge themselves to become more productive people. ASTA and sail training is about changing lives!

The American Sail Training Association is pleased to honor with special recognition our founding fathers: Barclay Warburton III, Russell B. Brown, Joseph C. Wylie, Norris D. Hoyt, Robin G. Wallace, Joseph Davis, Perry Lewis, and Bartlett S. Dunbar.

Special Recognition Award 2008

Henry H. Anderson, Jr.

Henry H. Anderson, Jr. received ASTA's Lifetime Achievement award in 1998. We often joke that after an individual receives the Lifetime Achievement Award, they tend to take a step back from the organization. However, Harry Anderson has done just the opposite. Since being presented with his award ten years ago, he has continued to give his time, energy, ideas, and financial support to ASTA and the world of sail training.

Harry grew up sailing in Oyster Bay on Long Island, New York. He quickly rose to the top of the local, regional and national sailing circuits. He sailed for both his prep school as well as Yale University. He went on to become Commodore of the Sewanhaka Yacht Club, and subsequently, Commodore of the prestigious New York Yacht Club (NYYC). He has been involved with several America's Cup campaigns for the NYYC, and calls some of the countries most accomplished sailors his friends. He has won numerous awards in the racing community, held international governing positions, and has supported college sailing programs for half a century. In addition to yachting, Harry is a founding member of ASTA, served many years as chairman of it's board, and founded the Henry H. Anderson, Jr. Sail Training Scholarship Program.

For many years, Harry has offered his downtown Newport home to house the ASTA summer interns - welcoming them into his home, preseting them with the keys, then asking them to not "burn down my house" - as he would leave the following morning to spend the month at his summer home in Canada! This simple example truly underscores Harry's incredible kindness, and generosity.

The American Sail Training Association is pleased to honor with special recognition one of our most dedicated and steadfast supporters, Henry H. Anderson, Jr.

ASTA's TALL SHIPS CHALLENGE® Series

Bermudan Sloop

The TALL SHIPS CHALLENGE® Race Series is a series of sailing races, cruises, crew rallies and maritime festivals organized by the American Sail Training Association in conjunction with United States and Canadian ports on the Pacific and Atlantic Coasts of North America and in the Great Lakes. Traditionally-rigged sailing vessels from Canada, the United States and many other countries are crewed by young people (either civilians or cadets) ages 13 - 25 who are engaged in sail training programs under the supervision of captains and professional crewmembers.

TALL SHIPS CHALLENGE® Series

The TALL SHIPS CHALLENGE® Race Series began in 2001 on the Great Lakes. Thirty vessels from six countries, and 1,000 sail trainees and cadets participated in the races, sail training rallies and port festivals in seven United States and Canadian ports. Detroit and Windsor celebrated their 300th Anniversary; additional ports were Kingston and Port Colborne, Ontario; Cleveland, Ohio; and Bay City and Muskegon, Michigan.

The 2002 series was sailed on the Pacific Coast of North America. Sixty vessels from seven countries participated in the series which included port festivals in Richmond, British Columbia; Seattle, Washington; San Francisco and Los Angeles, California. Races were sailed from the mouth of the Strait of Juan de Fuca to San Francisco and then on to Los Angeles. More than 1,200 sail trainees enjoyed the experience.

The 2003 series was again on the Great Lakes. Twenty-seven vessels from India, the Netherlands, British Virgin Islands, United States and Canada participated. Port festivals were held in Cleveland and Toledo, Ohio as part of the Ohio Bicentennial; Chicago, Illinois; Muskegon and Bay City, Michigan; and Sarnia, Ontario. Four races were held between ports and more than 1,000 trainees enjoyed the races and cruises aboard vessels in the fleet. Millions of spectators came to the city waterfronts to see the vessels and talk with their crew/trainees to learn about life under sail and the opportunities to sail on ASTA member vessels.

The 2004 TALL SHIPS CHALLENGE® Race Series brought vessels together from ten different countries: Belgium, Brazil, Canada, the Cook Islands, Mexico, Poland, Romania, the United Kingdom, the United States, and Uruguay. Across 2,300 nautical miles these traditional sailing vessels tested their crews in

Are you ready...

TALL SHIPS CHALLENGE® Series

friendly competition. The sailors aboard proudly displayed their ships to fascinated crowds in a dozen ports between race segments. Under blistering Florida sunshine and through impenetrable Nova Scotia fog, the ships' crews led their trainees in every aspect of running the vessels. Hand in hand with learning the ropes, the ships promoted team effort, responsibility, and personal development.

The 2005 TALL SHIPS CHALLENGE Race Series returned to the Pacific Coast. Seven United States and Canadian ports and nearly sixty traditionally-rigged sailing vessels from Canada, the United States, Mexico, New Zealand, Russia and other countries took part.   Ports included Victoria, Vancouver and Port Alberni, British Columbia; Tacoma, Washington; Channel Islands Harbor, Oxnard; Los Angeles and San Diego, California.

For the third time, the 2006 TALL SHIPS CHALLENGE® Race Series sailed into the Great Lakes. The fleet started in Cleveland, Ohio, raced to Bay City, Michigan, sailed to Green Bay, Wisconsin and finally were welcomed by over one million people in Chicago, Illinois. Throughout the summer, 22 vessels from the United States, Canada, Cook Islands and British Virgin Islands, took trainees on board to sail and show their competitive spirits in the Great Lakes.

The 2007 TALL SHIPS CHALLENGE® Race Series visited the Atlantic Coast ports of Charleston, South Carolina; Norfolk, Virginia; Newport, Rhode Island and Halifax, Nova Scotia. Participating vessels came from India, Indonesia, the Netherlands, England, Germany, Colombia, Brazil, Uruguay, France, Canada and the US. The ships were gorgeous, the crews enthusiastic and the public showed their support by the thousands.

for the Challenge?

The maritime festivals in each host port give visitors a chance to board the vessels and meet the crew and trainees and learn about the many varied opportunities to sail and travel on ASTA member vessels.

Racing is one of the most important components of the series. Historically, when two or more sailing vessels are found to be heading in the same direction, an impromptu race almost always ensues. The crews pay closer attention to the other ships and to the trim of their own sails in hopes of outdoing their counterparts.

But how can you compare the racing of a 60-foot sailboat with a 240-foot sailing ship carrying 10 times as much sail area? A special rating system developed in the European tall ships races is used to assign vessels of any size a relative performance factor. This gives all vessels an equal chance of winning if they are sailed well. Before the series starts, six pages of hull, rigging and sail measurements for each vessel are submitted to Sail Training International headquarters in England. They compute Time Correction Factors (TCFs) for each vessel using a program that has been fine-tuned over many years of competition. After each race, the ASTA race team multiplies the time it takes for a vessel to complete the course – its elapsed time – by its TCF in the race to determine the corrected time; corrected times are then compared to determine final standings.

Safety at sea is critical and each participating sailing vessel has been inspected and certified for its intended use either by a national maritime authority (the Coast Guard in the US) or by an internationally-endorsed society. At the beginning of the season, the safety equipment on each vessel is double-checked by the ASTA race team and any discrepancies are remedied prior to the first race.

While underway, racers use VHF or SSB radio to keep in contact once or twice daily with the race communications officer on the escort vessel and often with the ASTA race office by satellite-assisted email.

When the series starts, it is likely that not every trainee berth will have been spoken for and interested youth are encouraged to sail in a race or cruise between host ports. ASTA has a scholarship program for eligible youth. More information is available at www.sailtraining.org. Berths are also available for adults on a number of the participating vessels.

Since the first TALL SHIPS CHALLENGE® Race Series in 2001, ASTA and the host cities have strived to bring the experience of sail training to the North American public. As part of its continuing mission to encourage character building through sail training, both trainees and visitors have an opportunity to learn about life at sea aboard a tall ship. Whether it is learning to sail for the first time or learning about local maritime history, the TALL SHIPS CHALLENGE® Race Series brings to the public the opportunity to see and touch history. In this way, we can further our mission of education under sail through the unique experience that the TALL SHIPS CHALLENGE® Race Series offers to youth of all ages.

TALL SHIPS CHALLENGE®
Pacific Coast 2008

Hawaiian Chieftain

Irving Johnson

Lady Washington

Spirit of Dana Point

Seven ports along the Pacific Coast played host to the TALL SHIPS CHALLENGE® Race Series this summer. The Race Team and fleet of tall ships started in the Pacific Northwest surrounded by snowcapped mountains and favorable winds. From there, the fleet headed down the coast to the vibrant and bustling city of San Francisco, California, and then spent the month of August sailing and racing along the gorgeous Southern Californian coast.

Thirty-two vessels, some from as far away as New York, Connecticut and the British Virgin Islands, sailed into the spectacular Inner Harbour in Victoria, British Columbia. Outside of Victoria, with the Olympic Mountains rising majestically in the distance across the Strait of Juan de Fuca, the first race of the TALL SHIPS CHALLENGE® series pitted seven diverse sail training vessels against each other in a 16nm sprint to Port Angeles, Washington, with the sleek and quick *Lynx* the winner.

From Victoria, the fleet made their way to Tacoma, Washington, ASTA Port of the Year in 2005, for the Fourth of July weekend. Dazzling fireworks lit up the night on July 4th as revelers watched the display from the decks of "America's Tall Ship", the Coast Guard sail training vessel, Barque *Eagle*. The ships then headed back up to Canada to the two-time host city of Port Alberni, British Columbia.

For the second race of the series, the Canadian Navy's sail training vessel, HMCS *Oriole*, and the privateer *Lynx* raced the 740 nautical miles from Port Alberni, British Columbia to San Francisco, finishing under the Golden Gate Bridge within sight of each other. The San Francisco festival was spread out along the historic Embarcadero, allowing visitor's ample access to the ships while the crews were able to fully enjoy the downtown area of this exciting city.

From foggy San Francisco, the ships sailed down to Channel Islands Harbor in the seaside city of Oxnard, California. The third race of the series was also completed en route between *Lynx* and the USCG Barque *Eagle*, and ended in an upset when the *Eagle* beat the previously undefeated *Lynx*.

The fourth and final race of the series was sailed between *Californian*, *Seaward* and *Lynx*, with *Seaward* the winner. The ships arrived in San Pedro (Port of Los Angeles) with a spectacular Parade of Sail and for the next few days, visitors were able to board the ships berthed along a half mile of downtown waterfront.

Zodiac

The final port of the TALL SHIPS CHALLENGE® Race Series was San Diego. The downtown venue was thronged with visitors eager to board the fleet of 25 vessels. A new addition to the fleet was the Colombian Naval ship, *Gloria*, which greeted Parade of Sail spectators with an enthusiastic display of national pride. As she sailed in, the cadets were lined up on the yards (all the way to very top of the masts!), singing the national anthem. Local Colombians thronged the pier, singing along to the music and enthusiastically waving the Colombian colors.

Californian

We had a great time this summer and were able to experience some truly unique aspects of the Pacific Coast. The hospitality and genuine enthusiasm displayed by the host cities for the tall ships and their crews will make this a summer we won't soon forget. We met so many incredible, generous people along the way that 2011 can't come soon enough!

Lynx

TALL SHIPS CHALLENGE.

Bounty

Eagle

TALL SHIPS® ATLANTIC CHALLENGE 2009

Tecla

On a spectacular July day, the TALL SHIPS® ATLANTIC CHALLENGE fleet set their sails and departed Boston, Massachusetts for the sixth host port in the transatlantic series, Halifax, Nova Scotia. For the past three weeks, the fleet had been hosted first by Charleston, South Carolina and then by Boston. In between the port events, nine tall ships representing seven countries raced up the coast braving dicey weather, doldrums and heat. After years of careful planning, hundreds of invitations and thousands of nautical miles, the TALL SHIPS® ATLANTIC CHALLENGE had finally begun.

Urania

Billed as "the race of the decade", this trans-Atlantic event was the culmination of years of hard work on both sides of the pond. Working with Sail Training International (STI), based in Gosport, United Kingdom, the American Sail Training Association (ASTA) eagerly welcomed the international fleet of tall ships to the Eastern shores of the United States.

Capitan Miranda

Arriving from the tall ships event in Bermuda, eighteen vessels berthed along the waterfront in Charleston, South Carolina. Despite heat in the high nineties, thousands of people showed up to board vessels representing Russia, Romania, Belgium, the Netherlands, Uruguay, Bermuda, England, France, Germany and the United States. An international soiree was thrown one night and featured ship tours, food, drinks, and live music and entertainment. It was a warm and wonderful night that highlighted the majesty of the tall ships and their crews.

Virginia

The Parade of Sail out of Charleston was lovely with crowds lined up all along the harbor and surrounding islands, bidding a fond farewell to the tall ships. All of the sailors were the recipients of that famous Southern Hospitality that Charleston is best known for and many were sad to leave. Starting in the late afternoon, the ships made their way out of the harbor behind the U.S. Coast Guard Barque *Eagle* and ultimately followed by the *Spirit of South Carolina*. There were hundreds of spectator boats, many more than was expected considering it was a sultry Monday afternoon. As the ships made their way past Fort Sumter and out to sea, the spectator boats stayed behind in the harbor, forming a forlorn line of goodbyes. As the ships mustered for the start, raindrops began to fall and the weather forced the vessels to take their own time at the race start.

Ten days later, the ships arrived at Boston Harbor for the Sail Boston event. Thirty five vessels lined the harbor and millions of people came down to the waterfront. Five perfect summer days ensured that the event was a complete success. Vessels representing Argentina, Portugal and Brazil joined the fleet that had sailed up from Charleston. Boston is a city rich in maritime history and the tall ships fit smartly into the harbor view. Night receptions on board vessels filled the air with laughter and music, while the ships looked beautiful as their rigging was lit with strands of light.

Early on a Monday morning, the ships slipped out of their berths and headed north to Canada for the port event in Halifax, Nova Scotia. From there, they participated in the final leg of the TALL SHIPS® ATLANTIC CHALLENGE as they raced across the Atlantic to Belfast, Northern Ireland for the conclusion of the 7,000 nautical mile trans-Atlantic odyssey that started in May in Vigo, Spain.

Concordia

Cisne Branco

Picton Castle

Europa

Sagres

TALL SHIPS® ATLANTIC CHALLENGE 2009 Race Results

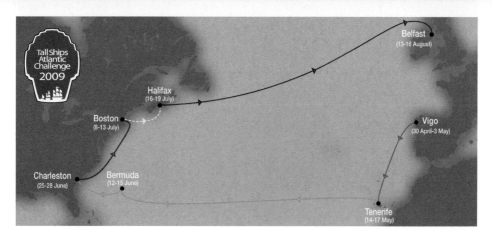

Overall Race Results-TALL SHIPS® ATLANTIC CHALLENGE 2009

Race One: Vigo, Spain to Tenerife, Canary Islands

Class A&B
1st - Tecla (NETH)
2nd - Kruzenshtern (RUS)
3rd – Jolie Brise (UK)

Class D
1st – Rona II (UK)
2nd – Urania (NETH)
3rd – Xsaar (BEL)

Race Two: Tenerife, Canary Islands to Bermuda

Class A&B
1st – Jolie Brise (UK)
2nd – Tecla (NETH)
3rd – Kruzenshtern (RUS)

Class D
1st – Xsaar (BEL)
2nd – Peter von Danzig (GER)
3rd – Rona II (UK)

Race Three: Bermuda to Charleston, South Carolina, USA

Class A
1st – Capitan Miranda (URU)
2nd – Europa (NETH)
3rd – Mircea (ROM)

Class B
1st – Pride of Baltimore II (US)
2nd – Tecla (NETH)
3rd - Jolie Brise (UK)

Class D
1st – Rona II (UK)
2nd – Xsaar (BEL)
3rd – Peter von Danzig (GER)

Race Four - Charleston, SC, USA to Boston, Massachusetts, USA

Class A
1st – Europa (NETH)
2nd – Mircea (ROM)
3rd – Eagle (US)

Class B
1st – Tecla (NETH)
2nd – Spirit of Bermuda (BER)

Class D
1st – Rona II (UK)
2nd – Urania (NETH)
3rd - Fazisi (USA)

Race Five: Halifax, Nova Scotia, Canada to Belfast, Northern Ireland

Class A
1st - Cisne Branco (BRAZ)
2nd - Europa (NETH)
3rd - Capitan Miranda (URU)

Class B:
1st - Tecla (NETH)
2nd - Jolie Brise (UK)
3rd - Etoile (FRA)

Class D:
1st - Rona II (UK)
2nd - Urania (NETH)
3rd - Peter von Danzig (GER)

Overall Winner for entire series: Tecla (NETH)

Great Lakes United
TALL SHIPS CHALLENGE® 2010

DULUTH, MINNESOTA
July 29 to August 1

TORONTO, ONTARIO
June 30 to July 4

GREEN BAY, WISCONSIN
August 12 to August 15

BAY CITY, MICHIGAN
July 15 to July 18

CHICAGO, ILLINOIS
August 26 to August 30

CLEVELAND, OHIO
July 7 to July 11

Great Lakes United
Union St-Laurent Grands Lacs

TALL SHIPS CHALLENGE 2010

The American Sail Training Association has partnered with Great Lakes United to bring a fleet of international tall ships to the Great Lakes, the world's second largest body of fresh water, as part of the Great Lakes United TALL SHIPS CHALLENGE® 2010 race series. Join us as the tall ships race through all five Great Lakes making port appearances in cities throughout the US and Canada. Two important initiatives sail along with the tall ships: water conservation education and youth sail training!

Official Host Ports

Toronto, Ontario: June 30 - July 4

Cleveland, Ohio: July 7 - 11

Bay City, Michigan: July 15 - 18
2001/2006 ASTA Port of the Year

Duluth, Minnesota: July 29 - August 1

Green Bay, Wisconsin: August 12 - 15

Chicago, Illinois: August 26 - 30
2003 ASTA Port of the Year

For information on how you can get involved, contact the ASTA office or visit our website at www.sailtraining.org

What Did YOU Do On Your Summer Vacation?

From the Logs of the ASTA Summer Interns

Each summer during the TALL SHIPS CHALLENGE® Race Series, the American Sail Training Association offers a team of young people the opportunity to serve as interns with the ASTA Race Team. Throughout the course of the summer series, the interns assist the race director, work in the race office, man the ASTA information booths, interact with the participating vessels and their crews and trainees, the port organizers and volunteers, and represent ASTA to the hundreds of thousands of people who come out to see the tall ships. Not to mention, sailing! Long days and hard work are a part of the job - but so are enduring friendships and memories that will last a lifetime. Since the first TALL SHIPS CHALLENGE® Series in the summer of 2001, young people from as far away as Japan and the United Kingdom, as well as Canada and the United States have had the chance to experience the CHALLENGE from this unique perspective.

2008 Summer Intern - Karen Quinn

I just graduated from Colgate University with a major in English and a minor in Caribbean Studies. I have been in love with sailing since my grandfather taught me to sail our sunfish on Little Lake Sunapee in New London, NH. Once I got a taste of the feel of the wind and spray in my face, I was hooked. As a result, I chose to build a 12- foot Shelback Dingy for my senior project in high school, and I spent a week that summer taking certification courses with the ASA. I've spent subsequent summers working for a charter yacht company, working as second mate on a 62-foot Swan, and selling tickets for excursions sailing out of Newport, RI. While I was at Colgate, I participated in a SEA Semester, studying Caribbean natural history, navigation, and oceanography on the *Corwith Cramer*, a 134-foot steel brigantine built as a research vessel. I'm looking forward to my internship with ASTA as a chance to combine my love of sailing, my passion for traveling (I spent three weeks in Asia between graduation and the beginning of my internship!), and my interest in travel writing.

Sailing with Elmo to Vancouver Island

Jesse and I clambered aboard the *Lady Washington*, or *"Lady,"* as she is so affectionately called in the tall ships circuit, and prepared ourselves for the transit back to Vancouver Island. We introduced ourselves to the captain and crew, who welcomed us very warmly with delicious dinner and lively conversation.

I have learned by hopping from ship to ship over the course of this summer that each vessel has its own unique personality, and *Lady* is no exception. I knew we were in for a treat when a petite, pretty brunette approached us and breezily introduced herself as "Bilgey." The captain, too, welcomed us with a friendly smile and a firm handshake, introducing himself matter-of-factly as Evil. Soon, we were chatting and laughing with Elmo, the tall, wiry engineer wearing oversized woman's sunglasses; Skook, the dynamic ship's cook who enjoys dancing and singing in the galley; Preston, a young man from Juneau, Alaska, whose preoccupation with "delicious hot wings" was a constant topic of ridicule; and Beth, the exasperated –but ever gracious –stewardess. I was delighted to join the cast of characters as we drifted away from Tacoma with a magnificently clear view of Mt. Rainier on the horizon. I climbed up on deck for my first watch at midnight that night. The four hour period drifted by as we discussed our favorite types of hot wings (Preston, of course, was in my watch group) while we quietly marveled at Seattle's glowing skyline off our starboard beam. I took my first shot at tiller steering under the supervision of my watch leader, Tim, who patiently guided me through the delicate process of steering the enormous ship.

When it was finally time to retire below decks, I regretted not bringing a warmer sleeping bag as I shivered in my bunk, trying to catch some much-needed shut-eye before breakfast. But in the wee hours of the morning, I came to fully appreciate my newfound family aboard the *Lady* as Skook lent me his warm, furry "transit hat" to keep for the rest of the trip, and Rob, the first mate, gingerly draped a wool blanket over me while I slept. Even as we headed into thick fog and high seas the next couple of days, I knew I had found a safe place to call home.

Saw Mills and Steam Trains in Port Alberni

Port Alberni, a quaint little mill town tucked away in the rugged wilderness of Vancouver Island, has all the heart and spirit of a city ten times its size. Beginning with the magnificent mountain panoramas at every angle, and ending with the unparalleled small town hospitality, Port Alberni encapsulates everything a Tall Ships port should.

When the ships arrived on Thursday, we attended a captain's reception at an old saw mill, where we were welcomed by the mayor of Port Alberni himself. The town arranged for transportation to the event aboard a steam engine train, with an energetic engineer narrating along the way. As we crept slowly up the hills and deeper into the evergreens, the air smelled fresh and clean, and we reclined in our seats and enjoyed the incredible views. Every person we passed waved jubilantly at the little train making its way slowly along the tracks. The event itself was catered by neighbors and friends of tall ships liaisons, and we sipped on native British Columbian wine from a local vineyard while chatting with the elated inhabitants of the surrounding area.

After a brief meet and greet, the captains were each formally presented with a cedar plank for salmon cooking, and given the chance to speak to the crowd. All of the captains agreed that Port Alberni deserves the highest praise for hosting the tall ships, and thanked the local people for their generosity and warmth. We will be sad to see the Port Alberni event come to a close tomorrow, as we board the Canadian naval vessel HMCS *Oriole* for the long transit to San Francisco.

A funny thing happened on my way to San Pedro

Early Monday morning, Jesse and I departed Channel Islands Harbor aboard *Lynx*, sailing in tandem with *Bounty, Seaward*, and *Californian* on our way to safe anchorage at Santa Cruz Island. Soon after getting underway, however, *Bounty's* crew found the wind unfavorable for square-rigging, so they furled her sails and motored off into the distance, leaving *Californian, Seaward*, and *Lynx* to coast side-by-side under moderate wind for most of the afternoon.

As the three ships approached the protected harbor on the northern side of the island, the trusty breeze died down considerably, and *Californian* and *Seaward* announced over the radio that they would surrender to the evening lull and motor the rest of the way into anchorage. Unwilling to strike sail just yet, Captain Craig and our *Lynx* crew bid farewell to the other two ships, and continued on to the eastern coast of the island in search of stronger winds.

Captain Craig assigned me to the helm just as we rounded the eastern tip of the island and our sails began to fill. The harsh California sunlight had waned to a rich, golden glow that bathed the dramatic, rocky coastlines of the Channel

Islands in magnificent late afternoon chiaroscuro. With orders to steer "full and by," Captain Craig left it to me to find *Lynx's* delicate point of balance on a close-haul. I used the same skills that I learned sailing my grandfather's 12-foot Sunfish to maintain equilibrium between the schooner's massive sail-area and her seemingly unfathomable keel. I concentrated on keeping the helm from turning up to weather and soon we were heeling over as the weight of the evening breeze pressed against our sails.

We spotted *Bounty* on the horizon, making her way to anchorage from the east, and Captain Craig ordered me to sail out to greet her. We tacked back and forth, beam-reaching on alternate port and starboard tacks, all the time getting closer and closer to *Bounty*. We tacked one final time and Captain Craig took over the helm as I rushed forward to grab my camera which was stowed in the foc'sle. Everyone gathered on the starboard side as we blasted by *Bounty,* only about twenty feet off our beam, waving and shouting to our friends up in the rigging.

Still reeling from our exciting fly-by sail, we turned *Lynx* towards the anchorage. We rounded the eastern tip again, this time from the south, and approached the harbor under full sail. We quickly lost momentum, however, as the wind died down and our sails began to luff in the protected harbor. Though we gradually slowed to a gentle float, the *Lynx* crew was too proud to switch on the ships' motor in front of *Californian* and *Seaward*, who had surrendered over an hour ago to dying winds. Saul, the first mate, thus ordered six of the crew (myself included) to tie a line to *Lynx's* bowsprit, and row the 100-ton ship the rest of the way with the wooden dinghy. When we had successfully rowed the ship to its anchorage, we cruised laps around *Seaward* and *Californian*, and their crews gathered on deck and applauded our efforts.

What a day! Exhausted from the exhilarating afternoon, we chowed down on dinner, and quickly retired to our bunks. My arms ached and my head spun as I struggled to fall asleep that night, already looking forward to whatever adventures the next day might have in store.

2008 Summer Intern - Jesse Kumbera

Growing up in a nautical family, I have always been fascinated by the sea. But my armchair sailing with authors like C.S. Forrester and Alexander Kent was no longer sufficient. During high school, when my insatiable wanderlust and curiosity finally took control, I set off on a missions trip to Malawi, Africa. Since then, my life has been one adventure after another. After finishing high school in Bellevue, Washington, I moved to Fullerton, California where I spent my days in class and my evenings and weekends working at the Disneyland Resort. This May, I completed my Bachelor of Arts degree in Psychology at Hope International University. However, much of my senior year was spent traveling and studying abroad culminating in a global circumnavigation with Semester at Sea. In addition to traveling at every chance I get, I also love sailing, flying, dancing, acting, and chasing my army of siblings about the house. In fact, one of the driving forces in my life is my abnormally large and complicated family. As the oldest of 11 siblings, my blended families certainly serve me life through a blender! The excitement never ends!

I cannot express how excited I am to participate in this internship for the summer of 2008. My siblings think I am going to be a pirate this summer, and that is fine by me! In 2005, I attended the Tall Ships® festival in Tacoma, Washington and decided that it was something I had to do. This summer I am looking forward to learning as much as I possibly can while immersed in the world of sailtraining. Some day I hope to combine my degree in psychology with my love of sailing; however, for now, I must content myself to sailing and exploring the world...what a rough life!

They are finally here!

They are finally here! After a few slow days, the ships have finally arrived and now the fun has begun. The night before the festival, the ships anchored out in the harbor and the crews came in to Fort Rodd Hill for a wonderful crew reception put on by the Victoria Tall Ships Society. Set against mountains in the background and a historic lighthouse on shore, the ships looked absolutely picturesque. On the next day, although the weather was a bit cooler than anticipated and the ships were not yet open for boarding, we had a fair amount of people visiting the festival. It was an excellent opportunity to get a feel for the atmosphere and to acclimate to our locations. This morning, we scurried around the docks delivering things to the various ships and meeting some of the crew members before the ships were open for boarding. I have to say that I was really looking forward to that part of the day and to meeting the crews. On top of all the pre-show excitement, the weather was absolutely beautiful with clear blue skies and a minimal amount of wind. An hour before the festival site opened, people were lining up to see the ships. It seems as if everyone is as excited about the festivities as I am! There are pirates and little pirates in training all over the festival nautical goodies to be had, and various costumes and uniforms from all different centuries. We will certainly have our hands full today with all this excitement. See you on the docks!

Adventure on Adventuress

What a whirlwind the past few days have been! The end of the festival in Victoria was filled with both sadness and excitement. With the ships closed and the vendors vacated, the festival grounds were quite ghostly. However, at the same time, I knew I would be sailing the next day so I was excited to see the ship and crew with whom I would be working. Finally, I learned that I would be on *Adventuress* for the next several days and for the race. When I arrived in the morning, I found that I was not the only one sailing on *Adventuress* for the first time that day. The Youth on Board program was joining the ship for the transit to Quartermaster Harbor (about three days). The youth were high school students between the ages of 14 and 17 who had applied for the opportunity to sail on one of three ships, *Zodiac, Mycia, and Adventuress*. Once everyone was on board, we set out from the dock and prepared to start the first race.

Honestly it was very exciting, albeit a bit anticlimactic. With large sailing ships, there is a flurry of orders to raise sails, pull in the docklines and fenders, stow gear and get the ship underway. After that there is not much to do until the next tack or change of direction. It was quite a beautiful sight standing on deck and watching the other ships prepare to cross the starting line with all of their sails set and ready to fly. When the starting gun was fired, the first ship began to make its way across the line. After that, the rest of the ships had 20 minutes to cross.

Sailing is not like most sports where everyone starts at the same time. Instead, each ship records the time it crosses the start and finish line and the the time is adjusted to account for an assortment of variables. Because of all that, the

winner of the race may not necessarily be the first one across the finish line. Despite the slow progress at the beginning, we had an excellent breeze blowing across the Straight of Juan de Fuca. In fact, *Adventuress* was sailing at maximum hull speed for much of the race at a blazing 10.5 knots!

The deck was heeled over so far that our stern caprail was awash several times. It was absolutely fantastic to watch the ship flying along so well. It looked as if she had been set free and was enjoying every minute of it. However, the same cannot be said of some of the passengers. For many of the students, and passengers, this was their first experience on a tall ship and so some were a bit green with the motion and others were sliding across the deck. Eventually, we had to drop sail and motor the rest of the way into Port Angeles so that we could clear customs and continue on our way.

After clearing customs and offloading our passengers, the captain decided that the crew and youth on board were tired so we anchored just outside of Port Angeles for the night. When the ship is anchored, those onboard must stand an hour of anchor watch at some point during the night to make sure that the ship is safe. The mate picked three different bearing points that we would measure throughout the night to make sure we were not drifting or dragging our anchor. We also monitored the weather conditions to make sure that they were still consistent. After a long day, the crew and youth were glad to relax, sing some shanties, and turn in for the night.

Day two was a bit more normal than the first day as far as routine goes. *Adventuress* doesn't race every day but does run education programs regularly. Being a passenger and a crew member, it was interesting for me to watch the program run in full swing. Everyone was assigned to a watch with crew watch leaders and began morning chores. My watch was responsible for the deck that morning so we pumped some sea water up to wash the deck and prepared for the morning sail. After that, we rotated through education and watch stations.

Although the program wasn't geared towards my age, I actually enjoyed it quite a bit! We learned about the environment of Puget Sound, sailing theory, boxing compasses, and knot tying. Even though I have lived in Puget Sound my whole life, I was amazed at the complexity of our ecosystem. Even down to the tiny phytoplankton whose shells are used in toothpaste, every bit of the Sound is interrelated. The kids were also soaking up all this knowledge and were ready to participate and share what they had learned with one another. After the hour rotation of the watch, my watch more or less went on 'break'. During that time we taught the kids how to make the Turk's head bracelets which are popular amongst sailors and enthusiasts. They also enjoyed drawing on the deck. In fact, when I saw someone pick up a stick of chalk and begin scribbling away, I had to look around to see if any of the crew thought this was strange. But to my delight, they actually used the deck as an enormous chalk board while they were teaching. By the end of the day, the deck was covered with food webs, sailboats, compasses, labeled deck paraphernalia, and a few extra doodles.

After a full day of sailing and teaching, we anchored in Blakely Harbor for the night and signed up for our anchor watches. The evenings festivities began when *Mycia* rafted up next to us for a visit and a game. With both groups of students onboard, our game of charades and CatchPhrase® was quite exciting! But, the clock eventually won and we all turned in for the night.

On our transit to Tacoma for the Parade of Sail, we took on a few more passengers and off loaded our youth program. As we set sail, there was only a light breeze so, to keep station with the ships fore and aft of us, we used our motor to aid the sails. It really wasn't until the last day that I became accustomed to the ships operations and orders. The first three days I felt a bit useless since I had never sailed on a tall ship before and wasn't sure what to do when an order was called. Since there was an education program onboard, the crew was employed in aiding the youth. Without any sort of indoctrination or sail training, I had to observe and ask as many questions as I could. Eventually everyone, including myself, would snap to their stations ready to haul on a line while the shantiman led in a round of 'Haul Away Joe' or 'Down to South Australia', after which a good '2, 6, heave!' would sheet the sail to proper trim.

Even though I felt a bit lost, I can now understand why people are so enraptured by sail training and specifically tall ships. I came into this sail with some sailing experience, but nowhere near the knowledge that these people have. They all take such pride in their ships but at the same time, they have a strong bond to the crew on their sister ships as well. It is a small but very close community. In fact, there is often a sense of brotherly competition and mischief between various vessels. All in all, I loved watching the crew do what they love and teach others as well. My journal now has several quickly scribbled shanties and notes about the passage. Although *Adventuress* is not continuing in the TALL SHIPS CHALLENGE® Race Series after Tacoma, I would love to sail with her again when the summer is over. In fact, I can't wait until San Diego when I will have two months worth of experience and a wealth of knowledge I can only imagine now.

2008 Summer Intern - Jovanna Hart

Ahoy! My name is Jovanna Hart, but most people call me Jo. This summer I will be interning for ASTA at the TALL SHIPS CHALLENGE® Series 2008 on the Pacific Coast. I just graduated from Ithaca College in Ithaca, New York with a B.S. in Integrated Marketing Communications. In the future, I'd like to apply my degree to a full-time career in advertising or event planning. That's why I'm so excited to take part in Tall Ships, because it involves events as well as many other elements I enjoy including water activities and traveling. I've been a competitive swimmer for 15 years including four years at Ithaca College. This past summer I was a member of the Cornell University Sailing Club where I became acquainted with small sailboats and the basics of sailing, and I was an intern for the Ithaca Downtown Partnership where I helped coordinate festivals and concerts. This internship with ASTA is a chance for me to combine these interests into one great experience. Being an intern in the TALL SHIPS CHALLENGE® Series will give me the opportunity to work with the public and gain new skills. I've traveled a fair bit and I love working in new environments with new people, and quite honestly, I can't think of a better way to do so then from the deck of a tall ship. I hope to see you all there! Anchors away!

Five down, just two to go

The *Spirit of Dana Point*, a schooner owned by the Ocean Institute in Dana Point, became my new home for the trek to San Pedro. I had the opportunity to sail with her to her homeport of Dana Point and I must say the Ocean Institute is quite a magnificent organization. Along with having two tall ships they have a plethora of other boats as well as a facility that incorporates tons of hands-on learning.

I witnessed everything from second graders dissecting squid eyeballs to a saltwater tank of plate-sized, multicolored starfish. It was great to see the children get involved and be truly enjoying it. During our time at the dock, I got to help out with boat repairs and preparation for the festival in San Pedro. This took about three days as we had damaged two sails quite badly and had to have them taken down and sewn. However, an expert, Jim, stitched them up in a hurry and before we knew it we were on our way to San Pedro, Port of Los Angeles.

San Pedro is one of the most industrial ports we've gone to this summer. It's pretty amazing to see the larger than life barges come into the port and then have Star Wars looking machines sort through and remove their enormous cargo. Being able to have a close-up view of this action in the harbor has made the festival unique and exciting in its own way.

Back to tall ships though! The parade of sail in San Pedro was one of the best yet. The inlet stretches straight down to the ocean so from the shore the lineup of ships was visible for miles. Areas along the waterfront were packed to the hilt and selected viewing spots had commentators reading off the order of ships and various facts about the vessels. The crowd interest was through the roof and representative of the enthusiasm the next few days would bring.

The festival will wrap up Sunday at 7 PM and then ASTA will be headed to our final port in San Diego. How fast this summer has gone! It feels like just yesterday we were wearing our wool sweaters and eating steamed clams in Victoria, but here we are in SoCal sporting tank tops and munching on In-N-Out burgers.

Our final voyage will be on the United States Coast Guard ship the barque *Eagle.* ASTA has worked in conjunction with the *Eagle* to create a two day educational program called "Eagle Seamanship" for this trip from San Pedro to San Diego. The program has accepted 22 kids age 16-19 who will be taught sail training via a real life, hands-on experience on the ship. Each participant will be treated as real crew by being given a watch schedule and be expected to fulfill certain duties throughout the trip. Members of the ASTA team will be overseeing the program elements while the permanent sailors aboard *Eagle* will be the sail instructors. Sailing aboard *Eagle* is a once in a lifetime opportunity not just for the participating teenagers, but also for us here at ASTA. Therefore, it should be a great sail training experience filled with learning and excitement.

Two Hundred Ten is a crowd

If you've been tracking our adventure as ASTA interns this summer you know that we've experienced ships of every shape and structure. The USCG Barque *Eagle* is no exception. The maximum number of crew and passengers I'd had on a tall ship up until this week was 26. The *Eagle* had 210. Measuring 295 feet in length and weighing 2,186 GRT, it was more than evident that we weren't on the schooner HMCS *Oriole* anymore.

Our adventure began on *Eagle* long before we left the San Pedro harbor. The night before we left port all the participants in ASTA's "EAGLE Seamanship" program gathered on the main deck of the Coast Guard training vessel to meet, greet, and see what we were getting ourselves into. The 22 youth seemed stoked. The carefully selected group was more than enthusiastic about playing name games and engaging in a few ice-breaker activities. After receiving our "Everything you'll ever need to know about EAGLE" booklets we were introduced to our bunks.

Now, one might think that being an overwhelmingly large vessel might lend the *Eagle* to having somewhat larger living quarters. Not so. Upon choosing one of the triple stacked bunks we all laid down to feel things out. Then I heard Karen say from the top level, "My head is wedged between two pipes labeled 'heat exhaust' and there is a fluorescent light laid over me like a tanning bed bulb". This made me feel better about my bottom bunk and the fact that I felt like I was being held in an underground cage that was constantly being kicked as my new shipmates attempted to maneuver through the tight walkway. However, after this initial introduction our bunks became home and we slept more than comfortably.

The size of the ship is what set this voyage apart from any other. Even after three days I was seeing people I didn't recognize and I'm pretty sure there are a good many rooms I never found. This is quite a change from the smaller crews we've traveled with before where we were in constant close communication and could see each other at all times on deck when handling lines.

Teamwork on the *Eagle* took on entirely new components. Here we needed megaphones and walkie-talkies to receive and return orders. Working together meant trusting the actions of other stations that were on an entirely different end of the ship, completely out of view. It was a foreign method of teamwork for us. After all was said and done, however, it was as efficient and rewarding as working on one of the smaller vessels. In fact, when I looked up at what was previously a line of bare yardarms and saw the endless masses of sail set tight in the wind miles above our heads, it was like no other experience I've had this summer.

A new aspect to this trip was that we were not only working with the *Eagle's* normal crew, but we were coming together with the kids in the EAGLE Seamanship program. Once aboard the ship these youth took the experience very seriously. They did everything from going aloft to calling out the order to "Heave-ho!" Although I felt comfortably knowledgeable with the typical routine of a ship, I think I learned a lot from interacting with and watching this group. One instance sticks out in my mind particularly because it involved going up into the rigging, which is something that flutters the hearts of even the most experienced sailors. On this occasion I went aloft with a young girl named Amy, who was 17 years old, to furl a staysail. We'd both furled a few sails out on the yards before, but this experience was totally new. Furthermore, I had watched crew members furl a staysail before and commented on how you must have to be a certified tight rope walker to accomplish such a feat. Despite this I went up and, although hoping for the best, I was immediately met by the fear I had expected. Amy worked her way out onto the line first. She did this without a sound and then looked back calmly, waiting for me to join her. After watching Amy I readied myself and decided to take my first move onto the thread-like line.

At this point I began ranting each step of the way, "Holy!" "Wow!" "Ahh!" "No way!" Then I'd look forward and see Amy smiling confidently, allowing herself to stand as a figure of hope, showing me that in the end I'd be alive and she was living, breathing proof of it. All in all, I can say this encounter was fascinating to me because I was the elder by six years, however I was definitely not the more mature of the two of us. I was uneasy and I let it show while Amy took on the leadership role. When we landed on the deck she raised her hand and said, "High five shipmate!" and we carried on with smiles from ear to ear.

I couldn't think of a better ending to a summer of sailing. The past few days have been a once in a lifetime opportunity on so many levels. Thanks to the *Eagle* and ASTA for making it happen!

2009 Summer Intern - Amelia Smith

Ahoy! I just graduated from New York University, and am extremely excited to begin my internship with the TALL SHIPS CHALLENGE® Series! I look forward to the opportunity to share my love of sailing with others while combining my passions for photography, history and writing.

As a kid, I lived aboard my parent's sailboat as we cruised from our home in Detroit, Michigan to the Bahamas and back. We would often come across tall ship festivals and events in the Great Lakes and along the East Coast. It wasn't until high school that I realized the large role organizations such as ASTA have in bringing together tall ships from across the globe into organized and memorable festivals and Challenges, when I raced aboard the *Pride of Baltimore II* from Newcastle, UK to Fredrikstad, NWY, continuing through the North Sea to Bremerhaven, GER. Most recently, I crossed the Atlantic aboard the tall ship *Prince William* in 2007.

At NYU, I have gained experience editing, designing, writing and taking photos for Seaport magazine as an intern in the publications department of the South Street Seaport Museum. I also worked as a free-lancer, writing feature articles for SpinSheet and PropTalk, sailing and boating magazines in Annapolis, MD while an intern at the Annapolis Maritime Museum.

Sailing has encompassed my life, and by the end of college my resume has taught me that as much as I may enjoy other things, they have yet to be done without a sailing connection! I hope to be lucky enough to continue in this direction well into the future, and am excited to be an intern with ASTA this summer!

At Sea on Schooner Virginia

With the festival in Charleston finished, it was time for us to move on to schooner *Virginia* and prepare for the education program bound for Norfolk, Virginia and then New London, CT. The morning was spent preparing for the students: laundry had to be picked up, groceries put away, soles (floors) cleaned and bunks made. At two in the afternoon, we welcomed aboard 12 students bewteen the ages of 13-17. They are part of schooner *Virginia's* educational programming, which teaches life skills and leadership through sail training.

Students began with a muster and then went down to find their bunks, claim a mug to label with their name and to learn about using the heads (marine

toilets) and watertight doors. After leaving the dock, we dropped the anchor and had dinner (Taco Tuesday!). Divided into watches, students learned how to clean the galley, deflate and stow the fenders and the 32 points of the compass for steering. The captain equated how the students would feel on their first day to a sponge that had a five gallon bucket of water dumped on to it. They seemed to absorb it quite well despite the heat and sheer volume of information. Then, in rotations, students learned about steering, lookout duties, and line handling. It has been great to assist them and move through the watch duties because we (Nelly and I) get instruction and learn about everything too!

Last night, everyone was part of a one hour anchor watch. With the students, we ran through a boat check and took bearings on the compass to ensure the ship maintained its position. It seemed to go by quickly, and soon I was sleeping again and ready for another day's activities.

Cool Breezes as Virginia heads home

Thursday on the 12 to 4 a.m. watch we had nine knots of speed but still some seasickness. The students worked hard to fill the rotations of helm, lookout, rough log and boat check. My rotation was rough log, so I walked the students through determining course ordered, course steered, wind direction and speed, sea direction and height, cloud type, and air temperature. It was a little challenging explaining wind and sea direction in the dark, but the students worked hard and powered through. Getting them through the rough log, I may have built more character than the students that watch, Ms. Cole (1st Mate) joked, as I stopped to grab some water.

Later that day, there was great excitement during our afternoon watch when dolphins appeared. There were not just one or two, but eight dolphins jumping and twirling around in the ship's wake. Some were speckled, others gray in color. Soonafter, we caught a Mahi Mahi on the fishing line, and student Zach cut it up for us.

After rounding Cape Fear, Cape Lookout and finally Cape Hatteras, the seas have calmed and left us with a steady wind. It was wonderful to wake up to a cool afternoon breeze instead of sweltering heat, and you could see it in the smiles of the students how big of a difference it made. With seasickness lessening, students have started building leadership as Junior Watch Officers (J-WO). The J-WO organizes the watch and leads rotations, making sure tasks are completed on time.

During watch, Ms. Cole led lessons on dead reckoning, and the students have picked it up quickly and incorporated it into their rough log. Instead of using the GPS to determine our position and plotting it on the chart, students read our nautical miles traveled on the taff rail and log it into the rough log. Combining the distance traveled with the course steered, students then plot our position on the chart using this "dead reckoning" method. On the watch change every four hours the watch leader plots our GPS position.

When not on watch, students have been learning their knot tying, compass points, aloft safety and rigging in order to be cleared to go aloft. It has been great to see the students helping to teach each other as they pick up more and more information. Their goal is to see the July 4th fireworks aloft in Norfolk!

A homecoming in Norfolk

Norfolk Harborfest for the 4th of July was phenomenal but, before delving into the event itself, I should start with the morning which was lively as well. At 5 a.m. I had a confused wake-up for anchor watch– I'd been off-watch and asleep during the midnight anchoring. It was a brisk morning, and I watched the sun rise, helped the students to complete the hourly boat check, and took bearings recorded in the log with students Zach and Lauren. As locals to the area, they were excited to recognize the coastline and explain where we were anchored.

During my engine room check I noted a higher than usual draw on the batteries and woke Aaron the engineer. It turned out the coffee-maker was on and I headed back up on deck. Our watch was nearing its end, and as the students and I waited to take bearings again, I leaned over to adjust the windscoop for the aft cabin. The engines roared on, which was odd because we were at anchor but I knew the engineer was up and around. Aaron came running up with a startled and confused look asking if I had turned the engines on. Apparently I had with my knee as I was leaning to move the windscoop. He quickly shut it off, but not before it woke the Captain who asked from the aft cabin what was going on. So embarrassing!!

After breakfast the students split up into watches and cleaned *Virginia* from top to bottom to ready her for parents and guests that evening. Then it was time for a swim break! Before I knew it, we were raising anchor and getting the sails loose and ready to enter Norfolk. We set the mainsail, foresail, staysail and the jib. I was on bow watch looking out mostly for little powerboats who wanted to take a closer look. It was a little stressful with so many pleasure craft out for the holidays, but also really great to see the entrance into downtown Norfolk. We passed lots of naval vessels dressed with flags in celebration, and finally Nauticus, the huge maritime museum. Soon we spotted *Capitan Miranda, Cisne Branco* and *Pride of Baltimore II*.

Schooner *Virginia* continued along the harbor side until we were opposite hundreds of people gathered along the waterfront for the festival. Turning into the wind, the students lowered the sails beautifully in a synchronized manner before docking alongside. Once ashore, the students were split up into three groups for a one-hour field trip, with Nelly, Nate and me each leading one. We went on board the tall ships and even had a private tour down below for the students on *Pride of Baltimore II*!

Once the students were back on board, they helped dress the ship with flags and prepared for their parents. They acted as docents on the ship during the reception that night, sharing what they had learned and experienced aboard the ship such as navigation, boat checks, sail handling and knot tying. As the dark settled in, the students enjoyed delicious lemon tarts and punch Carey the cook had prepared. The perfect end to a beautiful July 4th— smiling students aloft and on the main gaff watching two barges set off some impressive fireworks!

2009 Summer Intern - Nelly Turley

In May, I graduated with a BA in Social Anthropology from the University of Michigan, where I also got to take classes in naval navigation and oceanography. During my four years in Ann Arbor, I played on the Michigan's Ultimate Frisbee Team, braving everything from snowy to sweltering practices.

My love of travel took me on a gap year after high school, which is where I discovered tall ships. I've sailed twice for the Tall Ship Youth Trust, both as a crewmember and watch leader. I sailed aboard the *Stavros S. Nairchos* around England and Spain and loved every minute of it. I also had a chance to crew on a Swan 62 for Race Week in Antigua in 2005. One of the reasons I love sailing so much is the opportunity it presents to travel to so many different places.

Being able to spend the summer as an intern for the TALL SHIPS CHALLENGE® Series 2009 is a dream come true for me because I have loved sailing since I was nine and learned to sail in an El Toro, a dinghy about the size of a bathtub.

The Chocolate Pancake Dance

As *Pride of Baltimore II* sailed out of Hamilton, Bermuda and around the island to the start of Race Three, we were joined by hundreds of yachts, dinghies and even jet skis. It felt like a royal escort.

I hate to admit it, but I couldn't tell you when we crossed the starting line. I had never set foot on a schooner before and I was often concentrating so much on what I was doing, mostly hauling and trying not to fall over, that I wasn't always sure exactly what my hauling was achieving up in the rigging and by the time I was done I needed to move to another line.

The last I was aware, we were waiting for the other race committee boat to get into position. Then we were setting more sails and tacking, which involved a lot of hurry and hauling while trying not to slip on the deck.

It started pouring and there was as much water raining down on us from above as there was crashing over the bow. To add to the commotion on deck, the guest crew was lined up on the leeward side being sick, then the main runner block blew, but still *Pride* sped along, charging towards Charleston.

It wasn't until I looked up some time later and saw that all the little yachts and powerboats that had been with us were out of sight, and all you could see were the gray skies and tall ships surging forward. "Oh," I thought, "The race must have begun. I totally missed that. Oops"

It took some strategic blanket placement to make it so that I couldn't fall out of bed that night. This worked really well until we tacked and I found myself plastered against the hull like a magnet.

It was always more fun to be able to see our competition on the horizon (especially when they were behind us). One night *Urania* came up from behind and crossed over to our port side. At one point she was only 1.5 nautical miles away, it was eerie to see her silently moving behind us.

One afternoon, as I was lying sleepily in my bunk, I could see Rob, the cook, making German chocolate cake. Good smells are a luxury on a ship so that was always a bonus of sleeping by the galley. I have always been a fan of food, which was heightened on board because all I did was eat, sleep and haul on lines – and eating was the only thing I did that didn't make me sweat (it was very hot below decks). I always enjoyed walking through the galley and smelling what he's cooking – it's also great when we were on deck working and the sweet smell of dinner wafts up.

That night we got woken up during our standby watch (the four hours before our watch time) to help strike a sail. I have never been able to snap out of sleep as well as I did on *Pride*. It's probably because the person sent below to do wakeups isn't messing around and their urgency makes me snap awake. They say my name and I'm up, throwing on my glasses and scrambling up the ladder. This particular night we got up, struck a sail then were relieved back to sleep, then later woken up to set a sail. Both times I was awake enough only to know where I was and what I had to haul on.

During our night watch on the third day we saw a cruise ship, which first appeared as a glowing mass in the distance and it got so close off our port side that we could see individual windows. It looked like a skyscraper that had been knocked on its side, gliding across the water. We could see *Capitan Miranda* and a few other tall ships as tiny lights on the horizon making me feel like I had a posse out there on the water.

Since I am on watch from 12-4 in the morning and afternoon, I normally slept through breakfast. On the days I had duty, however, I had to get up early to clean the ship before watch. I hadn't had a breakfast in days and when I woke up that morning I smelled something on the griddle and literally jumped out of my bunk and into the galley shouting "Pancakes!" I may or may not have proceeded to go around the galley doing the chocolate chip pancake dance.

I fell asleep after my afternoon watch to the gentle rocking of the ship, as it moved slowly in the light winds only to wake up plastered against the hull, both hearing and feeling the water blowing by. "Well that's different," I thought. I went up on deck to find that we were cruising along at eight knots headed straight for Charleston!

Waaaay back in June

Way back in June, when I arrived in Hamilton, Bermuda on the *Bounty*, Captain Walbridge briefed us on some port etiquette, from bringing friends on board to letting other ship's crew members climb *Bounty's* rigging. I didn't really know anyone else that would want to come climb the rig so I didn't think too much about it until I visited the *Cisne Branco*. The *Cisne Branco* (or White Swan) is the Brazilian navy ship and was docked in front of the *Kruzenshtern* at the Bermuda tall ships event, where I had just had tea and cookies (baked on board) while they filled out a vessel survey. I decided to tour *Cisne Branco* and chatted with the radio operator, Mario. As I was walking away he said, "If you have any questions please, don't hesitate to ask." There was only one question that came to mind, "Can I climb your rig?" And so my quest to climb to go aloft on as many ships as I could began with that one simple question.

Being up in the rig, or over the side, still hasn't lost its luster for me. I know some seasoned sailors might shrug it off but I still consider it my favorite place on board (just ahead of my bunk and wherever the food is).

It took some time to find the officer on watch, and then for the next officer to change from his dress whites into climbing gear. I was given gloves, a harness and up we went! Once I got to the coarse yardarm of the *Cisne Branco* they have safety lines that follow the shrouds so you are clipped in at every moment. There were knots in the line so if you fell you didn't slip down the whole thing, while I appreciated the safety of it all I wasn't used to being clipped in while

climbing so I would get stuck and have to climb down, clip in above the knot then unclip again. Before I knew it, I was climbing the last few feet to the very top of the mast. Bruno, my guide, was right behind me and, after I touched the mast head lights, we climbed out onto the royal yard and chatted. Every cadet that joins the *Cisne Branco* has to climb to the top of the main mast with a certain degree of confidence as part of the application process to join the ship. Bruno was surprised at how well I had done and said I would have passed easily. After I climbed down, they invited me to the state room for a drink while they printed out a certificate that said I had made it to the top, which I will be sure to save in case I want to join the Brazilian Navy someday.

Mircea, the Romanian Naval ship, is home to the fastest climbing cadets in the TALL SHIPS ATLANTIC CHALLENGE® 2009. During every Parade of Sail, they run up the rig making it look as if the ship is being taken over by ants. At the Captains' Reception in Charleston, I met a crew member of *Mircea*, named Mircea. I told him how I was admiring the yellow rig and how I would like to climb it. He was a bit busy escorting small children up and down the steep gangway but said he would inquire for me.

Sure enough, the next morning I was outfitted with the most comfortable harness I have used and escorted up the rig! She's the biggest ship I have ever climbed on and her rig was fantastic and a breeze to climb. The lower shrouds weren't steep at all so up I went, over the tops and past the cross trees until Mircea told me that was high enough because of the wind. So we climbed out on one of the yardarms and took in the view. Her sails were hanging in their gear and billowing in the wind and her dress flags, which are color coordinated, were hanging just above us. Up there on the sunshine yellow yardarm, I was reminded of something I had overheard one of the cadets giving a tour the day before say: "It's a happy color and we are a happy people." That was definitely the vibe I was getting.

I can't decide what has been the most amazing part of the summer. It might be that I got to climb all over these gorgeous tall ships, meet people from all over the world (many of whom I plan on seeing again) or that I got to sail to Bermuda and up the East Coast on some of the most gorgeous ships I have ever laid eyes on. All of those things blow me out of the water but the most amazing thing has to be the fact that the experience was exactly what it had been cracked up to be. Sail training, racing and the festivals were everything I had expected and more. I had been looking forward to this internship since January, I took a week off my school work to perfect draft after draft of my application until the counselor at the career center said it was perfect because I wanted this position so bad. I tried to talk some sense into myself because there was no way that it could be everything I was imagining, there was no way it could be that good. But it was. Every ship I sailed on was different and gave me new experiences and outlooks on tall ship sailing. At the festivals, I could hardly find time to write my blogs because I was doing too many blog worthy things. Being an ASTA intern and a tall ship crew member in port magnified the experience because we had our crewmates, and interning gave us face time with the cadets and officers of all the other ships.

I am leaving to sail to Belfast in a few days and I'm not buying a plane ticket home. Some of my former shipmates have returned home to Europe and have extended invitations to visit and I intend take them up on their offers. There's also ten times as many ships over in Europe and who knows which one will need a extra pair of hands. I also know that the experience isn't unique to me; Amelia is going and intends to visit people she met on her first Atlantic crossing onboard the *Prince William* in 2007. This has been the time of my life and the best part is that it's not over yet.

2009 Summer Intern - Matt Maples

In the spring of 2007, Matthew Maples began his sailing adventures as an intern with the American Sail Training Association on the barque *Picton Castle*. His life has not been the same since. Since then, he has sailed on the twin brigantines *Irving Johnson* and *Exy Johnson*, the brig *Niagara*, and the schooner *Spirit of Massachusetts*. Now he sails again representing ASTA on the bark *Europa* to document several of the 2009 TALL SHIPS ATLANTIC CHALLENGE® festivals from the perspective of the ship and its crew.

Matthew graduated from Eastern Illinois University in 2007. He is a native of land-locked Bartlett, IL. His internship opportunity with ASTA infected him with a sailing "bug" that to this day persists in ailing him with a chronic-yet-delightful wanderlust over water.

Have you ever wanted to know what it is like to sail on a mighty wave-conquering tall ship? If so, read on! You may be surprised...

It is 1:17 A.M. I cannot sleep. This does not surprise me, for in a matter of hours I will be in the midst of another tall ship adventure. This always happens.

This time is different though. My excitement is so contagious that I feel as if the air around me will ignite. In the past, on the tall ships *Niagara* and *Spirit of Massachusetts* I was a deckhand. Now I will be an "embedded" photojournalist on board the Dutch bark *Europa*. I am to document via blog and photograph several of the 2009 TALL SHIPS ATLANTIC CHALLENGE® events from my perspective while on board *Europa*. I envision that this blog will reflect the spirit and perspective of its crew as we make our way from Hamilton, Bermuda to stop at Charleston, South Carolina; Boston, Massachusetts; and Halifax, Nova Scotia for this summer's ambitious TALL SHIPS ATLANTIC CHALLENGE® festivals.

It is here in this blog that I hope to capture the salted taste of daily life on a tall ship sailing in the midst of such a landmark summer of events. For not only am I undergoing a different tall ship experience for myself, but this summer marks a race series jointly organized by the American Sail Training Association and Sail Training International. Consequently, this particular TALL SHIPS ATLANTIC CHALLENGE® will be a unique experience for everyone involved. I have read the roster of participating vessels and my jaw plummets. This summer's events will see a majestic assortment of some of the world's most awe-inspiring sailing ships – these vessels of wind and wave that embody our personal ambitions, hopes, and the unstoppable force of human ingenuity and adventure. Indeed, these ships embody our hopes made manifest. In that respect, they are us. Perhaps that explains the intuitive connection that millions feel at the sight of canvas sails on the horizon.

For you, reader, this blog is your ticket to an inside perspective of the voyaging tall-ship. It will be updated frequently with observations and will periodically feature specials concerning interesting aspects of the ship, its personalities, and the port festivals. www.tallships.wordpress.com

In the past I was an intern for the American Sail Training Association, part of which included keeping a blog as I experienced my first taste of the tall ship life on board the *Picton Castle*. This blog however, will be more ambitious, as I am able to dedicate more time to it, and I also am able to experience things with eyes tempered by experience. I hope that you will enjoy this perspective of the voyaging tall ship and the 2009 Tall Ships® Races as seen firsthand from the deck. Check back often!

A steady wind takes us into limbo

June 22, 2009 – 1415 hours, 33.23.64′N x 75.46.68′W

Have you ever wondered what it would feel like, to be on the bow of a tall-ship underway? Maybe I can give you an idea.

Standing on the foredeck of a square-rigger, close-hauled and making good speed, is an awesome experience, especially at night. The deck bucks up and down with the waves, as if it were a never-ending roller-coaster ride. The methodical hammer blows of the bow smashes waves asunder, sending spray up the sides to land in your face. The seas crackle, as if like static. Bio-luminescent creatures, disturbed by our thundering presence, flash green in their multitudes, like twinkling stars in the black wake of our ship. Taut canvas ripples with the wind, whistling through the rigging, sounding as if a gallery of jeering ghosts were aloft. Far and away from land, with no light pollution, clouds become stains of spilled ink on an unimaginably clear, starry canvas, their presence betrayed only by their smothering of the celestial canvas. Inky tendrils of clouds, like a creeping hand, deviously envelop the sky in complete darkness. Meanwhile our lamps in the deckhouse sway, shifting shadows to dance across the deck.

Really though, it is something you will have to experience for yourself, which you can do. Just as many of the trainees on our ship are experiencing. I'll be writing in some of their stories in upcoming logs.

The visual description above was what it was like on my look-out shift on the foredeck last night. We have been making good speed since yesterday afternoon. A short rain and a passing front brought wind, and we have been making a steady way since. Yesterday afternoon and evening saw us busy setting and re-setting many of our sails. I was kept busy along with the crew in tying down or unfurling our highest square sails, staysails, outer jib and gaff tops'l.

I had to stop in the middle of writing this because an impromptu limbo competition broke out suddenly on the main-deck. I've seen shuffleboard done with deck brushes and rope mats before, but not limbo on a swaying deck!

Only Kylle de Lange, one of the *Europa's* deckhands, was spry enough to accomplish the feat. I fell on my back.

Captain Klaas said today that we made a good 120 miles to Charleston yesterday with 206 miles to go. Our rating in the race is now second in our class, fifth overall. We have moved up three places overall in the past few days, despite being the most northerly ship. This may work to our advantage. As Captain Klaas says, we are now experiencing more wind then the ships more south of us, also, we need not tack and have a straight course to Charleston. Our weather, shifting in all aspects over the past few days, has been explained as a low pressure system in our area stuck here by three high pressure systems. Thus explaining our phenomenon of seemingly random weather. *Capitan Miranda*, the sail-training vessel from Uruguay, is ahead of us by 70 miles. We are doing all we can to close the gap in the competition between the Class A vessels. We think that if the wind can keep up for us that we can give *Capitan Miranda* a surprise run for its money on the last leg of this race.

Boom! Flash! Storm!

June 21, 2009 – 1415 hours – 34.20.10′N x 73.21.42′W

Wow. Yesterday was one of the most intense days of sailing I've ever experienced. The wind picked up considerably in the afternoon, forcing us to take in our highest and most outboard sails. We would pile on sail and take it back in as soon as the wind got too intense for some of the canvas. All day we were heeled way over, sailing the ship to its optimum. Sprays of bitter salt water leapt over the deck often enough that the lookouts forward on the lee side needed to wear foul-weather gear. We "wore" ship twice, that is, to change direction by bringing our stern past the wind. The wind, increasing to force five, made the sails much more difficult to handle. Whenever we had to bring down the flying and outer jibs we would need to line people up, as many as a dozen, along the foredeck to haul in unison to bring the wind-whipped sails down. It was still difficult, even with a dozen straining bodies heaving on a single line fighting the wind for every pull.

When the sails get taken in, they need to be furled. At one point we took in the flying jib, the outermost head-sail on our jib-boom which protrudes from the bow of the ship. The flying jib was being furled by only one crew member, Erika Wasner. The sail, like a flailing bull, whipped about as Erika tried with great effort to bring it in. With the other crew members aloft furling the sky-sails, Erika asked for help to bring in the sail. I donned a harness quick as I could and half-dashed, somewhat blundered, my way out there. Not hesitating, I grabbed at the canvas trying to escape from our head-rig and the two of us started to violently hauled it in. Right behind me was Selange Gitschner, trainee, who bravely tackled the sail with us. We held the sail down while Erika tied it up and it was finally tamed. She later told me that I had made it to the scene just in time.

I was woken for watch at midnight. I groggily got up. The boat was rocking a good bit, but that was how I left it when I went to my bunk a few hours earlier. I stumbled out into an empty hallway making my way to the deck above. I came up on deck in time to enter a much more chaotic scene.

Boom! Flash! Storm! Everyone was donning full-body harnesses as lightning spiraled around the ship. The thud of thunder punctuated sentences. "Oh boy!" I thought, "We are going to get it now." I got my harness on and dashed out of the deckhouse just in time to help haul up the mainsail. For the next hour we kept taking in sail. Captain Klaas was giving orders from the quarter-deck; "Take in royals!", "Take in the mizzen royal staysail!" "Take in t'gallants!" "Take in Desmond!" The sails came in fast and furious, then furled and secured. Our trainees, bolstered by the lightning and rain, worked together at a level that we had not achieved yet in the daytime. As we wore ship to change course, I could see the trainees on the main braces, hauling away "2-6", "2-6" was their hauling cadence as they brought the main braces to bear on their new heading. Again on the fore braces, "2-6", "2-6", "2-6 heave!" as we muscled our way onto a new course.

I took the wheel after we wore ship. By then the rain had stopped, but bursts of fog lightning and gnarled chain lightning sliced the air around us, thunder booming across the waves, echoing among the dark void. Thankfully, the squall was not big; we were only in the midst of it for maybe ten minutes.

The reaction of our trainees to the situation surprised me. Instead of being worried or frightened by the prospect of a night-time stormy squall at sea most

seemed to be having fun, enjoying the atmospheric sky show going on all around us and unhesitatingly stepping up to the sail-handling challenges that rattled down in quick succession from the quarterdeck. Neil Forrest, trainee from Charleston, told me today that it was "awesome" and that it was just the kind of thrill-seeking adventure he was looking for. Sara Lagan, a Bermudan trainee, told me that the whole affair was "Brilliant! One of the most memorable parts so far" Was she scared though? "Nah! Well, only a little" she said.

In sharp contrast, today has been perfectly peachy. Sunny weather with a steady, if weak, wind. Far more relaxed and quite fitting for a sailors Sunday. Captain Klaas wants more wind though, a force four breeze exactly.

Belfast: A Bittersweet Conclusion

Here we are, Belfast. The relative quiet of the deckhouse on *Europa* barely conceals the roiling festivities of the opening day of the Belfast Maritime Festival. A short glance to my left reveals the legs of the crowd gathered on the quay, stacked tight against one another, trying to get as close to our ship as they can. Now a gangplank is being rigged, and the fences are being cleared away, and the people edge a bit closer, their silent excitement betrayed by eager faces. In a few moments they will come aboard as guests, to walk our deck, view our ship and hear our stories. It is quite a turn-around in a day, to transform our ship from a working, sailing ship into a highlight attraction at a maritime festival. No longer do we find ourselves bracing yards, furling sail and steering at the helm – our time-worn duties and sailing routines have been replaced. Now we have given our ship a thorough tidying. We have removed the "unsightly gear" like chain winches, canvas strops and tools. We now do the gangplank "switcharoo" by which we persistently tweak, adjust, and re-set our gangplank to compensate for the tide, which raise and lower us against the quay a dozen feet or so in a day! It is a different set of duties, but I am reminded in each one of these ports about how special what we are doing really is; these crowds of people who come to visit us and meet us in every port do so for a reason.

The conclusion of our cross-ocean voyage came with the onset of yesterday afternoon. We had anchored off the northern coast, next to an island called Muck Island, only a handful of miles from Belfast. A morning of sterile wind did little to move us on our way; despite our "sailing off the hook" (raising anchor and setting sail with no motor!). After a long drift, the wind came, to move us on our way.

As we neared Belfast a "foul wind" barred entry into the city via sail, forcing us to use our engines for the first time since Halifax. Taking in all our sail, I was allowed, for the third time in a row, to "call" the main mast – meaning that my job was to receive sail-handling orders from the Captain, ensure that all the lines were properly manned and then call out the orders and watch the sail to take it in; "Ease down halyard, haul away clews! Yard is in its lifts! Cast off sheets, haul away clews!" I called, as we, one by one and as quick as we could, took in the squares and brought down our fore and aft sails. It went more smoothly than previous times I thought. In ship's I've sailed on previously, this job was usually executed by a mate or very experienced AB.

Rounding the seaside town of White Head we saw, deep in the bay our first glimpse of Belfast – a moment of mixed emotions for many of us. It is always a good feeling to conclude a voyage and bring the ship, and the ship you, safely into port. Conclusions though, are less an ending, and more a transition. For those of us leaving the ship before she leaves Belfast, we are left in a strange limbo; hanging around and helping out on a ship that will leave soon without us. A movement from a home that we've come to know and make our own and a dread of leaving a place we enjoy so much. I am not the only one who feels this way.

Sean Og Maguire and Ciara Higgins, the two Belfast trainees I interviewed previously, feel much the same. Ciara felt mixed feelings when she saw Belfast, realizing that "it was the end of the voyage, we're going to have to get off." Even though she is excited to see her family in Belfast, she has become "used to having (her) own little family on board." Sean Og agrees; "You're used to everyone's personality on here, you know how to react to everyone here – but new people in the crowd, you react like "Ah! Ah! Get away from me!"

For Ciara and Sean Og, I followed up on my earlier interview, conducting another one today for the end of our voyage. They seem a little surprised by the outpouring of positive feelings that the people of Belfast and beyond have given the tall ships and themselves. The media has been extensively covering the Belfast trainees who crossed the Atlantic on several of the racing ships, following up on the en-route reporting of BBC's Julian Fowler.

Our trainees Sean Og and Ciara found themselves in an impromptu radio interview as they walked up the street, their *Europa* T-shirts giving them away to the eager questions of the press. Indeed, today, nearly all the newspapers of Belfast carry the image of the trainees on *Europa* as they came into port.

As for Sean Og and Ciara, I inquired to the reaction their own families gave them after finishing this momentous voyage; They found their families, as can be expected, beaming of their achievements. "I can't believe you came back alive!"

said Sean Og's parents. He says that they "were expecting me to be so hyper and fall overboard, or else get thrown overboard!"

For both of these trainees, they found out that they learned some things in addition to the usual seamanship of sails, knots and navigation. For Sean Og, he learned that "You can commit to something if you try. Usually I try something for two weeks and then, eh, I don't care anymore," he says, adding that, "This is something I want to do and experience a lot more."

Meeting, dealing with and making friends with new people was a highlight of the journey for them. Sean Og found that living with people who started out as complete strangers, who became fantastic friends. "You are with the people 24/7, you get to know them and not just the grim part of their personality," he says. "On a boat you are with people through ups and downs." Sean Og was a little surprised at how well everyone got along, "It's just so strange, if you are thrown in to a group of mixed people, some aren't going to gel well together and you'll usually get some bickers and fights, but there's nothing like that on board, it's all so good, laid back and relaxed."

"Most of us will probably be friends for life," says Ciara. She is impressed by the strength of the friendships she formed in a mere matter of weeks while on board, especially in her cabin that she shared with five other strangers who took on the familiarity of friendship. Ciara discovered, while immersed in an environment full of new people, that she was more approachable and friendlier than she had perceived herself to be.

One thing that I can relate to, with Sean and Ciara, is how huge the effect sailing on these ships is to many. I had read all about how it changed people, but I didn't expect it to be so much! Sean and Ciara found something similar. "Everybody said it was going to be really life-changing. I was thinking I would get on and get off and go back to my day job, but it's just so much different, everything just looks different. Being in the middle of the ocean," she says, "gives you time to think about what you want to do."

Sean found the experience so life-changing that he can't wait to come back sailing, whether for *Europa* or other ships. "I want to do more traveling, but I want my means of travel to be on a boat."

At the end of the day, the most vivid memories these two say they will have, is of the visceral experience of sailing at sea. For Ciara, climbing into the rigging was amazing. "I think I made myself afraid of heights, but then I just went and did it," she said. Sean Og found the rough weather we experienced with gale force winds for a handful of days to be his most exciting moment, "Although it was dangerous, you were safe – it was exciting and adrenaline-rushing, so many mixed emotions thrown into one."

No doubt this experience has been an "experience of a lifetime" for Sean Og, Ciara and the dozens of other trainees aboard these ships. This particular group of trainees we have had on *Europa* have been the most enthusiastic, energetic, willing and capable trainees I have ever encountered among the handful of ships I have sailed on before. I believe that a number of them will return to sailing on tall ships, and sooner than they expect!

It is a bittersweet return to port, bringing us to new places, to meet new people. But every port brings the end of a voyage for someone. This time, it is the Belfast trainees and myself. We've all seen some amazing things, done things we didn't think we could do and pushed ourselves a bit farther, learned something more. All these things bring changes. Changes only truly felt as one disembarks from their ship, leaving their new-found home and family. These ships though, have a way of re-uniting shipmates, as I have witnessed, again and again in the ports that we sailed to for this summer's TALL SHIPS ATLANTIC CHALLENGE® . We have made some fantastic new friends, of all ages from all around the world. Who, though soon to be separated, will undoubtedly keep their friendships through our shared voyage together. For some of us, there may yet be more.

It is easy to forget, deep in our routines at sea about the real meaning of what we are doing, but it is always easy to remember when we come into port, to the cheers of the crowds that what we are sailing represents something special to so many people. I think it is only in port, when we come back that we realize how unique what we are doing really is. These ships have a strong cultural meaning – of daring, adventure, perseverance and romantically "getting away from it all" These huge amounts of eager visitors are the testament to the strength of the symbolism people see in tall ships.

In that way, their visit means much to us who sail these ships. Hopefully our stories will inspire some of them to give tall ship sailing a try, it is more accessible than most people think.

My voyage, though extended, is soon to end, and in an excellent way. I will probably find my way onto a rolling deck again soon, though I do not know when, as of yet. I hope you enjoyed this blog and please leave your criticism, for I am inspired to continue this sort of writing with the next ship I find myself on. Thank You, Bon Voyage and Fair Winds!

The Sail Training Experience

"ASTA member vessels and programs foster opportunities for intensive personal development -- intensive life experience in order to advance leadership development, an utter reverence for nature, a sense of time and place, an appreciation for history, and teamwork ability. Sail training really teaches the qualities of stewardship, resourcefulness, pride, humility, bravery, strength and grace. And we learn to sail, too."

Eight Days on the Corwith Cramer

By Destiny Freeman

When I first learned about Science At SEA, I had no clue what a great experience it would be. Not only did we learn about oceanography and navigation, but we used that knowledge to work as a team with a common goal: to have an enjoyable trip aboard the SSV *Corwith Cramer.*

Before boarding the *Corwith Cramer*, we spent ten days at the SEA campus studying oceanography, navigation, and maritime studies. We learned about plate tectonics and neutral buoyancy along with other important topics. When we were not in the classroom, we would have free time or go on a field trip to a salt marsh or Woods Hole Oceanographic Institution's Core Lab. Throughout all of these activities, we were also coming closer together as a group. After the first day we all noted how we felt like we had known each other our entire lives. This made the trip even more amazing because we were able to work successfully as a team.

Although we have all gone our separate ways, we will always remember our journey aboard the SSV *Corwith Cramer*. From meeting great people to learning new skills, this was a trip that I would recommend to all high school students.

Log July 11, 2009

Today at the salt marsh my group collected data on the depth, temperature, and salinity at eight different spots. We also took note of the speed of the current. Unlike at Quissett Harbor, we used a computer to collect all of our information. Towards the mouth of the marsh, which was where we took our first water measurements, the water was relatively deep. Since most of the group did not want to enter the deeper water, Mac volunteered to go

and get the measurements. We found that the water in these first few spots was cold, salty, and had a strong current. Also, most of the wildlife, however small, was in these areas; we saw small fish, green crabs, and tons of hermit crabs. We waded further into the marsh and found that the water became warmer with a weaker current and lower salt content. Also, there were fewer animals and they were larger. We went fairly far into the marsh and had to stop when Dave got stuck in some deep mud. Enensa went to help him but ended up also getting stuck. Our group helped both of them out, but in the process Enensa ended up

losing his shoe. We were about to give up looking for the shoe when Dave pulled a large clump of mud out of the water that was the shoe. The walk back to shore was difficult because the current had gained strength and the water was much higher. When we all got back to shore we talked about our findings and mapped the marsh on large poster boards. Afterwards, we had Beach Olympics. Our first challenge was to create a boat with natural items located on the beach. Our group decided to use an already made hole and we just had to expand it. Then we all sat inside and sang a verse of "Row Your Boat." Our "hole" idea was too time-consuming and we came in last place. The second challenge was a crab-walking race. Once again, we came in last. The third challenge was to find certain crabs and grasses that we may have seen during our research earlier that day. Our team found as many items as the other groups but we lost points for finishing a couple minutes after time was called. In the end, our watch earned about ten points.

Log July 17, 2009

In oceanography we presented our zooplankton projects. Jordan and I did our presentation on the Portuguese Man-of-War and made a model out of a water bottle, paper, shoelaces, and celery leaves. We told the class identification tips and fun facts about the organisms. In nautical science we watched a movie that demonstrated what to do when there is a man overboard or you have to abandon ship. Then Terry brought out two insulation suits and Emily and Lewis raced to put them on in a minute. Emily was able to mostly put the suit on, but Lewis couldn't even get his legs in. At 1300 we had labs with Carl, Terry and Mary.

Mary had us test the density of different plastics in relation to different densities of water. Then Terry had us take apart a diesel engine and he explained the role of all the different parts. Carl discussed the history of steamboats with us. That evening we all walked to the Madden Center where Terry and Mary talked to us about life aboard the SSV *Corwith Cramer.*

Log July 20, 2009

42 degrees 35.1' N by 70 degrees 40.2' W

We started at the harbor in Gloucester and used the engine because of lack of wind. We hauled up the main stays'l and the forestays'l. We are headed to Greatsouth Channel. B watch was woken up at 0600 and had twenty minutes before breakfast. We mustered at the quarter deck and then walked around learning the names of the lines and sails. Afterwards we had orientation in which we learned how to deploy science equipment, how to put entries into the log book, how to do boat checks including in the engine room, and we went through all the emergency procedures. We all ate lunch and B watch was relieved. During my free time Dave tried to teach me how to play guitar and we all sat around on the bow. Then we helped set the main stays'l and the forestays'l.

Log July 21, 2009

Noon: 42 degrees 42.5' N by 69 degrees 18.2' W
Midnight:42 degrees 08.4' N by 69 degrees 39.1' W
Sailing South/Southwest. West along Nantucket Shoals. All the lowers and the JT are up.

My morning began with my watch working the midnight shift from 2300 to 0300. None of us got very much sleep (I got 2 hours worth), but we were all excited to work this shift. During the shift I was a lookout on the bow, hauled up the mains'l (after untying it), directed the helm, and did a boat check. Although the most challenging, hauling up the mains'l was also the most fun. The bioluminescent plankton was interesting to watch as the waves hit them. At one time I actually saw a bird dive into the water and come out covered in the plankton so that the bird appeared to be bioluminescent. Overall the shift was amazing, but I would be lying if I said that I wasn't glad to get some sleep once we were relieved by C watch. I awoke three hours later to breakfast and could not fall back asleep. At 1300 I reported to the lab for watch and was told to do a 50-count for some phytoplankton that was caught that morning. I had to count dinoflagellets and diatoms that I found until I reached a total of fifty. I decided to go beyond that and do a hundred-count of the phytoplankton; mostly because I accidentally went past fifty.

Log July 22, 2009

Direction Traveled: 180 – 190 degrees PSC
Today my watch worked from 0300 to 0700.
The sky was completely covered with clouds
and there was a dense fog. On top of that,
there was a light rain, cold air, and seas 4-5ft.
During the watch I taught Henrik how to do
boat checks, I plotted our position on the chart,
directed the helm, and was a bow lookout. The
shift was a little boring and half of my watch
became sea-sick. After breakfast and dawn

clean-up I got five hours of wonderful sleep. At 1430 we had class and my watch
reported on the weather. After class we separated into our groups and talked
about our projects that are due Friday. Next, I enjoyed my free time by hanging
out on the bow with anyone off-watch. I was then on-watch from 1900 to 2300
in the lab. We started off the watch by learning how to set up the Neuston Net.
Then Katie Hunter timed us to see how quickly and accurately we could set it up.

Our first try we did it in 4 minutes and the second time
in 2 minutes 20 seconds. Both Hunter (Scientist) and
Coleen (1st Mate) said that it was the fastest they have
ever seen it done. Plus, we made only one or two tiny
mistakes. It was important for us to know how to set up
the net accurately and quickly because we were going
to have to do the same process again in the dark.
During the rest of the watch we mainly winkled, which
is a process that finds the oxygen content in the water
samples. It is a boring and long process, but we get to
wear strange hats to make it more interesting.

Log July 25, 2009

Sailing under 4 lowers, JT, and fish. c/o 310 degrees PSC
My day began with dawn watch during which I worked
on my project and learned the lines. Gabe walked around the deck teaching me
lines for about an hour and a half before it all sunk in. When I took the test I got
all eight of them right. Now I can go aloft if I decide to. Once my watch finished
breakfast we cleaned the common areas. While we were cleaning out the
buckets on the science deck, Dave reached out to get the bucket I was cleaning,
and it fell into the water. We had to lower the small motor boat so that we could
retrieve it. Once we finished cleaning, Nolan, Jasmine, Jordan and I went out on
the bowsprit. It was really cool to be able to hang out on a net suspended just
a few feet above the water. Then I had to go to the library to do a mock group
presentation for Hunter. At 1430 we had class and we presented our projects
to everyone. My group's project was on physical properties of the water. We
explained the temperature and salinity changes along our cruise track and the
data from the CDOM and the transmissometer. The CDOM measures the amount
of Color Dissolved Organic Matter in the water. As we got further from shore the
CDOM lowered, meaning that there was less "stuff" in the water. Conversely, the

transmissometer increased as we got further from shore. The transmissometer measures the amount of light that can pass through water, so less "stuff" in the water means more light passing through. Once class was over, a few people went aloft and the rest of us went on the bowsprit. Afterwards, we had dinner and went on deck for watch. During watch we mainly worked on our journals.

Log July 26, 2009

Anchored right outside Woods Hole.
This morning we had our big field day. We cleaned EVERYTHING and it took about four hours. I was so glad I changed into old clothing because I got so gross and dirty. We also had journal reviews. I had done all my journals but I didn't plot our course on my chart. It ended up not being a problem. Once cleaning and journal reviews were over, a few of us hung out on the bowsprit. Around 1500 we were able to go swimming. Surprisingly, the water was not that cold. It actually felt really nice. We all tried climbing a line that was hanging off the side of the ship, but only Mary (Chief Scientist) and Lewis could do it. I made it to where my feet could barely get out of the water and I was surprised I could even do that. After we were told to come back on deck, most of us shampooed our hair and rinsed with the hose on the science deck. That evening we had a line challenge in which each watch had a stack of cards with the names of lines that we had to individually find. When my turn came around, I got the toughest one, the Fish Peak Jigger. I knew where the fish peak halyard was, but the jigger was not on the other side like they usually are. Finally Gabe and Coleen gave little hints and I looked up and saw that it was on the traveler. I couldn't believe it! Halfway through our stack we got a card that instructed Jasmine to tell one of the scientists a pick-up line. Chuck told her to say "Hey baby, can I buy you a fish sandwich?" It didn't make sense and Jasmine was told to think of another one. Jordan told her a good pick-up line and we were able to move onto our next card. Our last card told us to make a conga line and walk around the ship, so we did just that. My watch was so happy when we won the challenge! That night we drank swizzle and had a gear-adrift auction. It was hilarious watching people humiliate themselves for a lost jacket or water bottle. I was very thankful that none of my stuff had been in gear-adrift. After the festivities we went to sleep.

This concludes my experience at SEA. I learned so much and brought back memories that I will forever cherish. Before this trip I forgot how much I loved the sailing aspect of being out at sea. I began with mostly science on my mind and left with the desire to sail my entire life.

Aboard a White Bird of the Sea
My Adventure at Science at Sea III

By Rosalind Waltz-Peters

You stand alone in the bow of the ship. Below you, in the inky water, wave crests shine like the moon with bright, white phosphorescence, while above you, the twinkling stars outshine even the waves. As you observe the horizon, where sea and sky meld into darkness, you see not a single artificial light, for you and your fellow crew are the only people for miles in any direction and all is peaceful: the sliver path of moonlight from your ship to the horizon, the creak of sails, the salt breeze in your face. From time to time you look up into the sky, and wish upon a shooting star.

This particular shipboard experience, though not exactly a teaching experience in and of itself, provided a wonderful and calm period for contemplation of what I had learned during my time at Science at Sea III. Some of these lessons were very specific to sailing, while others will have applications throughout my life. Due to the challenging demands of the land course, I became a more efficient student. We had six hours of classes every day, with an additional evening lecture on some days. Between these commitments and daily chores, one had to prioritize and work very effectively to get all of the daily homework, journal entries, and long term projects done. Normally, I am a perfectionist, but with the work load at camp I learned how to do a good, solid job without spending too long on the details, which made each individual assignment quick enough to allow me to complete everything decently. I also learned better community living skills as I lived in a dorm room with two other girls while on land and onboard the one hundred thirty-four foot sailing ship, the S.S.V. *Corwith Cramer*, with thirty-seven other people while at sea. At sea, the only personal space was your tiny bunk, so you learned to be forever amicable, as you spent all of your free time in public spaces. When I live at college, I will make an attempt to act in what I quickly discovered is the thoughtful, community way: keeping your things contained in one area, being quiet late at night, taking short showers and in general, not tying up the community bathroom any longer than necessary. Both working faster but at a slightly less perfect level and community living skills will serve me well for college and life, but these skills will also help me now, particularly my improved study skills, as I am taking six honors courses this year.

More exciting were the skills I learned that pertained directly to sailing. On shore, there were three main classes. The first was Maritime Studies. In this, we covered the history and origins of sailing, its effect on various countries, and the images associated with it. I found our discussion on what had motivated people throughout time to go to sea, and the past and present day significance of "going to sea" fascinating. I was also amazed at how much of an extension of my freshman world-history class Maritime Studies was. It linked into many of our major units, such as imperialism, and gave me a whole new perspective on many of the historical events we had covered and their connections to each other.

Once on a boat, I also had a greater appreciation for the genius that had gone into designing our ship, the S.S.V. *Corwith Cramer,* and the luxury I was living in, compared to historical seafaring.

A second class we took on land was Oceanography. In this class I learned a great deal about winds and currents. Some of this information linked into what I already knew about the Gulf Stream and Atlantic Conveyor Current, but it also helped broaden my knowledge. It also prepared our group for the scientific work we would be doing on the ship by teaching us about scientific instruments, from Neuston tows, to secchi disks, to transmissometers. While on shore, we learned transecting and how accurate a transect was as a sampling of a whole. Discovering how to transect, we slogged through a salt marsh and swam across a harbor on transecting routes, stopping periodically to record changes in surface features (in the case of the salt marsh) and depth and bottom type (in the case of the harbor).The data we later recorded on board the S.S.V. *Corwith Cramer* was transect data, our transect being the ship's route through a small portion of the Atlantic Ocean. These activities were not only very exciting and hands on, but taught me a new scientific skill.

Linking to what we had learned in Oceanography about currents and winds, were our lessons in Nautical Science. These had the most practical applications on board the ship. We learned basic navigation with a chart, dividers, and triangles, as well as how to calculate true, magnetic, and ship's compass courses. Towards the end of the land course, we had a "Nautical Olympics" in which we competed in knot tying, boxing the thirty-two points of the compass, and setting, striking, and furling a sail, among other skills.

Even more nautical science was taught on board the ship. For the ship's log, we took hourly weather observations. I became competent at identifying direction of the winds and seas as well as their strength and height (respectively) by eye and feel when I completed log entries. We were taught how to steer a course, and spent about an hour of every watch we were on deck at the helm. Additionally, I am proud to say that I can now identify every sail on the S.S.V. *Corwith Cramer.*

By the time I disembarked, I could name every line on the ship as well. These feats not withstanding, my proudest accomplishment aboard the S.S.V. *Corwith Cramer* was to climb nearly all one hundred ten feet of the *Cramer's* foremast. Climbing the ratlines without being clipped onto anything as I moved terrified me, particularly when I had to go through the hole in the higher of the two small platforms attached to the mast. There seemed to be no footholds below it, nor any handhold above it. To make matters worse, I could barely squeeze through, it was so small. Still, when I persevered and got through it and up even higher on the ratlines, about six feet from the top of the mast, I was triumphant. I had conquered my fears and shown myself that when I set my mind to it, I could do even the most seemingly impossible things on the ship.

The number of scientific skills taught aboard the ship nearly matched the number of nautical skills gained. I had my first experience operating a hydrowinch and J-frame to deploy scientific apparatus. From the samples we collected in various nets and tows, I was taught how to perform a Winkler Titration to test for dissolved oxygen in water samples and how to filter chlorophyll a out of other seawater samples. I also helped with a hundred count of zooplankton, in which I struggled to identify and differentiate between copepods and other organisms. Though I thought the lab work was very interesting and I loved its new challenges, I believe the most enthralling events were when we saw a pod of pilot whales and the several occasions when we say manta rays (with small cleaning fish attached) or dolphins (Atlantic Spotted or Bottle-Nosed).

Overall, I feel I had a once in a lifetime experience at SAS III. From learning the basics of seamanship to discovering more about oceanography and marine biology, I believe I had a unique experience which may have influenced the course of my life. From being on a ship for a week, I also gained some memories which I will cherish for life: having twenty dolphins racing the prow of the ship, watching the sun rise over a sea that looked like quicksilver, clinging to the top of a mast and feeling I was seeing forever, being on the lone vessel with ocean in every direction, as far as the eye could see, and standing at the bow of ship in the most peace I can remember. I can only hope that someday I will once again have the pleasure of being part of the crew on a sailing ship. Thank you for helping make sailing aboard the S.S.V. *Corwith Cramer* possible for me.

Life of a Sailor

By Marann Fengler

Yes, it's a cheesy title. Yes, it's the name of a "sailing station" a lot of us have to teach. It's also what we do, part of who we are.

I've had a weird day. I woke up this morning, packed and ready to head out to meet *Lynx* in Hawaii.

I figured I'd be sweltering in a tiny bunk tonight, waiting to see how my sexy schooner danced in aqua water, but circumstances conspired against me, and when I finish this note, I'll climb into my big, comfortable bed in California, and try to sleep - despite its hardships, missing my boat, missing the life of a sailor.

It's funny how the weather, the look of a day, the feel of a breeze can take your mind places... This beautiful, not-too-hot day, that began with the expectation of weeks of sailing in tropical trade winds, has made me reflect on what I love about what I do, and I find myself longing for a boat. Days like this are what the sailor in me lives for. They are the reward for all the suffering she endures.

Last summer, there were many days when I wondered what I was doing on a boat, why I willingly was putting myself through what, at times, seemed more or less like torture. I know I haven't experienced anything near the scariest or worst conditions the sea has to offer, but I have been in a few hairy situations that made me question the wisdom of my decision to become a sailor. What I do is inherently risky - for example: standing on a piece of served rope of not much greater diameter than my thumb, 75 - 80 feet in the air... It isn't the safest way in the world to make your living.

Scrambling over footropes is only one aspect of the craziness of boats. The life is uncomfortable and far from glamorous. You sleep with a bunch of other people, in cramped quarters where privacy is almost non-existent, and where every snore and fart is public knowledge. You deal with complaining or puking passengers and fellow shipmates. You get filthy, covered in pine tar, fluid film, or "slush" (Vaseline used to keep the masts lubricated). You have almost no time off and work 14-15 hour (or more) days rather frequently. Your hands get torn up and so sore and swollen from use, you can hardly close them. You wear the same clothes for days on end - mostly because you're too tired to change them.

Then there are the dangerous bits. You find yourself called out of your rack at odd hours because the wind has decided to dictate that you take in or set sail. You're on deck in your foul weather gear, freezing, trying to haul on lines in the darkness, while waves wash over you. Maybe some crisis requires your help - say, the course truss broke and there's a 700 lb yard hanging from the topsail, swinging and swaying in ways it never was meant to. It's got to be fixed or at least tamed now. The boat and the ocean don't care that it's 2:18 in the morning and you've finally managed to get warm and fall asleep after your last watch.

You see waves, towering double-digit feet above your boat and wonder how you don't get swallowed completely. You watch gaping holes drop open beside you, and as the dreadful lean gets worse, fear your boat will heel so far she'll tumble to the bottom and never come back. You hear something rip loose below decks and crash across a compartment, and you hope it didn't crush anyone. You watch geysers come through your scuppers as the rail goes under and a torrent of green water buries your midships guns. You slip on a wet deck, grab whatever you can to keep from going overboard, and feel your heart pound so hard you think it's going to burst from your foulie-clad chest. Wind and swell pick up to where the boat won't respond to the helm, and you pray to God you don't get knocked down. You stand at that helm so long you feel like you're going to collapse. Sometimes you come off watch and you do collapse. You feel colder than you've ever felt in your life. Every muscle in your body aches.

You find mystery bruises on the rare days you get to shower. Sometimes you're on deck for 4 or more hours without ever seeing the sun - and you can't understand how the night could possibly be so long. Exhaustion and sleep deprivation drive you to tears or nearly there, but you don't cry. You suck it up for the sake of your shipmates. Boat first, then crew, then you. That's your credo. You give more than you ever thought you had in you, yet still the boat and ocean demand more.

So why even bother? For personal growth? To challenge yourself? Learn courage? Sure, but perhaps more... for days like today.

All I had to do was glance out a window to know what it would feel like to be sailing today. Bright sun, warm on your skin, good breeze, fresh in your face. You could dial a boat in really well in these conditions and feel like you were flying. The sea would sparkle. You might get lucky and be chased by dolphins, who'd play under your bowsprit and make you wish you could join them. (Last summer, J.P. climbed down to the martingale to try and touch one. It came up right beneath him and blew. He got dolphin exhale all over him, but do you think he cared?)

Sailing on a day like this one would be magic. On days like this, the breeze fills the sails till they're shaped perfectly, drawing as well as they can. The boat skims the water, hardly seeming to touch it. It gives you a sensation of overwhelming joy, pure exhilaration, soaring. You feel no fear; you feel radiant, peaceful, refreshed, strong, like you can take on the world. You look up, up, up to the top of the rig, watch the pendant standing straight out and the mast vibrating ever so slightly, and feel like the luckiest person on earth.

If you're (silly enough to be) below in a rack, you can hear water streaming along the hull. It's a comforting sound, a bit like sandpaper being pushed slowly across a very long piece of wood. Every so often, the boat will hit a bigger swell and jump a little, sending tiny waterfalls of spray over the bow - if you're on *Lynx*, you might get drenched. But the day being what it is, you'll dry soon enough.

It's hard to remember days like this during dark, cold, stormy nights when you're wondering how you'll live to see another day. But you do see another, and then, sooner or later, there comes another glorious, sunny day like today to remind you why you brave it all, and how fortunate you are.

Am I being melodramatic? Romantic? Exaggerating? Probably. Wouldn't be the first time. But I have had the privilege of knowing every feeling I've described here, and they all add up to being vibrantly alive. So while I'm sad I won't be enjoying beautiful days in Hawaii on a boat I love with people I love, I feel extremely grateful for all the beautiful days I've had, and I choose to believe there are more beautiful days on boats in my future. I am truly blessed to be a part of this amazing brother/sisterhood of tall ship sailors, and to know that no matter where I am, if there's a tall ship nearby, there's a good chance I'll be able to tag along on a sail and indulge this brutal, wonderful passion of mine.

What a Long, Strange Voyage It Has Been...

By Matthew Maples

Again I found myself on a tall ship in Charleston Harbor. Above me, three masts of wind-catching canvas obscured the blue sky. Sun-warmed wood lent life to a deck beneath the roughened leather soles of my bare feet. Now free of dock lines, the ship heaved gently forward through the waves. Around us, a swarm of white pleasure boats escorted us to the harbor entrance. Ahead and behind us was a parade of beautiful tall ships dressed in their most colorful flags. But wait, this scene is familiar. Two summers ago, I also left the harbor of Charleston on a three-masted barque in a parade of sail, a farewell festivity to crown a TALL SHIPS CHALLENGE® port festival. As I stood on the deck of the three masted barque *Europa* during this summer's 2009 TALL SHIPS ATLANTIC CHALLENGE®, it was a profound moment to recall that 2007 event because that was my very first day on a tall ship. It is there that the similarities end. I was on a different barque-rigged ship this time. Not the *Picton Castle* of old, but on the Dutch vessel *Europa*. And this time, I knew what I was doing!

My first day of sailing on *Picton Castle* was a very confusing one for me. In quick succession, Captain Moreland called out orders to set sail. I understood neither the names of the sails, nor the lines that control them which looked like a vine-choked jungle of confusion. I was both humbled and awed as I watched the crew and experienced trainees of *Picton Castle* erupt into a flurry of controlled chaos that saw hands hauling on and casting off lines. I was startled by the shouts of repeated orders, calls and commands, full of words that made no sense. Amid this sensory overload, I found I could do little more than help others haul on lines.

That was two years ago. My summer on *Picton Castle* endowed me with the experience I needed to begin working as crew on other tall ships. Since then, I have worked the decks of *Irving* and *Exy Johnson*, U.S. Brig *Niagara* and *Spirit of Massachusetts.* Now, as a deckhand on the *Europa,* I knew just how to raise those sails.

Being a deckhand on a tall ship does not only mean being able to hand, reef and steer, I find that it also means being in a mid-level leadership role. Before sailing tall ships I was never someone who went out of their way to take the lead in a situation. Being able to communicate effectively is a skill I had to become competent in as soon as I knew my way around a tall ship. When the mate or captain tells me to "Take in t'gallants", I put trainees into stations so that that every line is manned. I then call the orders while watching to ensure that the order is carried out quickly and safely.

As the orders to set sail come from the quarterdeck, I lead the new crew to the pin rail and put lines in their hands followed with a short instruction. I can see myself reflected in their bewildered faces. With that first memory still fresh in mind, I like to make it a point to go out of my way to explain things to trainees in quiet moments. My favorite things to teach are the lines, sails and helm. It can be really frustrating trying to teach someone how to "drive a car on ice", but with patience and practice they get it. When trainees become disillusioned at their first time steering, I relate to them that on my first time at the helm, a mate on *Picton Castle* asked me if I was trying to write my name with the wake.

There is one lesson I have learned that rises above all others and that is to have the confidence to allow others to truly grow in their skills by allowing them to take some real control. I always appreciated it when watch-leaders or mates would encourage me to experience an aspect of their duties. On *Europa*, I was allowed to be mast captain and call the commands for the main mast for taking in sail and bracing the yards. Understanding why the mates wanted things to happen in a certain way doesn't make sense until seen from their vantage point. With their patience and confidence as an example I, in turn, made it a point to let trainees fill in for my role by calling commands and working the sails.

Crossing the North Atlantic Ocean from Nova Scotia to Ireland on *Europa* this summer, was where I saw the manifestation of these changes in myself and these aspects of sail training take full effect. On board we had a full complement of trainees, most of them young, all of whom were extraordinarily eager to learn. Of the 35 or so, 18 were from Northern Ireland and were being sponsored by the city of Belfast for the TALL SHIPS ATLANTIC CHALLENGE® 2009 race. Our passage would take about three weeks and in that time the crew would do our best to make sailors out of these trainees. Ever since I was a kid reading about Columbus, I wondered what it must be like to sail across that vast expanse. To me, crossing the ocean was a rite of passage and a true challenge.

As we left Nova Scotia in our wake, we did so in the company of *Mircea, Sagres, Eagle,* and *Kruzenshtern*. In solidarity we flew great spreads of canvas as five barques, all built in pre-war Germany, once again united over time, made for the open ocean and to Europe. I can find no words that can convey the excitement on board a tall ship now free of its dock-lines and heading out towards the vast, azure horizon. All the pent-up anxiety from time in port spent stockpiling supplies and maintenance is released with the sails and made manifest in the sonic bellows of the ship's horn as she signals the beginning of a voyage. That initial loud departure quickly gives way to the graceful silence of the open ocean. From then on, the creaking of the ship and lapping of water on the hull becomes the soundtrack to our conversations on the quarterdeck.

We first headed southeast which gave us a warm, trade-wind crossing for the first week and a half. Sunshine, sunbathing, warm wind and the tweaking of studding sails characterized the beginning of our voyage. Meanwhile, our compatriots farther north endured the chill and fog of the more northern latitudes.

Having experienced rougher weather at sea, I appreciated the sun but our eager trainees were thirsting for something more challenging. They got what they wanted in our last week as we headed north and into the fog, rain and wild winds of the grey North Atlantic. For several days, we saw our speed increase to 10, 11, even 12 knots as the winds increased, topping at near gale-force. At its height, we were surfing our hull down waves over twenty feet high running with topsails, trysail and foresail to keep our bow down. It was exciting for us to see waves crashing over the rail on the main deck, burying the pin-rail behind a waterfall. Once, while at the helm, another crew member and I were steering when a surprise wave snuck over the rail on the poop deck with enough force to pick up the heavy, wooden, traction floorboards we weren't standing on and nearly carried them over the side! The bosun, who has spent many seasons on *Europa,* said that he had never seen the helm "pooped" like that.

The morning of our 19th day at sea revealed the northwest coast of Ireland to us, its rounded hills and sawed-off, craggy coastline silhouetted in the sunrise. Many of our Northern Irish trainees were less excited though, as the sight made them realize their ocean odyssey was in its final act. Trainees Sean and Ciara reflected on what they had seen, how far they had come, and they realized they would greatly miss sailing, especially on *Europa* with their family of shipmates. Sean was all abuzz with his plans to continue sailing, "I want to do more traveling, but I want my means of travel to be on a boat." I fear he has acquired the sailing "bug" that infects one with an insatiable necessity for adventure and a loathing for anything that smacks of banality.

I am often asked why I want to return to sea and my answer is to get away from the noise. Among my favorite moments is during a quiet night watch, far from land's light and noise pollution, where the ocean possesses a solemn serenity that is rarely equaled. As the sails propel our floating community forward, little is to be heard beyond waves, wind and whispers. A clear night sky serves to heighten awareness to the many stars once hidden by land's light pollution and now shining unhindered. Andy Dodd, insightful *Europa* bartender, shares my sentiments and he once told me that his favorite thing about going to sea was for the refuge, "I get a solace, a peace you don't get from day to day life…time for yourself to work things out and appreciate the more simple things in life." After her first tall ship voyage I asked Ciara what the best part of being at sea was and she shared that, "Being in the middle of the ocean gives you time to think about what you want to do."

For some, to come onto deck and see nothing but water in all directions is unnerving and lonely. For others, like Andy, Ciara and I, it is a welcome respite from the distractions of normalcy and an opportunity for introspection.

Ultimately, though, it is the tall ship community that pulls me back to the deck and sails. A tall ship, alone on the ocean is a veritable floating community. To work, eat, and socialize together with a small group of very different people is a lifestyle that many in contemporary western-style society are not accustomed to. I find that the proximity forces us to find connections and creates a bond close enough to be called a family. On ship we stick our necks out for each other, share bad jokes, peel potatoes for dinner and share in an adventure. Time and again, I see shipmates rise up to help their friends long past their own working hours. I see shipmates pop into the galley, smiling and willing to help clean dishes, or even to lend an ear to the thoughtful on a late-night watch at the helm.

It is a different way of life than many are used to, but I feel it brings out the best in people. A small community brought together by teamwork and camaraderie which is tested daily by trials and adventures. Sailing onboard these tall ships definitely brings out the best in me and that feeling will keep bringing me back to the sea, again and again.

Tall Ship:
A Cultural Evolution

By Karen Quinn

On a still, moonless evening in June on the coastal waters of the Pacific Ocean, my new shipmate invited me to engage in a venerable and exclusive ritual aboard the 1812 privateer ship *Lynx.* When I had climbed onto the ship twenty-four hours earlier, I was merely an outsider, an observer, a passenger. The *Lynx* crew was a well-oiled machine that sailed the ship with unrivaled efficiency and professionalism, and my bumbling presence on board felt like an annoyance. As I descended apprehensively into the belly of the ship, I stole one last glance at the receding shoreline. I was about to be immersed into an age-old tradition of the tall ship, and simultaneously experience and contribute to the evolution of that tradition.

I took my place at the table in the saloon. My companions, still bundled up in old-fashioned woolen pea coats, neck scarves and knitted knickers, crowded around the tiny dining area laughing and exchanging barbs. We grabbed our plates and cups from an antique hutch that was hand-carved for *Lynx* to represent an 1812 period piece. The captain of the ship removed his cap to expose his long, silvery hair before he hunkered down at the head of the table, just as he would have almost two centuries ago. His first mate, distant and intimidating despite his mere twenty years, sat opposite the captain. The bosun, who wore his earnest vivacity on his tattered sleeve, offered jokes and tales to entertain the ragged crew.

The scene's charming antiquity quickly dissipated, however, when the ship's cook, a noisy, opinionated chick from LA with a penchant for bad rap music, suddenly emerged from the galley with a value-sized bag of Tostitos and several cans of Diet Coke. As we dined on tacos with salsa and sour cream, the crew, who had been living aboard the 130-foot ship for several months, sailing from port to port, discussed their latest Facebook friendships, quoted their favorite movies and television shows, and compared the features of their digital cameras.

The conversation turned serious when the engineer, a cantankerous malcontent with intensely blue eyes, weathered skin and tattooed arms, addressed his shipmates. He suggested ways in which the crew could function and communicate more efficiently when under sail. His companions listened intently, and when the first mate chimed in with a few suggestions of his own, the crew remained silent and reflective. They discussed the wind and the weather, the conditions of the canvas and rigging aboard the ship, *Lynx's* hierarchy of command, and the following day's schedule. Though a GPS system had been installed right next to the ship's binnacle several years ago, the sailors still worked together to hone their navigational skills and harness the wind. The current crew was made up of characters from all walks of modern life, but their mission remained the same as it had been in 1812.

My immersion in simple tall ship rituals such as nightly dinner in the *Lynx* saloon granted me the opportunity to experience a culture on the brink of extinction. The American Sail Training Association seeks to preserve and promote maritime heritage by encouraging young people from all over the world to participate actively in maritime legacy. Participants in sailing programs often experience deeply profound personal development during their time at sea. I found, however, that my own revelations were far less introspective than I had anticipated. Instead, I became fascinated by the anthropological implications of globalization on a remote culture, and the ways in which maritime heritage becomes both diluted and enriched by this process.

In his 2000 article for National Geographic "Global Culture," Joel L. Swerdlow argues that "the rapid disappearance of remote cultures is part of a larger trend. Human societies have always mixed and changed," he observes, "but goods, people, and ideas move farther and faster today, spreading an urban-oriented, technology-based culture around the globe." In the nautical world, the process of globalization negates an ancient institution by replacing sailing ships with motor liners and tankers. In fact, water travel in general has become almost obsolete, and the practice of sailing has become naught but a luxury for the wealthy. The world's vastness, which Christopher Columbus himself set out to encounter, has shrunk with the advent of technologies that seem to collapse space and time. All that remains is a trove of literature, cartography, art, music, and tradition to remind us of the wonder of discovery and to capture an experience that seems to hold no place in the modern world.

Why then maintain the tall ship? Why perpetuate this outdated method of transportation? Over the centuries during which sailors have developed their lingo, behavior, and artistic expression, they have formed one of the world's most unique and fascinating subcultures. I have come to realize that this "subculture," though endangered, still exists today. Modern tall ship crews like the one on *Lynx* have indeed adopted the "technology-based," "urban-oriented" global culture that Swerdlow discusses in his article, but they also maintain the ancient codes and principles of operating a ship when underway. We maintain the tall ship and the old fashioned maritime culture because there is something in our blood, something passed down to us from our fathers and their fathers before them, that draws us to the sea. We long for the solitude found only beneath a starry sky miles from civilization, and we crave the camaraderie practiced only on the deck of a sailing ship. Like Ahab's assorted crew, modern tall ship sailors come from all over the world and every walk of life to participate in this legacy that we have inherited. By preserving the tall ship, we have the opportunity to discover and explore this cultural heritage, and to appreciate something more profound about ourselves.

In order to make these unique discoveries and participate in this heritage, we must first understand the "roots" of tall ship culture; the things that remain invariable. For example, though modern global culture is increasingly "flat," as Thomas Friedman puts it in his book *The World is Flat*, tall ship culture continues to revolve around hierarchy and chain of command. Unlike the increasing homogeneity and democratization of the rest of the world, the tall ship depends on distinctions between the chain of command. To an outsider, the sometimes dogged preservation of these dated structures can be difficult to understand. One evening in Southern California, I sat and listened to my shipmates discuss a particularly difficult passage from British Columbia to San Francisco. During the mid-watch on a very windy night, the sailors on watch began to feel anxious. They woke the captain and suggested that they slow down and "take in canvas" to minimize hazard to the sailors and inevitable damage to the ship. The captain refused their request. Though the sailors stood the remainder of the watch in fear for their lives as the sails ripped and the ship careened through the treacherous sea on an impossible course, they didn't dare act against the captain's orders. The sailors, though disappointed by the captain's decision that night, always respect and obey his commands without question.

This is because tall ship culture revolves around a reverence for experience, where the most skilled and knowledgeable sailor is assigned to be in charge of the rest. I wondered to myself why, if the sailors knew they were in immediate danger, didn't they just take the sails down against the captain's orders? He would have slept through the night and never known the difference! But even in this world where individuals are responsible only for themselves, the tall ship must maintain meritocracy because it ultimately saves lives.

But even as tall ship culture remains constant in many ways, it also survives and expands in the modern world because sailors embrace the technological advancements that have come with globalization. GPS and radar allow ships to travel greater distances and make safer passages. Backup engines facilitate navigation through heavy traffic channels. Ships' generators constantly supply fresh water and electrical power. But even with these modern luxuries, sailors remain conscious about saving water and conserving energy. Sailors go for days and even weeks at a time with no showers, phones, ice or internet. Under these conditions, self-reliance replaces vanity; solidarity replaces discord. In his article "Vanishing Cultures," Wade Davis argues that "endangered" societies must be "willing and able to embrace the new on their own terms, while rejecting anything that implies the total violation of their way of life." Tall ship sailors and advocates have done just that. The endangered sailors on *Lynx* that windy night contributed unique skills and knowledge in order to make it safely through the night, utilizing GPS and radar to stay the course while still maintaining the structural configuration of a tall ship crew. The captain knew, even from his dark and peaceful cabin, that his comprehensive and progressive crew could be trusted to run the ship while he slept.

Perhaps the tall ship "way of life" remains functional and practical in the 21st century because it is not only affected by globalization, but also contributes to it. Early sailors and explorers set out to sea in order to trade foreign goods, discover new lands, and interact with new peoples. Sailors were, in fact, some of the original globetrotters in that they forged the advent of world commerce and the international exchange of ideas. Today, tall ship sailors form a network of intellectual, creative, and adventurous people who travel the world and continue to share ideas and form friendships beyond social divides.

At the end of my summer internship with the American Sail Training Association, I attended yet another tall ship ritual during which I realized that I had become part of this distinctive and complex culture. I sat on the deck of *Kaisei* laughing and clapping along while crewmembers from every ship in the TALL SHIPS CHALLENGE® fleet sang sea shanties and played instruments. We celebrated the end of the summer and our return to normalcy. I looked around at my many new friends and companions. An US Coast Guard officer from *Eagle*, dressed in his "civilian" clothing, played an accordion and sang Colombian love songs. His friend, a proud Texan, wore a tattered cowboy hat and donned a folk guitar, trying to keep up with the chords and laughing all the while. Timid cadets from the Colombian ship *Gloria* grinned and sang along in Spanish and their perfectly pressed white shirts and meticulously parted hair stood out in the crowd of unkempt sailors. On the opposite side of the ship, three girls sat with their arms wrapped around each other, cleaned and dressed up for the first time in weeks, and belted out shanties. The scruffy *Bounty* crew bid farewell to one another, discussing future ventures but knowing fairly well that their travels may never bring them together again. And though I did not belong to one particular crew, I realized that night that I did belong to the greater fraternity of tall ship sailors, a company of people who are inextricably bound by the momentous experience of life on the sea. Once indoctrinated into the tall ship culture, we become life-long members. We are connected through hundreds of generations to explorers before us, and way finders before them, and anonymous ancient sea farers before them. Preserving the tall ships and encouraging young people to set sail fortifies these bonds and reinforces our connection to the earth, to the sea, and to each other. Tall ship culture, though fundamentally antique, continues to evolve and contribute to the global culture, uniting people from all over the world in a collective intellectual movement that brings us, as it always has, back to the sea.

You Simply Will Not Know Until You Try It!

By Jovanna Hart

Describing the experience of sailing aboard a tall ship is a delusional effort. It is similar to believing you can adequately describe the taste, smell, texture and pure joy of indulging in ice cream to someone that has never experienced the pleasure. No amount of reading, photo viewing, or story listening can give you a true understanding of the sensation. It must be experienced first hand.

Sailing on a tall ship is a voyage that consumes your every sense. Seeing the lofty, wooden structure, your crew, and the physics involved. Hearing the water rushing against the hull, the booms crashing, the commands shouted across the deck. The taste of the salt air and a much-appreciated cup of hot coffee during a cold morning watch. The pure smell of the open air and the occasional unpleasant gasps of bilge tanks. Feeling the strain of twisted line in your palms, salt-crusted canvas against your hands, ocean spray against your face, and the connection created amid a hardworking crew. The sail training experience is nothing you'll find in a book, photograph, model, or museum. You simply will not know until you try it.

That said, the mission statement of the American Sail Training Association (ASTA) has a strong purpose: "To encourage character building through sail training, promote sail training to the North American public, and support education under sail." Bringing passengers aboard these ships is the only way that the incredible experiences and feelings they hold can become valued. That is why ASTA and its members are necessary. They strive to bring the absolutely incredible experience of sailing a tall ship to as many people as possible.

When I accepted the internship with ASTA this past summer, I was a virgin to the world of tall ships. Coming from inland Pennsylvania, it was not often I'd seen boats, let alone ones on such a unique and grand scale. I'd seen one tall ship in my lifetime on a trip to Corpus Christi, Texas. I was absolutely astounded by it. I took almost 40 pictures of it sitting idle at dockside. Therefore, you can imagine how stunned I was when I found out there was an entire industry surrounding hundreds of ships such as that one.

Becoming a part of the ASTA family is what prompted me to discover and continue with tall ship sailing. This industry is such an interesting niche. Every component is unlike any other group or job circuit I've ever been a part of. First of all, there are the ships. These vessels are homes and classrooms, a place for work and escape. They are beautiful from far away with their masts towering high above the water with their massive sails filled with powerful, steady wind. Their decks are crowded with lines, an organized chaos at first glance. The lines appear to be a mass of confusion; a puzzle that could never possibly be understood. However, all it takes is a voyage or two and the chaos becomes understood one line at a time.

Then, there are the people. A very interesting circle, I might say. Despite the number of members ASTA has, it is a small circle. Everyone knows everyone. Many are storytellers, teachers, and observers. You meet individuals who pride themselves on being dirtied with tar for days on end and have the ability to defy any rational human fear of heights. You meet musicians of somewhat obscure instruments, such as a tin whistle expert or a well versed accordion player. This past summer, I came to find that tall ship sailors even have a unified dance style. Although it lacks any sort of clear steps, it's somehow distinct with flailing limbs and flowing movements.

Finally, there is an entirely new vocabulary to learn. However, it's not usually learning the definitions that are difficult, but learning to drop a good portion of the letters in a word, adding an apostrophe somewhere and pronouncing it entirely different from how it is was originally spelled. That's where the confusion is created.

In general, tall ship sailing is a free spirited, but hardworking, way of living. It is a way of life built out of genuine people who care about others, the work they do while out at sea, and passing along their knowledge.

There are a thousand things that stick out in my mind from this summer and beyond. For instance, being rocked to sleep for the first time that I can remember, falling into place in a hierarchical structure, and giving every single one of my belongings a lanyard. However, I think it's the people that have struck me the most- those from ASTA, festival attendees, sailors, captains, and anyone with enthusiasm for this community and style of living. These people realize that tall ships have an irreplaceable presence in the world. It is these individuals that give tall ships their personality and the stamina to continue thriving as one of the most valuable parts of our nautical history.

I Loved It!

By Amelia Smith

When the wind blows against my face and light spray dampens my hair, I come alive with excitement. Sailing has always had this effect on me, but this summer's sail training opportunities, through the ASTA internship program, has been one of the most rewarding and amazing summers of my life. It provided me the opportunity to work within the tall ship community by assisting with festival events and sharing my love of tall ship sailing with the public. I was also able to see the importance of sail training and education for youth first-hand by travelling to exciting ports and meeting crew aboard ships from many other countries. I loved it!

There is a feeling of togetherness among those who share a voyage. It is born of shared experiences: making it through an exhilarating storm, watching a smile of confidence on a student's face, baking cookies for each other in the middle of the night, or even dissolving into pure glee at the sight of dolphins.

My favorite such experience was a storm while aboard Schooner *Virginia* during the celestial navigation crossing from Hamilton, Bermuda to Charleston, South Carolina. Dark clouds and lightning surrounded the ship just after dinner on a Sunday night. Stinging rain in sideways sheets stirred up the phosphorescence and decreased visibility. As the wind reached upwards of 55 knots, the ship's bell began to clang eerily on it's own, adding to the chill from the shift in temperature. Lightning lingered in the distance for 11 hours. Finally the stormy night was over and as the sun rose in the east, a warm breeze filled our sails and the swells calmed down.

Captain Edick said. "We'd been watching the squall line on the radar for a couple of hours, and the wind shifted around west to northwest almost like it was drawing us in." It took about three hours to get through the squall line. Then Schooner *Virginia* turned west and ran parallel to where the lightning was striking. "I've never seen anything like that," Captain Edick said about the lightning. After seeing three lightening strikes only yards from the boat, Aaron, a deckhand, says he tried to keep people laughing. "I felt like we were in good hands and knew the boat and crew could handle it."

From Charleston, I continued aboard Schooner *Virginia* to Norfolk as part of an educational program for high-schoolers. Being on an education voyage was something I'd never before experienced from a non-student perspective. It was great to see the skepticism and tired crabbiness on a kid's face slowly turn in to a sense of accomplishment and joy when they learned a new knot or remembered their compass points. The highlight, during Norfolk's Harborfest on the 4th of July, was when Schooner *Virginia* came inside the harbor opposite hundreds of people gathered along the waterfront for the festival. Turning into the wind, the students lowered the sails beautifully in a synchronized manner before docking alongside. They helped dress the ship with flags and prepared to greet their parents. They acted as docents on the ship during the reception that night, sharing with their parents what they had learned such as navigation, boat checks, sail handling and knot tying. The perfect end to a beautiful July 4th— smiling students aloft and on the main gaff watching two barges set off impressive fireworks!

Working as a team is necessary and strong bonds are forged though these shared experiences and hard work. I've heard the phrase, "Living on a ship with someone for one week is like knowing them for months." I can't imagine the close connection felt after an entire sailing season, but got a glimpse when the TALL SHIPS ATLANTIC CHALLENGE® fleet arrived in Boston, Massachusetts. Many sailors made the trip into the city to meet former shipmates they hadn't seen in ages. One person I spoke with at a crew party made a fitting observation, saying he had never been among so many people who knew each other, or were only one person away from finding a friend in common.

Boston's festival ended on a quiet Monday morning. A calm enveloped the harbor as the sun rose. Some ships had slipped out at dawn, and now it was time for *Etoile* and *Belle Poule* to be on their way. They began with a bagpiper on their bow, the crisp music carrying across the harbor. Still tied together, as the French sister-ships often are, they backed off the dock and into the harbor. It was a beautiful sight. I saw the national pride and culture they had carried thousands of miles to share with the TALL SHIPS ATLANTIC CHALLENGE® international fleet. I saw this moment as a farewell from all the ships and a fitting tribute for all the experiences every crewmember was able to share in together throughout the summer.

The Friendships, the Feelings, the Ships and the Ports

By Jesse Kumbera

The friendships, the feelings, the ships, and the ports. How could one possibly encapsulate in a single article the amazing adventure I had the privilege of living this summer? Looking back, I remember how fantastically excited I was to receive the e-mail telling me I had been accepted for the ASTA internship. I almost fell out of the chair in my little cubicle at school. After a previous semester of traveling, I was tired of rotting in an office. Now, I was looking at the prospect of facing the sea again and I could hardly believe my luck. I would no longer be confined to the ships in my books or the tall tales of other sailors. This time, I would tell my own stories of my own ships. After years of watching ships like *Adventuress, Lady Washington,* and *Eagle*, I would now have the opportunity to experience the ships first hand.

As I reflect on this past summer, I look back with a different kind of pride. From the outside observer looking in on a crew, it must seem a fairly exclusive group. But as a crewmember, I can completely understand why we remain so insular. In this little microcosm of the world, we lived together, ate together and, for our ship and one another, did things any reasonable person would understandably have

refused to do. I loved my fellow crew. I was frustrated with them, sick around them, and even dunked into the ocean with them. That kind of living immediately builds lifetime friends.

With the unique opportunity to sail on several different ships in a short period of time (two and a half months), it took me a while to process the vast amount of information I was taking in. I remember sitting on the grass with the other summer intern, Jo, in front of the Parliament Building in Victoria, British Columbia, and soaking in the sun before the festival started. We didn't know what was expected of us just yet or with whom we would be sailing after the event was over, but we knew we were waiting in the calm before the storm. Two days later, the ships arrived, the festival opened, and the vistors came down to the waterfront. They came to dip their toes into the world of sailors and to taste the adventure of life at sea.

Having sailed on five different ships over the course of the summer's TALL SHIPS CHALLENGE® Pacific Coast Race Series, I lived many different aspects of the sail training experience. On *Adventuress*, a 133' gaff rigged topsail schooner, I enjoyed the exhilaration of a race as we sped along at 10.5 knots heeled over to a 45 degree angle from Victoria, BC to Port Angeles, WA. I learned how to live with the bare minimum and how to share that experience with teens from the area. While most of the teens were not too happy about the idea of a vegetarian boat, they were quick to defend it when we came alongside their peers on *Zodiac* (another boat hosting the same program). This was their ship and they wouldn't stand any slights from anyone else about it. They learned how to adapt to the situation and they learned to find pride in the individuality of their experience.

On *Lady Washington,* a 112' brig, I spent the most time handling the sails either aloft in the rigging or hauling from the deck, and I have the blisters to prove it! While on board, I learned that despite the many miles of rigging aboard a ship, there is a sense of cohesion and organization to the madness. I will never forget the first time I climbed up and over the futtock shrouds, despite the very real danger of falling, and taking in the view all around me. Looking around at the beautiful inlet of Port Alberni, British Columbia, I could see the lush green mountains on either side sheltering us from the harsh wind. Looking below me, I saw the strength of the ship in her wide deck, her sails, and in her rig.

Sailing on HMCS *Oriole,* a 102' Marconi rigged ketch, from Port Alberni to San Francisco, California, I learned how to watch for damage control and to put the needs of the ship before personal comfort. With 20 foot swells chasing us and winds gusting to 40 knots, I quickly figured out that action is the best prevention of disaster. Despite the relative inexperience of some new crew, we were able to pull together when the headsails burst and the main required reefing. One of the most important lessons I took away from sailing with the Canadian Navy is that one should have many sets of extra clothes, as this was the wettest boat I have ever been on. On *Lady Washington*, the waist high rails and high sides were sufficient to guard us from the waves. On *Oriole,* the toe high rails welcomed them aboard to explore the insides of our jackets, boots, and pant legs.

From San Francisco to Oxnard, I sailed aboard *Lynx,* a 122' square topsail schooner. There I learned that the closeness of a crew can be one of the most rewarding aspects of sailing as well as one of the most stifling. With about three weeks on *Lynx,* I realized what constant maintenance is required for a ship like her to thrive. I again spent most of my time aloft but this time, I was covered in Vaseline and lanolin. In Oxnard, went to the maritime museum with the crew and watched the exhibits come alive. Each model was scrutinized and each line discussed. The one memory I treasure most about *Lynx* was sitting around the table, which was too small for everyone at one time, and watching arms shooting in every direction with people bouncing between four different conversations. It was loud, it was cramped, it was hectic and it was home.

On *Eagle*, a 295' three-masted barque, I learned about discipline and leadership during our two day sail from San Pedro to San Diego. Being a US Coast Guard vessel manned by Coast Guard personnel, I came to understand the strict procedures and teamwork necessary for running such a huge vessel. One person cannot handle any of her sails while bearing any sort of load, so the direct application of teamwork was unavoidable. Like *Adventuress, Eagle* also hosted an education program. The Tall Ships® Youth Adventure program brought onboard about 20 students from the various summer ports and challenged them to get into the routine of sailing. Some students complied with enthusiasm, while some wondered what they had done to deserve the punishment of a 4-8 am watch. To others, it was a questionably planned publicity stunt designed to make them work. But the transformation

came when we arrived into San Diego Harbor just two short days later. I watched them change as they realized that it really didn't matter how many hours they had been up or how uncomfortable they were. The point was that they had left home with doubt and returned with full of pride and accomplishment. They were able to look out on the several hundred people gathered just to see the ships arrive and realize that they were participating in something that most people only dream about. Later during the festival, I heard several of them retelling stories to their friends and family saying, "You see that sail way up there? That's the main royal. I helped furl that sail today."

Perhaps I learned the most from the transformations I saw in these kids because it mirrored my own. I am now able to spin my own tales and share my own stories about the tall ship family. And that is exactly what it is, a family. At a large crew party put on by the LA Maritime Institute in San Pedro, CA, a crew member approached me. I had only sailed with this man for a few short days, but I greeted him warmly and he said, "Isn't this great! It's like a big family reunion only now you are part of it." It hit me like a breaking wave to realize that he was completely right. I looked around the room and saw the family I had sailed with all summer. Each crew had a different flavor, each captain a different style, each ship her idiosyncrasies. But all of them accomplished one goal, to spread the tradition of tall ship sailing and share the joy of learning about oneself through the sea and sail training.

Photo by Matt Maples

Photo by Thad Koza

Photo by Matt Maples

Photo by Thad Koza

Photo by Matt Maples

Photo by Matt Maples

U.S. COAST GUARD

Photo by Matt Maples

Photo by Anders Rauk

Photo by Matt Maples

Photo by Matt Mapl

About Sail Training

"For some, sail training offers first time successes. For others, it is a much needed refresher course in life when we find ourselves, for instance, knocking hats off passerby's or staring too long at funeral processions -- which Herman Melville describes as "high time to get to sea" in Moby Dick. For all, sail training offers an absolutely unique experience."

Take Responsibility For Your Adventure!

One of the most important products of sail training is the development of a sense of judgment about what and whom you can rely on, and to what degree. This applies to: the compass, the weather forecast, your shipmates, the depths on the chart, the strength of the anchor cable, the vigilance of the lookout on the other ship, and many other things. Sail training also builds a reasoned sense of self-reliance. All of this starts from the moment you begin to think about a voyage. Use the information in this Directory to begin to evaluate and decide what might be the best sail training experience for you.

Recognize who you are dealing with and what is included. When you book a sail training trip, you are dealing with the vessel owner or its representatives— ASTA is not involved. You must evaluate whether the financial and business arrangements make sense for you. If there is connecting travel involved, for example, find out if you must make the arrangements, or if it is somehow tied into those you make with the vessel. What happens if you miss your ship because your plane is delayed, or vice versa? Do you need trip insurance? Have you confirmed with the vessel owner any possible customs or immigration issues? Will you need a passport or a pre-purchased air ticket? You must seek out the answers to these questions.

Make informed, responsible decisions about risk and safety, level of challenge, physical suitability and other important issues. One of the important reasons to embark on a sail training trip is to engage the world in a different, stimulating, and challenging way—if you want to stay warm and dry, you should stay at home by the fireplace. Much of the point is to come face-to-face with the elements. At the very least, this probably means that you will find yourself wet, chilled, or tired at some point in a challenging voyage. But everyone's threshold for this is different, and you need to find out what you are likely to be experiencing in order to find out if it is well matched for you.

Since the beginning of time, going to sea has been recognized as carrying an element of risk. These days, we more commonly think about risk in connection with highway travel or aviation, but the idea is the same: you get a pre-flight safety brief on an airliner, you get a lifeboat drill on a cruise ship. Part of the value of sail training is addressing these issues head on. You need to decide whether you are comfortable with the combination of risks and safety measures connected with your proposed sail training trip.

For example, will you be able to go aloft? Will trips in smaller craft be involved? Will you be expected to stand watch at night? Do the demands of the ship match your physical and health capabilities? Are you on medication that will (or may) become necessary during the voyage, or do you have a condition (for example, hemophilia or epilepsy) that may require special access to medical attention; if so, is the vessel operator aware of this? Will you be able to get up and down the ladders, in and out of your berth, and along a heeled-over deck? If there is an emergency, will you be needed to handle safety equipment or to help operate the vessel?

Remember that sail training is often not intended to be like a vacation. Some vessels, on the other hand, may offer leisurely voyages, where very little will be asked of you. You should arrive at a clear understanding of these issues prior to setting sail.

In short, you must satisfy yourself that the trip you are looking into is the right thing for you to do, considering safety, risk, suitability, challenge, comfort, convenience, educational value, cost, and any other factors you consider important.

> In short, you must satisfy yourself that the trip you are looking into is the right thing for you to do, considering safety, risk, suitability, challenge, comfort, convenience, educational value, cost, and any other factors you consider important.

Does the American Sail Training Association have a hand in any of this? In a word—no! ASTA is your "bulletin board" to introduce you to opportunities. However, the American Sail Training Association does not operate any vessels, and has no ability or authority to inspect, approve, or even recommend vessels or programs because programs are constantly evolving and changing.

The American Sail Training Association is a nonprofit organization with a limited staff. It serves as a forum for the sail training community, but it has no authority over what programs are offered, or how vessels are operated. The information in this Directory is supplied by the vessel operators, and ASTA can not possibly verify all the information, nor visit all the ships in order to evaluate programs. For these reasons, you must take the information in this Directory as a starting point only, subject to change and correction, and proceed directly with the vessel operator. The American Sail Training Association is not an agent or business partner for the vessel operators, and is not a travel agent.

ASTA believes in the value of sail training as a concept, but remember, from the moment you step beyond looking at this book, the decision and the resulting experiences rest with you.

Choosing A Sail Training Program

There are as many sail training programs as there are ships, and choosing the right one depends a great deal on your personal needs and desires. Sail training differs from going on a cruise ship, in that you are expected to take part in the running of the ship by handling sails and lines and standing watch, as well as working in the galley (the ship's kitchen) or performing routine cleaning or maintenance duties. To what degree depends on the sail training program you select.

Do you want a program that specializes in marine biology or adventure travel? Would you like to ship out for a day, a week, a school semester—or, for as long as it takes to circumnavigate the world? Are you interested in maritime history? In celestial navigation? Whales? Do you want the unique challenge of climbing aloft in a square-rigger? A race across the Atlantic? Maine lobster dinners aboard classic windjammers? Exotic ports of call? Will you be bringing your wheelchair? Would you like to receive academic credit?

The answers to the above questions provide a profile for just some of the options available to you. As to what sail training programs require of you—beyond an eager willingness to get the most out of your voyage—the requirements are few:

SAFETY FIRST!

Take a close look at the vessel's credentials. In the US, check to see if the vessel operates under United States Coast Guard regulations. Does the vessel currently hold a USCG-issued Certificate of Inspection (see pg 102 "Regulations for Vessels") or comparable certification from the authorities of the country in which it is registered? If it is a non-US vessel you should ensure that the vessel operates in accordance with the maritime safety rules of that country. In most cases this is supervised by a government agency similar to the US Coast Guard.

Talk to the program provider! Ask questions! Read the organization or company's literature, check out their website and, most importantly, visit the ship if you can. Get a sense of the professionalism of the operation and the quality of its program. Find out about the experience level of the captain and officers. How long have they served the ship you are looking into? If you will be joining the vessel in a distant port, or if it does not hold a current USCG Certificate of Inspection, be especially diligent in your research. Ask the program operator for the names of past trainees or clients and give them a call and ask about their experience. The amazingly diverse range of sail training opportunities featured in this book provides each of us with a variety of options.

EXPERIENCE

With very few exceptions, no prior sailing experience is required of trainees. Some programs do accept non-paying volunteers as crewmembers, but typically require experience in similar vessels or a long-term commitment—or both. Paying positions typically require a license—"Able-bodied Seaman" papers document a minimum of 180 days spent underway and successfully passing an exam administered by the US Coast Guard. Licenses are awarded to crew based on additional time underway, the tonnage of vessels served in, waters sailed, technical training, and additional testing. Trainees are encouraged to have the ability to feel comfortable in and around the water; however, many programs have no formal swimming requirements.

AGE

Most voyages are planned with a specific age group in mind. This varies from program to program, but many sail training programs start accepting unaccompanied trainees from the age of 14 (ninth grade). Ask what the composition of the ship's complement will be and, if you plan to send a young person on an extended voyage, what the in-port supervisory arrangements will be. Day sails and dockside education programs are readily available for elementary school students and overnight trips can be arranged for older school groups as well. There are a tremendous variety of adventure programs for adults of all ages, including "Elderhostel" voyages for seniors.

ACADEMIC CREDIT

Some vessels are tied directly to academic institutions that grant credit to trainees who successfully complete sail training programs as part of a course of study or project in a wide range of subjects. Some educational institutions will also grant credit for on-board independent study.

CO-EDUCATION

Just about every sail training vessel in the US sails with both male and female professional crew and programs are typically co-ed. Others are designed specifically for groups such as the Girl Scouts or in conjunction with a single-gender school or affiliated program.

COST

Prices vary considerably depending on the nature and the duration of the program and the type of vessel. Some vessels have limited financial assistance available, and some trainees, Scouting, and school groups have successfully sought private, business, and/or community support . Check with the sail training program you are interested in to see what opportunities may be available. The American Sail Training Association offers sail training scholarships and criteria and applications can be found on the ASTA website, or by calling the ASTA office.

Regulation of Vessels

Virtually all vessels are subject to some form of regulation by the national maritime authority of their "flag state"—the country in which they are registered. In the United States, these regulations are written and enforced by the United States Coast Guard, pursuant to laws enacted by Congress. Under the Safety of Life at Sea (SOLAS) Convention, administered by the International Maritime Organization (IMO), vessels of any nation signatory to the convention and over a certain size, or carrying more than 12 passengers and operating internationally, must comply with the requirements of the Convention with regard to construction, safety equipment, manning, crew training, etc. Compliance is documented in a "SOLAS Certificate" issued by the ship's national maritime authority.

US-registered vessels listed in this directory will generally fall into one of the following categories: Small Passenger Vessel, Sailing School Vessel, Oceanographic Research Vessel, and Uninspected Vessel. For each category there is a comprehensive set of regulatory requirements governing construction and arrangement, watertight integrity and stability, lifesaving and firefighting equipment, machinery and electrical systems, vessel control and equipment, and operations.

With the exception of Uninspected Vessels, all categories of US-registered vessel are subject to Coast Guard inspection on an annual basis. Upon satisfactory completion of the inspection, a Certificate of Inspection (COI) is issued, and must be permanently displayed on board the vessel. The COI spells out what waters the vessel may operate in (its authorized route), how many passengers or sailing school students may be carried, how many crew must be carried and what qualifications the master and crew must have, the requirement for and location of lifesaving and firefighting equipment, and so forth. Although not inspected annually, Uninspected Vessels (which are generally vessels less than 65 feet in length and carrying six or fewer passengers for hire) must still comply with requirements for safety equipment and a licensed skipper. The type of COI to be issued to inspected vessels is determined by both the size and construction of the vessel and the operating intentions of the owner. Some vessels carry dual certification.

The Coast Guard also prescribes the qualifications for the officers and crew of inspected vessels, and requires both that they have certain minimum levels of experience and training, and that they be examined and issued licenses or documents before they can lawfully serve on board. The following page gives a brief description of the various types of certifications governing the operation of US-flagged vessels.

Sailing School Vessels (SSV) are inspected under Title 46, Subchapter R of the Code of Federal Regulations (CFR). An SSV is a vessel of less than 500 gross tons carrying six or more sailing school students or instructors, principally propelled by sail, and operated by a nonprofit educational organization exclusively for the purpose of sailing education. Sailing School Vessels are required to pass regular inspection by the USCG in order to maintain their certification.

Passenger Vessels are certified according to size and number of passengers (not engaged in educational activities or in the operation of the vessel) carried under Title 46 of the CFR:

Subchapter C – Uninspected vessels which operate with no more than six passengers.

Subchapter T – Small passenger vessels of under 100 gross tons that carry more than six passengers and are required to pass regular USCG inspection of the ship and all onboard equipment.

Subchapter K – Small passenger vessels of under 100 gross tons that carry more than 150 passengers and are required to pass regular USCG inspection of the ship and all onboard equipment.

Subchapter H – Passenger vessels more than 100 gross tons that carry passengers for hire and are required to pass regular USCG inspection of the ship and all onboard equipment.

Attraction Vessel certification is required whenever a vessel is open to public boarding or conducts dockside programs. The vessel may be permanently moored to a pier, or it may also be certified under one or more of the above subchapters, but the Attraction Vessel COI (ATCOI) certifies its safety for dockside programs and visitation only. Oceanographic Research Vessels (ORV) are certified under Subchapter U of Title 46 of the CFR. An ORV is a vessel employed exclusively in either oceanographic (saltwater) or limnologic (freshwater) instruction and/or research, and is not necessarily equipped for passengers or other non-professionals. For more information, access the United States Coast Guard through the link on ASTA's website or contact the Government Printing Office for the above listed sections of the Code of Federal Regulations.

ASTA

Shipping Out

While often similar, each sail training vessel has its own list of suggested items so be sure to ask for it! The list shown on this and the following page is intended as an example of what you might be expected to bring. This list is from the website of the Bark *Europa* (www.barkeuropa.com).

Since 1994 the barque *Europa* has roamed the seas of the world and built up the reputation of a ship that really sails. A professional crew of 14 and a complement of 48 voyage crewmembers of all ages and nationalities sail her. Tall ships enthusiasts, some with no sailing experience, take the wheel, hoist the yards, navigate, etc. In a light breeze 30 sails bellow from *Europa*, taking her towards the horizon. (See page 163)

Recommended packing list
(List may vary slightly depending on the voyage)

Luggage
Suitcases take up a lot of space in your cabin and cannot be stowed, so we ask you only to use sturdy but soft luggage bags.

~ Luggage labels: Please make sure that you luggage is clearly labeled with your name and destination on the outside of your luggage and also put a second label or big piece of paper inside your luggage with detailed information. Also mention the ship's phone number and name.

Documents:
Bring vital documents in your carry on luggage but keep photocopies in your luggage.

~ Passport
~ Visa: It is important that you check with your own embassy for visa requirements pertaining to each country you visit during your trip on EUROPA
~ The letter of BARK EUROPA certifying that you are a bona fide crew member of EUROPA. You will receive this letter two weeks before your embarkation
~ A printout of email-addresses and telephone-numbers of loved ones at home.
~ Certificates of medical and travel insurance. We strongly advise that you arrange these insurances for you trip on EUROPA

Clothing

~ On board and ashore it is common to wear casual clothing.
~ Windproof and watertight gear to prevent you from getting wet from splashing waves, rain, deck cleaning etc. It is also important to have good shoes for these foul weather conditions
~ Clothing for all types of weather (Layers!)
~ Enough clothes for your entire voyage.
~ Socks, underwear, nightwear.
~ Comfortable shoes, like sneakers, sport shoes. When climbing in the rigging or working on deck you need to wear shoes that are closed and stay on your feet
~ Rubber boots (non-slippery)
~ Swimming clothes

Other

~ Extra pair of prescription glasses or contact lenses
~ Sunglasses (uv filter) with cord
~ Sunscreen. The sun is very strong out at sea.
~ Photo and film equipment. Memory cards, blank CD's or a spare memory stick to store your photographs.
~ Personal medicines and toiletries
~ Wall socket adaptor (if applicable). Electricity on board is 220Volt/50Hertz, standard European plugs with two circular metal pins.
~ On board you can pay (your bar bill & souvenirs) in cash. We do not accept credit cards.

Don't bring

~ Jewelry
~ You are not allowed to bring your own drinks or large amounts of food on board.

Washing

There is a washing machine on board. However its use is limited. We can only use it if there is not too much swell. Please bring hand washable and easy drying clothes with you.

Sleeping

Your bunk has a duvet with cover, one pillow with pillowcase and a sheet, so you do not need to bring a sleeping bag. Towels will be provided too. If you sleep light you might like to think about taking ear plugs.

Medical Care

If you have or have had a disorder or sickness for which you use medication we ask you to inform us in advance and bring enough medication for the entire voyage. Because we live close to each other on board the ship, colds or influenza are easily passed on to others. We advise you to take an anti-influenza injection before departure. If you have questions about a specific health problem, we advise you to get in touch with the office. We can put you in contact with one of the ship's doctors.

Seasickness

A sailing ship under sail is steadier in the water in strong winds than a motor vessel. Healthy eating and sleep are the best ways to prevent seasickness. If you fear that you might be susceptible to seasickness, you can bring anti-seasickness pills.

What is a Tall Ship?

Full-Rigged Ship

A tall ship is not a strictly defined type of sailing vessel. Most of us use the term to mean a large traditionally rigged sailing vessel, whether or not it is technically a "ship". The United States Coast Guard's training ship *Eagle*, for example, is technically a "barque". A tall ship can also be a schooner, brigantine, barquentine, brig, ketch, sloop, or a full-rigged ship depending on the number of masts and the cut of the sails.

For the purposes of classification and race rating, the American Sail Training Association adheres to the descriptions found in the Racing and Sailing Rules and Special Regulations established by Sail Training International.

CLASS A
All square-rigged vessels and all other vessels over 40m (131 feet) length overall (LOA)

CLASS B
Traditional-rigged vessels with a LOA of less than 40m (131 feet) and with a waterline length (LWL) of at least 9.14m (30 feet).

CLASS C
Modern-rigged vessels with a LOA of less than 40m (131 feet) and with a LWL of at least 9.14m (30 feet), not carrying spinnaker-like sails.

CLASS D

Modern-rigged vessels with a LOA of less than 40m (131 feet) and with a LWL of at least 9.14m (30 feet), carrying spinnaker-like sails.

Ship Shapes

Sail training vessels are as varied as the programs operated onboard them. Below are examples of the different rig configurations used by ASTA's Member Vessels. On the following page you will find a diagram of the different sails carried by a full-rigged ship as well as a glossary of terms commonly used in this book.

Two-Masted Schooner

Topsail Schooner

Three-Masted Schooner

Brigantine

Brig

Barquentine

Barque

Ship Rigging Identification

1. Bowsprit	12. Fore upper topsail	22. Main lower topgallant sail	32. Mizzen upper topgallant sail
2. Martingale	13. Fore lower topsail	23. Main upper topsail	33. Mizzen lower topgallant sail
3. Figurehead	14. Foresail, Fore course	24. Main lower topsail	34. Mizzen upper topsail
4. Flying Jib	15. Main royal staysail	25. Mainsail, Main course	35. Mizzen lower topsail
5. Outer jib	16. Main topgallant staysail	26. Mizzen royal staysail	36. Crossjack, Mizzen course
6. Inner jib	17. Main middle staysail	27. Mizzen topgallant staysail	37. Jigger topgallant staysail
7. Fore topmast staysail	18. Main topmast staysail	28. Mizzen middle staysail	38. Jigger topmast staysail
8. Foremast	19. Mainmast	29. Mizzen topmast staysail	39. Jigger staysail
9. Fore royal	20. Main royal	30. Mizzen mast	40. Jigger mast
10. Fore upper topgallant sail	21. Main upper topgallant sail	31. Mizzen royal	41. Gaff topsail
11. Fore lower topgallant sail			42. Spanker

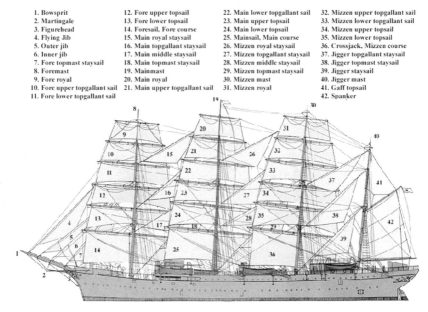

Sparred length - The length between the extremities of any spars that overhang the bow or the stern of a vessel, such as a bowsprit or a boomkin.

LOA- Length overall. The length between the forwardmost and the aftermost points on the hull of a vessel.

LOD - Length on deck. The length between the forwardmost and the aftermost points on a specified deck measured along the deck, excluding sheer.

Sheer - The fore-and-aft curvature of a vessel's main deck from bow to stern.

LWL - Length on the waterline. The length between the forwardmost and the after most points on a vessel's waterline.

DRAFT - The depth of water required to float a vessel.

BEAM- Width of a vessel at its widest part.

RIG HEIGHT - Maximum height of rig above waterline.

FREEBOARD - The vertical distance from the waterline to the freeboard deck, usually measured amidships.

FREEBOARD DECK - The uppermost deck that is designed to be watertight.

GRT - Gross registered tonnage. The volume, expressed in units of 100 cubic feet to the ton, of a vessel's total enclosed spaces below the weather deck and enclosed spaces above the deck including the bridge and accommodations.

ASTA Member Vessels

"From coastal cruising with gourmet cooking to blue water voyaging these ships are all in the business of enrichment. As diverse an agenda as this may seem at first glance, these ships all provide sail training. The common denominator is that each uses the wind and sea to teach us something else. Sail training, like reading, is not a subject in and of itself. It is a means to an end. We at ASTA often say that sail training is not learning to sail, it is learning from sailing. From the ship, from the sea, and perhaps most importantly, from yourself."

SPECIFICATIONS

Flag: USA
Rig: Gaff schooner
Homeport: New York, New York
Normal cruising waters:
New York Harbor
Sparred length: 80'
LOA: 65'
LOD: 64' 6"
LWL: 58'
Draft: 8'
Beam: 16'
Rig height: 62'
Freeboard: 3' 4"
Sail area: 1,850 square feet
Tons: 41 GRT
Power: twin 65 HP diesels
Hull: wood

ADIRONDACK

The schooner *Adirondack* is the third of five schooners to come out of the Scarano Boat Building yard, beginning with the 59-foot schooner *Madeline* and the 61-foot *Woodwind* in 1991, followed by the 105-foot schooner *America* in 1995, and a sister ship, *Adirondack II*, launched in 1999. *Adirondack* combines the virtues of turn-of-the-century schooner yachts with the latest in laminated wood technology. Offering an enviable combination of stability and speed, *Adirondack* fulfills the builder and owner's ambition of providing a quality sail for people of all ages and experience.

Who sails: School groups from elementary through college, private and corporate charters, families, and individuals of all ages
Program type: Sail training with paying trainees, passenger day sails
Built: 1994: Albany, NY, Scarano Boat
Coast Guard certification: Passenger Vessel (Subchapter T)
Crew: 3 **Trainees-passengers**: 49 daysails
Contact: Classic Harbor Line, Chelsea Piers, Suite 5912, 23rd St. at Hudson River, NY, NY 10011 USA
Tel: 212-827-1825 **Fax:** 646-349-5963
E-mail: info@Sail-NYC.com
Website: www.Sail-NYC.com

SPECIFICATIONS

Flag: USA
Rig: Gaff schooner
Homeport: Newport, Rhode Island
Normal cruising waters:
Narragansett Bay
Sparred length: 80'
LOA: 65'
LOD: 64' 6"
LWL: 58'
Draft: 8'
Beam: 16'
Rig height: 62'
Freeboard: 3' 4"
Sail area: 1,850 square feet
Tons: 41 GRT
Power: twin 60 HP diesels
Hull: wood

ADIRONDACK II

Who sails: Private charters, families, and individuals of all ages
Program type: Sail training with paying trainees, passenger day sails
Built: 1999: Albany, NY, Scarano Boat
Coast Guard certification: Passenger Vessel (Subchapter T)
Crew: 3 **Trainees-passengers:** 65 daysails
Contact: Sailing Excursions, Inc., Bowens Wharf, PO Box 1155, Newport, RI 02840 USA
Tel: 401-862-8441; 401-847-0000
Fax: 518-463-3403
E-mail: info@Sail-Newport.com
Website: www.Sail-Newport.com

The schooner *Adirondack II* was launched in August of 1999. The near-sister ship of the *Adirondack* joins the fleet of schooners known for their performance-oriented design/construction, combined with classic traditional aesthetics. With its wide-open cockpit, *Adirondack II* can comfortably accommodate groups of up to 65 trainees/passengers. While dockside, spacious cockpit doghouses double as serving space for food and beverages or classroom navigation paperwork. *Adirondack II* affirms that modern wood composite construction and 19th century elegance blend seamlessly to the benefit of all.

SPECIFICATIONS

Flag: USA
Rig: Gaff topsail schooner
Homeport:
Port Townsend, Washington
Normal cruising waters:
Puget Sound and San Juan
Islands
Sparred length: 133'
LOD: 101'
LWL: 71'
Draft: 12'
Beam: 21'
Rig height: 110'
Sail area: 5,478 square feet
Tons: 82 GRT
Power: 250 HP diesel
Hull: wood

ADVENTURESS

The 1913 schooner *Adventuress* sails to increase awareness of the majesty and vulnerability of Puget Sound. Founded in 1989, the non-profit environmental education organization, Sound Experience, provides hands-on education aboard *Adventuress* to thousands of young people annually and partners with youth-serving organizations to reach Puget Sound area at-risk teenagers. Volunteer and paid crew receive environmental and sail training. The ship's apprentice program for youth ages 14 – 18 and month-long internships for adult sailor/educators also feature extensive sail training. The non-competitive environment fosters cooperation, teamwork, and leadership skills. A National Historic Landmark and a Puget Sound treasure, the *Adventuress* is truly a boat for the people, providing empowering, life-changing experiences to more than 3,500 youth and adults each year.

Who sails: Schools and other groups from elementary through college, individuals and families
Program type: Sea education in marine science, maritime history, and ecology; passenger day and overnight sails; dockside interpretation during port visits
Season: March - October
Designer: B. B. Crowninshield
Built: 1913: East Boothbay, ME, Rice Brothers
Coast Guard certification: Passenger Vessel (Subchapter T)
Crew: 4-5, with an additional 8-10 instructors
Trainees-passengers: 45 daysails, 25 overnight
Contact: Catherine Collins, Executive Director, Sound Experience, PO Box 1390, Port Townsend, WA 98368 USA
Tel: 360-379-0438 **Fax:** 360-379-0439
E-mail: mail@soundexp.org
Web site: www.soundexp.org

SPECIFICATIONS

Flag: USA
Rig: Schooner
Homeport: Bivalve, New Jersey
Normal Cruising waters:
Delaware Bay, Delaware River, New
Jersey Coastal Waters
Sparred length: 115'
LOA: 85'
LOD: 81' 7"
LWL: 78' 3"
Draft: 6'
Beam: 22' 1"
Rig height: 67' 8"
Freeboard: 3' 6"
Sail area: 3,560 square feet
Tons: 57 GRT
Power: 225 HP diesel
Hull: wood

A. J. MEERWALD

Who sails: School groups 4th grade through college, private and corporate charters, individuals of all ages
Program type: Sail training for professional crew, volunteers, paying trainees; 3-hour educational sails, summer camp, family sails, teacher workshops, overnight programs, team building, theme sails; sea education in marine science, maritime history, ecology, and watershed awareness
Season: April 1 - November 1
Designer: Charles H. Stowman & Sons
Built: 1928: Dorchester, NJ, Charles H. Stowman & Sons
Coast Guard certification: Passenger Vessel (Subchapter T)
Crew: 11 **Trainees-passengers:** 45 daysails, 12 overnight
Contact: Meghan E. Wren, Executive Director, Bayshore Discovery Project, 2800 High Street-Bivalve, Port Norris, NJ 08349 USA
Tel: 856-785-2060 **Fax:** 856-785-2893
E-mail: info@bayshorediscoveryproject.org
Website: www.bayshorediscoveryproject.org

The Bayshore Discovery Project operates the schooner *A. J. Meerwald*, New Jersey's official tall ship, as an experiential classroom. This authentically restored ,1928 Delaware Bay oyster schooner sails from her homeport of Bivalve, New Jersey as well as annual visits to cities and coastal towns throughout New Jersey, Pennsylvania, Delaware, and occasional special trips into the Chesapeake and the Northeast Atlantic Seaboard. Students range from 4th graders to senior citizens. Subject matter ranges from the history of Delaware Bay oystering to present water quality issues. Motivating people to take care of the environment, the history and the culture of New Jersey's Bayshore region are the primary goals of all activities on the *A. J. Meerwald*, regardless of their target audience, length of program, and/or port of origin. The Bayshore Discovery Project also conducts shore-based programs, lecture series, hosts Delaware Bay Days (the second weekend in June), and provides leadership on watershed issues throughout the Delaware Estuary. Members and volunteers are the lifeblood of the organization and are always welcome.

SPECIFICATIONS

Flag: USA
Rig: Gaff schooner
Homeport: Vineyard Haven, Massachusetts
Normal cruising waters: Southern New England
Sparred length: 126'
LOA: 90'
LOD: 85'
LWL: 78'
Draft: 12' 6"
Beam: 21'
Rig height: 94'
Freeboard: 5'
Sail area: 5,000 square feet
Tons: 85 GRT
Power: twin diesels
Hull: wood

ALABAMA

The ex-pilot schooner *Alabama* is an authentic example of a typical Gloucester fishing schooner of the early 1900s. She was built for the Mobile Bar Pilot Association in Pensacola, Florida in 1926 and designed by the greatest New England designer of Gloucester schooners, Thomas F. McManus. After a major three year reconstruction, the summer of 1998 marked her first year sailing the waters of southern New England joining the *Shenandoah* in The Black Dog Tall Ships fleet of Martha's Vineyard. The *Alabama* runs six-day sailing trips for youth ages 9 to 16 from late June through late August and is available for day and sunset sails and private charter each year from Memorial Day through Columbus Day.

Who sails: School groups elementary through college, private and corporate charters, and individuals of all ages
Program type: Sail training for paying trainees ages 9 - 16; private charters and public days sails
Designer: Thomas F. McManus
Built: 1926: Pensacola, FL, Pensacola Shipbuilding Company
Coast Guard certification: Passenger Vessel (Subchapter T)
Crew: 6 **Trainees-passengers:** 49 daysails, 27 overnight
Contact: Coastwise Packet Co., dba The Black Dog Tall Ships, PO Box 429, Vineyard Haven, MA 02568 USA
Tel: 508-693-1699 **Fax:** 508-693-1881
E-mail: office@theblackdogtallships.com
Website: www.theblackdogtallships.com

SPECIFICATIONS

Flag: USA
Rig: 3-masted gaff topsail schooner
Homeport: Yorktown, Virginia
Normal cruising waters:
Chesapeake Bay (summer),
Caribbean (winter)
Sparred length: 105'
LOA: 105'
LOD: 80'
LWL: 65'
Draft: 8'
Beam: 20'
Rig height: 63'
Freeboard: 5'
Sail area: 2,778 square feet
Tons: 85 GRT
Power: 130 HP John Deere
Hull: steel

ALLIANCE

Who sails: Groups and individuals of all ages
Program type: Daysails and weekly charters
Designer: Tom Colvin
Built: 1995: Palm Coast, Florida, Treworgy Yachts
Coast Guard certification: Passenger Vessel (Subchapter T)
Crew: 4 **Trainees-passengers:** 49 daysails, 12 overnight
Contact: Laura Lohse, Yorktown Sailing Charters, P.O. Box 238, Yorktown, VA 23690 USA
Tel: 757-639-1233
E-mail: info@schooneralliance.com
Website: www.schooneralliance.com

Alliance was built in Florida in 1995 by Treworgy Yachts as the *Kathryn B.* for the windjammer charter trade. She sailed the waters of Penobscot Bay, Maine and the Caribbean Islands with weekly charter guests. In 2005, Yorktown Sailing Charters purchased her and started a public day sail business in Yorktown, Virginia, renaming her *Alliance* in honor of the French and American alliance that won the battle for independence in 1781. She sails in Virginia from May through October carrying up to 49 passengers on two and three hour cruises. In the winter, *Alliance* offers weekly charters in the Caribbean Islands. During the spring and fall, she offers overnight charters on the Chesapeake Bay. Throughout the year *Alliance* works with the Mid Atlantic Maritime Academy (MAMA) offering training cruises that meet the academic requirements for USCG 6-pack and 100 ton masters license. She can accommodate up to 12 guests for overnight cruises with a crew of four.

SPECIFICATIONS

Flag: USA
Rig: Schooner, 2-masted
Homeport: San Francisco, California
Normal cruising waters:
San Francisco Bay
Sparred length: 88'
LOA: 62'
LOD: 61' 4"
LWL: 59' 5"
Draft: 3' 6"
Beam: 23' 6"
Rig height: 76'
Freeboard: 4'
Sail area: 2,684 square feet
Tons: 47 GRT
Power: twin diesels
Hull: wood

ALMA

The last of approximately 400 scow schooners that carried cargo in the San Francisco Bay area at the turn of the century, *Alma* was built at Hunter's Point in San Francisco Bay in 1891. Today she is owned and operated by the San Francisco Maritime National Historical Park and docked at Hyde Street Pier near Fisherman's Wharf. From March to November, the *Alma* sails with a part volunteer/part professional crew on board, representing and interpreting a time when commerce moved by boat around the Bay. The volunteer program enables trainees to learn about traditional sailing and wooden boat maintenance. No fees are required as all crew volunteer to sail and maintain the *Alma* and other park vessels. The Park offers ranger-led interpretive sails on Thursdays and Saturdays from March to November.

Who sails: Park visitors, school groups, scout groups, families and individuals of all ages
Program type: A science and sailing based curriculum for students in grades 4-8, sail training, ranger-led interpretive programs under sail. Affiliated groups include the SF Maritime National Park Association, San Francisco Maritime National Historical Park, and the National Park Service.
Built: 1891: San Francisco, CA, Fred Siemers
Designer: Fred Siemers
Crew: 5 **Trainees-passengers:** 80 daysails
Contact: Lynn Cullivan, Management Assistant, San Francisco Maritime National Historical Park, Building E, Fort Mason Center, San Francisco, CA 94123 USA
Tel: 415-561-7006 **Fax:** 415-556-1624
E-mail: lynn_cullivan@nps.gov
Website: www.nps.gov/safr/historyculture/alma.htm

SPECIFICATIONS

Flag: Republic of Vanuatu
Rig: Main topsail schooner
Homeport: Port Vila, Republic of Vanuatu
Normal cruising waters: Tropical waters worldwide
Sparred length: 126'
LOA: 92'
LWL: 87'
Draft: 10'
Beam: 19'
Rig height: 85'
Freeboard: 2' 6"
Sail area: 5,700 square feet
Tons: 87 GRT
Power: Wichmann 2-cycle diesel 160 HP
Hull: riveted steel

ALVEI

Who sails: Adults 18 and over
Program type: Sail training for volunteers and paying trainees; sea education based on informal in-house participation; coastal and offshore passages
Season: Year-round
Designer: Hull unknown, accommodations and rigging, Evan Logan
Built: 1920: Montrose, Scotland
Certification: Vanuatu Maritime Authority, Charter Vessel (pending final topsides inspection)
Crew: 6 volunteer crew and 12 paying trainees
Trainees-passengers: 36 daysails, 18 overnight
Contact: Evan Logan, Owner/Operator, Alvei Sail Training Cooperative, PO Box 415, Nelson, New Zealand
Tel: 6421-111-8501 **Fax:** 643-546-8505
E-mail: alvei@yahoo.com
Website: www.alvei.com or www.alvei.de

Underway since 1995, *Alvei* makes both long Trade Wind passages using the old sailing ship routes and shorter passages among the islands of the South Pacific. From December through April, *Alvei* sails coastal waters of Australia or New Zealand. From April to December, there is a long, deep-sea passage north to the tropics, followed by inter-island passages among the islands between Tahiti and New Guinea. *Alvei* works with Project MARC, (Medical Aid to Remote Communities). From June to October she carries doctors, medical supplies, technicians and materials to Islands in Vanuatu. *Alvei* operates as a non-profit sailing co-operative. Everyone contributes both work and money toward the operation of the vessel. There are no paid positions. Duties include steering, lookout, standing watch, sail handling, anchoring and docking, along with maintenance projects such as painting, tarring, sewing, cooking and rigging. Lessons on seamanship, boat handling and navigation are provided.

SPECIFICATIONS

Flag: USA
Rig: Schooner, 3-masted
Homeport: Long Beach, California
Normal cruising waters:
Southern California
Sparred length: 129'
LOA: 105'
LOD: 101'
LWL: 92'
Draft: 10'
Beam: 22'
Rig height: 98'
Freeboard: 6'
Sail area: 4,900 square feet
Tons: 203 GRT
Power: diesel
Hull: wood

AMERICAN PRIDE

The graceful, 3-masted schooner *American Pride* was built in 1941, as a 2-masted "schooner-dragger" and launched as the *Virginia*. She spent over forty years commercially fishing the Grand Banks and George's Banks. Her career spanned the New England ports of New Bedford and Gloucester, Massachusetts and Rockland, Maine. She was a working fishing boat, spending weeks at sea in search of cod, haddock, flounder, and ocean perch. In 1986, she was completely rebuilt in Thomaston, Maine, and certified by the US Coast Guard. The restoration included adding a third mast, watertight bulkheads, new deck, bulwarks, interior, rigging and machinery. She was renamed the *Natalie Todd* and operated as a charter boat out of Bar Harbor, Maine. In October of 1996, she was purchased by the Children's Maritime Foundation, and began her historic 7,500 mile sail through the Panama Canal to her new home in Rainbow Harbor, Long Beach, California. The once successful fishing schooner now majestically sails the waters of Southern California.

Who sails: School groups elementary through college, private and corporate charters, and individuals of all ages
Program type: Scientific or living history educational programs, sail training, team building, sailing adventures
Season: Year-round
Built: 1941: Brooklyn, NY, Muller Boatworks
Coast Guard certification: Passenger Vessel (Subchapter T)
Crew: 6 (paid and volunteer) **Trainees-passengers:** 100 daysails, 48 overnight
Contact: Helen H. Clinton, Director, Children's Maritime Foundation, 4676 Lakeview Ave #109-E, Yorba Linda, CA 92886 USA
Tel: 714-970-8800 **Fax:** 714-970-8474
E-mail: theamericanpride@aol.com
Website: www.americanpride.org

SPECIFICATIONS

Flag: Italy
Rig: Full-rigged ship
Homeport: La Spezia, Italy
Normal cruising waters:
Worldwide
Sparred length: 330'
Draft: 23' 6"
Beam: 50' 9"
Hull: steel

Photo by Thad Koza

AMERIGO VESPUCCI

Who sails: Junior officers of the Italian Navy
Program type: Sail training
Season: Year-round
Built: 1931
Contact: Embassy of Italy, 3000 Whitehaven Street, NW, Washington DC 20008 USA
Tel: 202-612-4400 **Fax:** 202-518-2151
Website: www.ambwashingtondc.esteri.it/ambasciata_washington

The pride of the Italian Navy, *Amerigo Vespucci* conjures up memories of men-of-war from two centuries ago. Riding high in the water, with triple decks indicated by painted stripes, *Amerigo Vespucci* is a gracious 20th century goodwill ambassador, as well as a symbol of Italy's global maritime heritage and tradition. Named for the great explorer and cartographer of the 17th century, this elegant, full-rigged ship is a grand visitor to many ceremonial parades of sail. Since her launch, *Amerigo Vespucci* has been used to train junior officers of the Italian Navy.

SPECIFICATIONS

Flag: USA
Rig: Topsail schooner
Homeport: New Haven, Connecticut
Normal cruising waters:
East Coast of the United States
Sparred length: 129'
LOA: 85'
LOD: 81'
LWL: 79'
Draft: 10' 6"
Beam: 23'
Rig height: 100'
Sail area: 5,200 square feet
Power: Cat 3304 x 2,135
Hull: wood

AMISTAD

AMISTAD America, Inc. is a national, non-profit educational organization that promotes improved relationships between races and cultures by acknowledging our common experiences and encouraging dialogue that is based on respect. The inherent lessons and legacies of freedom, justice, perseverance, cooperation and leadership arising from the historic Amistad Incident of 1839 are symbolized by the re-created *Amistad*, Connecticut's flagship and tall ship ambassador. The Freedom Schooner visits ports nationally and internationally as an ambassador for friendship and goodwill. It serves as a floating classroom, icon and as a monument to the millions of souls that were broken or lost as a result of the insidious transatlantic slave trade. The vessel offers an important message for all Americans about our collective history and future. The homeport for Freedom Schooner *Amistad* is Long Wharf Pier in New Haven, Connecticut.

Who sails: School groups elementary through college
Program type: Sail training for crew and apprentices and paying trainees; maritime history and a full range of programming are expected; sea education in cooperation with accredited institutions and other groups; passenger day sails and dockside interpretation during home and port visits
Designer: Tri-Coastal Marine
Built: 1998 – 2000: Mystic Seaport, Mystic, CT
Coast Guard certification: Passenger Vessel (Subchapter T), Sailing School Vessel (Subchapter R)
Crew: 8, combination paid and volunteer
Trainees-passengers: 49 daysails
Contact: AMISTAD America, Inc., 746 Chapel Street, Suite 300, New Haven, CT 06510 USA
Tel: 203-495-1839 or 866-AMISTAD
Fax: 203-495-9647
E-mail: operations@amistadamerica.org
Website: www.amistadamerica.org

SPECIFICATIONS

Flag: USA
Rig: Gaff topsail schooner
Homeport: Camden, Maine
Normal cruising waters:
Maine to the Florida Keys
Sparred length: 86'
LOA: 82'
LOD: 65'
LWL: 53'
Draft: 10' 6"
Beam: 18' 9"
Rig height: 75'
Freeboard: 8'
Sail area: 2,815 square feet
Tons: 63 GRT
Power: 210 HP diesel
Hull: wood

Photo by Greg Currier Photography

APPLEDORE II

Who sails: School groups elementary through college, families, and individuals of all ages
Program type: Sail training for crew and apprentices; sea education based on informal in-house programming; passenger day sails
Season: June – October (Maine)
December – May (Florida)
Designer: Bud McIntosh
Built: 1978: South Bristol, ME, Gamage Shipyard, Herb Smith
Coast Guard certification: Passenger Vessel (Subchapter T)
Crew: 7 **Trainees-passengers:** 49 daysails, 26 overnight
Contact: John P. McKean, President, Schooner Exploration Associates, Ltd. (summer) "O" Lily Pond Drive, Camden, ME 04843 USA (winter) PO Box 4114, Key West, FL 33041-4414 USA
Tel: 207-236-8353 (year round); 305-304-9222 (winter only)
E-mail: sail@appledore2.com

The *Appledore II* is a traditional gaff-rigged schooner designed for ocean sailing. Launched in 1978, she circumnavigated the world on her maiden voyage. From her homeport of Camden, Maine, the *Appledore II* makes day sails from late June through mid-October. During the winter months, she operates out of Key West, Florida, offering day sails, snorkeling trips on North America's only living coral reef, and sunset cruises. Committed to sail training, the crew of the *Appledore II* are trained in sailing and marlinspike seamanship through operation of the vessel on day sails as well as two 2,000 mile offshore voyages yearly. Those interested should contact the *Appledore II* for possible payroll and/or volunteer positions.

SPECIFICATIONS

Flag: USA
Rig: Topsail schooner
Homeport: Bay City, Michigan
Normal cruising waters:
Saginaw Bay and Lake Huron
Sparred length: 85'
LOD: 65'
LWL: 53'
Draft: 8' 6"
Beam: 18' 5"
Rig height: 76'
Freeboard: 6'
Sail area: 3,560 square feet
Tons: 48 GRT
Power: 135 HP diesel
Hull: steel

APPLEDORE IV

The schooner *Appledore IV* is owned and operated by BaySail, a 501(C)3 non-profit corporation. Tall ship adventures aboard the *Appledore IV* further BaySail's mission: "To foster environmental stewardship of the Saginaw Bay watershed and the Great Lakes ecosystem and to provide personal development opportunities for learners of all ages through shipboard and land based educational experiences." BaySail's environmental education program, Science Under Sail, begins and ends in the classroom with materials designed to prepare students for their sailing experience and reinforce the lessons learned while on board the *Appledore IV*. During the three-and-a-half-hour excursion, trained volunteer teachers lead small groups of students through hands-on activities including collecting and analyzing water, sediment, and plankton samples. Land use, maritime history, navigation, and weather observation are also discussed. To date over 30,000 K-12 students have taken part in BaySail's award winning education programs.

Who sails: School groups elementary through college and individuals of all ages.
Program type: Half-day K-12 marine science and ecology education; public sails and private charters. **Affiliated institutions include:** Saginaw Valley State University, Delta College, and the Boy's and Girl's Clubs of Michigan.
Season: April – October
Designer: Bud McIntosh
Built: 1989: Palm Coast, FL, Treworgy Yachts
Coast Guard certification: Passenger Vessel (Subchapter T)
Crew: 4 **Trainees-passengers:** 48 daysails, 18 overnight
Contact: Roger Nugent, Executive Director, BaySail, 107 Fifth Street, Bay City, MI 48708 USA
Tel: 989-895-5193 **Fax:** 989-460-1472
E-mail: info@baysailbaycity.org
Website: www.baysailbaycity.org

SPECIFICATIONS

Flag: USA
Rig: Gaff topsail schooner,
Homeport: Bay City, Michigan
Normal cruising waters:
Great Lakes
Sparred length: 65'
LOD: 58'
LWL: 49'
Draft: 7' 6"
Beam: 14'
Rig height: 63' 6"
Freeboard: 4'
Tons: 34 GRT
Power: 90 HP diesel
Hull: steel

APPLEDORE V

Who sails: Youth ages 12 – 18.
Program type: Youth Sail Training. Affiliated with Boy's and Girl's Clubs of Michigan.
Season: April to October
Designer: Bud McIntosh
Built: 1992: Palm Coast, FL, Treworgy Yachts
Coast Guard certification: Passenger Vessel (Subchapter T)
Crew: 2 **Youth Officers:** 2 **Passengers:** 29 daysails, 9 overnight.
Contact: Roger C. Nugent, Executive Director, BaySail, 107 Fifth Street, Bay City, MI 48708 USA
Tel: 989-895-5193 **Fax:** 989-460-1472
E-mail: info@baysailbaycity.org
Website: www.baysailbaycity.org

The *Appledore V* delivers BaySail's youth sail training program "Windward Bound". During the 5 to 10-day Windward Bound voyages, *Appledore V* is sailed by a professional captain and mate, two youth officers, and nine youth trainees. On their regular watches trainees are involved in every aspect of running the ship, from navigating and steering, to galley duty and manning the oars in *Appledore's* tender on trips ashore. Selected Windward Bound voyages also include a freshwater science curriculum which combines traditional sailing with study of Great Lakes habitats, aquatic species, shoreline geology, water quality, and nautical science. Trainees who successfully complete a summer training voyage become eligible to join the year-round program and train to qualify as youth officers. In the fall, the *Appledore V* sails Lake Huron's beautiful Cheneaux Islands and the North Channel on 3 to 5 day training voyages for adults. The *Appledore V* is owned and operated by BaySail, a 501(C)3 non-profit corporation.

SPECIFICATIONS

Flag: USA
Rig: Schooner
Homeport: Newport, Rhode Island
Normal cruising waters:
Narragansett Bay
Sparred length: 80'
LOD: 63'
LWL: 52'
Draft: 6' 6"
Beam: 17'
Rig height: 63'
Freeboard: 4' 6"
Sail area: 2,000 square feet
Power: diesel
Hull: steel

Photo by Thad Koza

AQUIDNECK

The Schooner *Aquidneck* (Ah-quid-neck) is a traditional, gaff rigged, topsail schooner. *Aquidneck* is named after Aquidneck Island, the island where Newport is located and is an Indian name meaning 'Isle of Peace'. With a length of 80-feet and a beam of 17-feet, the Schooner *Aquidneck* is our largest boat and one of the largest daysail schooners in New England. She is US Coast Guard inspected for up to 49 guests. Reminiscent of coasting schooners that were built to carry freight and passengers at the turn of the century, the Schooner *Aquidneck* was designed specifically to carry guests in comfort and safety. Her cabin tops are the perfect height for comfortable seating. Her large beam provides stability and allows guests plenty of room to move about with ease. She offers a terrific, tall ship style sailing experience.

Who sails: Individuals of all ages.
Program type: Passenger day sails, private charters
Season: April – October
Designer: Charles Wittholtz
Built: 2004: Long Island, New York
Coast Guard certification: Passenger Vessel (Subchapter T)
Crew: 3 **Trainees-passengers:** 49 daysails
Contact: John Hirschler, Sightsailing, Inc., 32 Bowen's Wharf, Newport, RI 02840 USA
Tel: 800-709-7245 or 401-849-3333
E-mail: info@sightsailing.com
Website: www.sightsailing.com

SPECIFICATIONS

Flag: USA
Rig: Schooner
Homeport: Newport, Rhode Island
Normal cruising waters:
East Coast/Caribbean
Sparred length: 160'
LOA: 140'
LWL: 120'
Draft: 12' 5"
Beam: 24'
Rig height: 75'
Freeboard: 8'
Tons: 91 GRT
Power: Cat 3196 diesel 490 HP
Hull: aluminum

ARABELLA

Who sails: Adults 16 and up
Program type: Adventure travel cruises, overnight passengers
Season: Year round
Built: 1983: Palmer Johnson/custom
Coast Guard certification: Passenger Vessel (Subchapter T)
Crew: 8 **Trainees-passengers:** 149 daysails, 40 overnight
Contact: Courtney van Beuren, Marketing Coordinator, Classic Cruises of Newport/Atlantic Star Lines, Christies Landing, Newport, RI 02840 USA
Tel: 800-395-1343 **Fax:** 401-849-3023
E-mail: reservations@cruisearabella.com
Website: www.cruisearabella.com

The sailing yacht *Arabella* is a stunning 160-foot 3-masted tall ship that combines the elegance of a classic yacht with modern conveniences and amenities. She has 20 well appointed cabins, which can be booked individually, and feature private bathrooms, satellite TV, and individual climate control. Her beautiful teak decks entice with a hot water spa and shaded cabana seating. Her sailing yacht elegance and tall ship presence offer the perfect sailing experience.

SPECIFICATIONS

Flag: USA
Rig: Gaff topsail schooner
Homeport: Mystic, Connecticut
Normal cruising waters:
Fishers Island, Block Island and
Long Island Sounds
Sparred length: 81'
LOD: 56'
LWL: 48'
Draft: 7' 6"
Beam: 20'
Rig height: 75'
Freeboard: 5'
Sail area: 1,800 square feet
Tons: 20 GRT
Power: 100 HP diesel
Hull: Honduran mahogany
on white oak frames

ARGIA

Argia Cruises operates the *Argia* out of Mystic, Connecticut during the months of May through October. She is a replica of a 19th century schooner, designed and built by Captain Frank Fulchiero for the day passenger trade. She carries 49 passengers on the waters of Block Island and Long Island Sounds for two to three hour day sails, charters, and marine science/coastal ecology programs. The Coastal Ecology Program utilizes various sampling and testing techniques to provide students with a better understanding of marine and coastal ecosystems. Volunteer and intern positions are available for this program which runs in spring and fall. Paid crew positions include: deckhand, 1st and 2nd mate, licensed captain, educator and assistant educator.

Who sails: All ages
Program type: Sail training for paying trainees and passengers; sea education in marine science, maritime history, and ecology in cooperation with accredited institutions and other groups; passenger day sails
Season: May – October
Designer: Frank Fulchiero
Built: 1986: Reedville, VA and Mystic, CT, Frank Fulchiero and Jennings Boat Yard
Coast Guard certification: Passenger Vessel (Subchapter T) Inland
Crew: 5 **Trainees-passengers:** 49 daysails
Contact: Molly Arps, Argia Cruises, 15 Holmes Street, Schooner Wharf, Mystic, CT 06355 USA
Tel: 860-572-1407 **Fax:** 860-536-0000
E-mail: molly.arps@yahoo.com
Website: www.sailawaynewengland.com

SPECIFICATIONS

Flag: United Kingdom
Rig: Schooner, 2-masted
Homeport: Road Harbour, British Virgin Islands
Normal cruising waters: Worldwide
Sparred length: 112'
LOA: 101'
LOD: 94'
LWL: 71'
Draft: 10'
Beam: 25'
Rig height: 102'
Freeboard: 6'
Sail area: 4,700 square feet
Tons: 130 GRT
Power: 425 HP diesel
Hull: Steel

ARGO

Who sails: High school graduates and college age students (fall, spring, and summer)
Program type: Experiential education semesters for high school graduates and college students; accredited academics with sail and scuba training and adventure travel; service projects and adventure travel
Season: Year-round
Designer: Langan Design Associates
Built: 2006: Marsun Shipyard, Thailand
Certification: MCA (UK) inspected Small Commercial Vessel up to 24 meters LWL, Catergory 0 unrestricted ocean service
Crew: 7 **Trainees:** 26
Contact: Sea|mester, P.O. Box 5477, Sarasota, FL 34277 USA
Tel: 941-924-6789 or 800-317-6789
Fax: 941-924-6075
E-mail: info@seamester.com
Website: www.seamester.com

S/Y *Argo* is a 2-masted staysail schooner that measures 112-feet overall and accommodates 26 students and seven professional crew on ocean voyages around the globe. *Argo* is certified and inspected by the British Maritime and Coast Guard Agency as a Category 0 vessel, allowing her unrestricted operation in the world's oceans. Sailing under the Sea|mester flag, *Argo* circumnavigates the globe offering students the chance to cross oceans while furthering their educational and personal goals in a highly experiential college-level academic environment. Sea|mester offers 40 and 90-day voyages aboard *Argo* during the fall, spring, and summer quarters. Under the guidance of professional staff, students learn through interaction and involvement with a focus on oceanography, marine science, leadership, and professional mariner training. Students earn certificates in sailing and scuba diving from IYT (International Yachtmaster Training) and PADI (Professional Association of Diving Instructors). No experience is necessary. Programs are available to high school seniors, graduates, and college students.

SPECIFICATIONS

Flag: Indonesia
Rig: Schooner
Homeport: Jakarta, Indonesia
Normal cruising waters:
Worldwide
Sparred length: 129'
Draft: 9'
Beam: 22'
Hull: steel

ARUNG SAMUDERA

In 1995, the Indonesian government celebrated their golden anniversary of independence by hosting a conference, heralded the Arung Samudera '95, to draw attention to the archipelago nation. At the conclusion of the conference, a 129-foot staysail schooner purchased in New Zealand was commissioned as Indonesia's first sail training ship. Known originally as *Adventurer*, the schooner was built in 1991 to serve as a sail training vessel based in Auckland, New Zealand. She was renamed Kri *Arung Samudera* to reflect her new home and service. The honorific "kri" is used just as "HMS" is used in Britain to designate a ship in service of the Royal Navy. Together the words "arung" and "samudera" in this context mean "cruise the ocean" a fitting goal for this adventurous schooner. *Arung Samudera* embarked on a circumnavigation of the globe as her first assignment.

Program type: Sail training vessel of the Indonesian Navy
Built: 1991
Contact: Embassy of the Republic of Indonesia, 2020 Massachusetts Avenue, NW, Washington DC 20036 USA
Tel: 202-775-5200 **Fax:** 202-775-5365
Website: www.embassyofindonesia.org

SPECIFICATIONS

Flag: USA
Rig: Gaff topsail schooner
Homeport: Newport, Rhode Island
Normal cruising waters:
Narragansett Bay
Sparred length: 101'
LOD: 80'
Draft: 8'
Beam: 17' 6"
Rig height: 82'
Sail area: 2,800 square feet
Tons: 53 GRT
Hull: wood

AURORA

Who sails: School groups elementary through college, individuals, families, corporate and social groups
Program type: Passenger day sails and informal sail training
Designer: Newbert & Wallace
Built: 1947: Thomaston, ME, Newbert & Wallace
Coast Guard certification: Passenger Vessel (Subchapter T)
Crew: 3 **Trainees-passengers:** 75 daysails
Contact: IDC Charters, Inc. Goat Island Marina, Newport, RI 02840 USA
Tel: 401-849-6683
Website: www.newportexperience.com

Formerly known as the *Francis Todd*, the *Aurora* is a 2-masted schooner built in 1947 for work in the fishing industry. She retired from fishery work in 1991 and has since been rebuilt to offer ample seating, a spacious deck plan, and amenability to charter arrangements. Perfect for entertaining and special occasions, the *Aurora* is inspected and certified by the US Coast Guard as a passenger vessel. She is stable, seaworthy, and professionally maintained for comfort and safety. Based in Newport, Rhode Island, the *Aurora* sails New England waters and Narragansett Bay and is available for day sails and private charter.

SPECIFICATIONS

Flag: USA
Rig: Full-rigged ship
Homeport:
San Francisco, California
Sparred length: 301'
LOD: 256'
Draft: 22' 7"
Beam: 38' 6"
Rig height: 145'
Tons: 1,689 GRT
Hull: steel

BALCLUTHA

The 3-masted, riveted steel ship *Balclutha* was built in Glasgow, Scotland, in 1886 "to the highest class in Lloyd's Registry." As a deepwaterman, *Balclutha* and a 26-man crew rounded Cape Horn with grain for Great Britain, and later ran Pacific Coast lumber to Australia. Each year as a salmon packet, the vessel carried hundreds of men (with boats and supplies) to the salmon fishing grounds of Alaska. She was rescued from decay by the San Francisco Bay Area community in 1954, and has been restored as a memorial to the men and times of the grand days of sail. Today the vessel hosts a slate of unique school education programs presented by the San Francisco Maritime National Park Association and is open to the public as part of the San Francisco Maritime National Historical Park.

Program type: Dockside sea education in maritime history
Designer: Charles Connell
Built: 1886: Scotland, Charles
Contact: Lynn Cullivan, Management Assistant, San Francisco Maritime National Historical Park, Building E, Fort Mason Center, San Francisco, CA 94123 USA
Tel: 415-561-7006 **Fax:** 415-556-1624
E-mail: lynn_cullivan@nps.gov
Website: www.nps.gov/safr/historyculture/balclutha.htm

SPECIFICATIONS

Flag: USA
Rig: Gaff topsail schooner, 2-masted
Homeport: Oxnard, California
Normal cruising waters: Coastal California and other offshore islands
Sparred length: 136'
LOA: 129'
LOD: 94'
LWL: 85'
Draft: 10'
Beam: 23'
Rig height: 100'
Freeboard: 5' 8"
Sail area: 6,300 square feet
Tons: 95 GRT
Power: 210 HP diesel
Hull: wood

Photo from the Port of LA Collection

BILL OF RIGHTS

Who sails: Primarily youth
Program type: Educational
Season: Year-round
Designer: McCurdy, Rhodes & Bates
Built: 1971: South Bristol, ME, Harvey F. Gamage Shipyard
Coast Guard certification: Passenger Vessel (Subchapter T)
Crew: 5 (day), 8 (overnight), 4 instructors
Trainees-passengers: 83 daysails, 32 overnight
Contact: Captain Stephen Taylor, American Tall Ship Institute, PO Box 20509, Oxnard, CA 93034
Tel: 805-320-7447
E-mail: Stephen@americantallship.org
Website: www.americantallship.org

The *Bill of Rights* is operated by the non-profit American Tall Ship Institute in her new homeport of Oxnard, California. The American Tall Ship Institute provides positive youth development programs, as well as educational and sailing opportunities to local schools, youth groups, and non-profits in Ventura County. The *Bill of Rights* is a fully certified passenger vessel under USCG Subchapter T.

SPECIFICATIONS

Flag: Canada
Rig: Brigantine
Homeport: Ottawa, Ontario, Canada
Normal Cruising Waters: Upper Ottawa River
Sparred length: 90'
LOA: 87'
LOD: 68'
LWL: 57'
Draft: 6'
Beam: 15'
Rig height: 60'
Freeboard: 3'
Sail area: 2,300 square feet
Tons: 40 GRT
Power: 235 HP diesel
Hull: steel

Photo by Cal Vandergeest

BLACK JACK

On May 2, 1904, *G. B. Pattee II*, a steam tugboat, was launched in Quyon, Quebec, Canada. She worked the logging industry for 50 years on the Upper Ottawa River. In 1952 the hull was purchased by the late Captain Thomas G. Fuller and converted into a tall ship brigantine, *Black Jack*, for a family yacht. On May 2, 2004, after a major refit, *Black Jack* was re-christened and launched at Britannia Yacht Club by Her Excellency, the Right Honorable Adrienne Clarkson, Canada's Governor General. At the same time, the vessel was designated Ottawa's Signature Vessel by the City of Ottawa. Bytown Brigantine was founded by the Thomas G. Fuller Family as a charitable foundation to provide opportunities for youth to experience adventure in the time honored traditions inherent in square rigged sailing. *Black Jack* is now the centerpiece of the Black Jack Island Adventure Camp, a 10-day program where youth 12-15 sail this tall ship or one of our 27-foot navy whalers as well as participating in other various camp activities.

Who sails: Middle school 12 – 15 year olds
Program type: Sail training for paying trainees; Island Adventure Camp; overnight voyages; bursary programs available
Season: Summer and fall
Built: 1904: Scotland
Certification: Sailing School Vessel, Inland/Minor Waters
Crew: 4 high school and university students
Trainees-passengers: 15 daysails; 12 overnight
Contact: Bytown Brigantine, 2700 Queensview Drive, Ottawa, Ontario K2B 8H6 Canada
Tel: 613-596-6258 **Fax:** 613-596-5947
E-mail: tallshipinfo@tallshipsadventure.org
Website: www.tallshipsadventure.org

SPECIFICATIONS

Flag: Canada
Rig: Gaff topsail schooner
Homeport: Lunenburg, Nova Scotia, Canada
Normal Cruising Waters: East Coast of Canada and the United States
Sparred length: 181'
LOD: 143'
LWL: 112'
Draft: 16'
Beam: 27'
Rig height: 132'
Sail area: 11,139 square feet
Tons: 191 GRT
Power: 250 HP twin diesels
Hull: wood

BLUENOSE II

Who sails: Individuals and groups
Program type: Sail training for crew; passenger day sails; dockside interpretation
Season: April through September
Designer: William J. Roue, Halifax, Nova Scotia, Canada
Built: 1963: Lunenburg, Nova Scotia, Canada, Smith & Rhuland Shipyards
Certification: Canadian Coast Guard certified
Crew: 18
Contact: Director of Operations, Lunenburg Marine Museum Society, PO Box 1363, Lunenburg, Nova Scotia B0J 2C0 Canada
Tel: 866-579-4909 or 902-634-4794
Fax: 902-634-8052
E-mail: bluenose@gov.ns.ca
Website: www.schoonerbluenose2.ca

The original *Bluenose*, launched on March 26, 1921, was a typical Nova Scotia Grand Banks fishing schooner. Built at Lunenburg both for fishing and for the International Fishermen's Trophy series of races between Canada and the United States, *Bluenose* was undefeated under her legendary master, Captain Angus J. Walters of Lunenburg. Her likeness became a national emblem and is depicted on stamps and the ten-cent coin of Canada. Launched on July 24, 1963, *Bluenose II* was built from the same plans at the same yard and by some of the same men. The only difference lies in the accommodations for the coed crew of 18 and the modern navigation and communication instruments. She serves as a goodwill ambassador for the Provence of Nova Scotia, participating in tall ship events throughout the Western Hemisphere. Her 12 deckhands receive instructions from her officers in all matters of seamanship. Today she sails in the best *Bluenose* tradition, and all officers and deckhands are encouraged to enhance their skills and certifications.

SPECIFICATIONS

Flag: USA
Rig: Full rigged ship
Homeport: Greenport, Long Island, New York
Normal cruising waters: East Coast US, Canada, Florida and Europe (upon request)
Sparred length: 180'
LOD: 120'
Draft: 13'
Beam: 30'
Rig height: 115'
Freeboard: 12'
Sail area: 10,000 square feet
Tons: 412 GRT
Power: (2) twin 375 John Deere diesel
Hull: wood

BOUNTY

HMS *Bounty* was built for the 1962 movie "Mutiny on the Bounty" by MGM Studios in Lunenburg, Nova Scotia to tell the story of the famous maritime mutiny that occurred in the South Pacific in 1789. Now owned and operated by the HMS Bounty Organization LLC, she makes Greenport, Long Island, NY her homeport. The ship carries 18 full-time paid crewmembers working side by side with our sail trainees and passengers. When docked in port, the *Bounty* is open for dockside tours, private functions and educational programs. She offers day sails for individuals and groups, sail passages, and corporate sail training and is available for private functions, film production, commercials and documentaries. Strongly dedicated to the educational development of today's youth, *Bounty* works closely with universities and other non-profit organizations to provide leadership learning and youth education-at-sea programs. The mission of the *Bounty* is to preserve the skills of square rigged sailing in conjunction with youth education and sail training.

Who sails: Students, individuals, and groups of all ages
Program type: Sail passages, dockside interpretations, school groups
Season: Year-round
Designer: British Admiralty
Built: 1960: Lunenburg, Nova Scotia, Smith & Rhuland
Coast Guard certification: Moored Attraction Vessel
Crew: 18 **Trainees-passengers:** 12
Contact: Margaret Ramsey, Executive Director, HMS Bounty Organization LLC, 2806 Ship Wheel Drive, North Myrtle Beach, SC 29582 USA
Tel: 631-584-7900 **Fax:** 843-280-6856
E-mail: mramsey@tallshipbounty.org
Website: www.tallshipbounty.org

SPECIFICATIONS

Flag: USA
Rig: Schooner
Homeport: Castine, Maine
Sparred length: 100'
LOA: 88'
LOD: 83'
LWL: 72'
Draft: 10'
Beam: 20'
Rig height: 70'
Freeboard: 4'
Sail area: 2,000 square feet
Tons: 66 GRT
Power: 190 HP diesel
Hull: wood

Photo by Captain Wendell Corey

BOWDOIN

Who sails: Students of the Maine Maritime Academy
Program type: Sail training
Season: June to October
Designer: William Hand
Built: 1921, East Boothbay, ME, Hodgdon Brothers Shipyard
Coast Guard certification: Sailing School Vessel (Subchapter R), Passenger Vessel (Subchapter T), Ocean
Crew: 6 **Trainees-passengers:** 40 daysails, 11 overnight
Contact: Tim Leach, Marine Operations Manager, Castine, ME, 04421 USA
Tel: 207-326-2364 **Fax:** 207-326-2377
E-mail: john.worth@mma.edu
Website: www.mma.edu

The schooner *Bowdoin* is the flaghip of Maine Maritime Academy (MMA) sail training fleet, and the official sailing vessel of the state of Maine. Built in 1921 for exploring the Arctic waters, she is one of the strongest wooden vessels ever constructed. Between 1921 and 1954 she made 26 voyages above the Arctic Circle under the command of explorer Donald B. MacMillian. Today, *Bowdoin* serves the students of MMA, the state of Maine, and New England. She is the flagship of MMA's Sail Training Curriculum in which students learn to sail and manage traditional and modern sailing vessels. *Bowdoin's* sailing grounds include New England, Nova Scotia, Newfoundland, Labrador, and Greenland. Training afloat is performed on the Academy's fleet of over 100 vessels, including a 500-foot training ship, a 35-foot schooner, a Tugboat, five Colgate 26's, and numerous other sailing and power vessels from 15 to 50 feet. In 2008, *Bowdoin* made a return to the Arctic with Maine Maritime Academy students and continues in the tradition of Admiral MacMillan in carrying young people to the northern latitudes.

135

SPECIFICATIONS

Flag: USA
Rig: Cutter/sloop
Homeport: Wickford, Rhode Island
Normal cruising waters:
Narragansett Bay, Rhode Island
Sparred length: 63'
LOA: 58'
LOD: 55'
LWL: 53'
Draft: 2' 6"
Beam: 18'
Rig height: 59'
Freeboard: 4' 6"
Sail area: 1,317 square feet
Tons: 60 GRT
Power: 135 HP Ford
Hull: riveted iron

BRANDARIS

Brandaris, the 63-foot Dutch-design sailing vessel, was launched in 1938 as the private yacht of William De Vries Lentsch, Jr., shipyard owner and famous Dutch designer. After a colorful escape from German occupation in WWII, *Brandaris* participated in the evacuation of Dunkirk. Now berthed in Wickford, Rhode Island, she is available for excursions, sailing charters, and special occasion functions from weddings to funerals. *Brandaris* also offers a Classroom Afloat program featuring educational field trips and curriculum-based experiential learning programs. Many of these programs have received sponsorship from corporate and grant-based underwriters at no charge to schools.

Who sails: School groups from elementary through college; individuals and families; charter groups
Program type: Sail training for volunteer and paying trainees; sea education in marine science, maritime history, and ecology, in cooperation with organized groups; passenger day sails and overnight voyages
Designer: William De Vries Lentsch, Jr.
Built: 1938: Amsterdam, The Netherlands, Amsterdam Shipyard
Coast Guard certification: Passenger Vessel (Subchapter T) Inland, Near Coastal
Crew: 2 **Trainees-passengers:** 32 daysails
Contact: Captain Douglas Somers, Owner, Brandaris Sailing Charters/Friends of Brandaris, 39 Ocean Avenue, Wickford, RI 02852 USA
Tel: 401-294-1481 **Fax:** 401-294-9098
E-mail: brandaris@earthlink.net

SPECIFICATIONS

Flag: USA
Rig: Gaff schooner, 2-masted
Homeport: Mystic Seaport, Mystic, Connecticut
Normal cruising waters:
New England
Sparred length: 74'
LOD: 61' 6"
LWL: 49'
Draft: 9'
Beam: 14' 8"
Rig height: 81'
Tons: 30 GRT
Power: 97 HP diesel
Hull: wood

BRILLIANT

Who sails: Teens ages 15–19 and adults 20+; participants must be physically fit, agile, and competent swimmers; affiliated institution is Mystic Seaport

Program type: Sail training with paying trainees; sea education in cooperation with individuals and organized groups such as Scouts and schools.

Season: May through October

Designer: Sparkman & Stephens

Built: 1932: City Island, New York, Henry B. Nevins

Coast Guard certification: Sailing School Vessel (Subchapter R), Passenger Vessel (Subchapter T)

Crew: 2-3 **Trainees-passengers:** 10 daysails, 9 overnight

Contact: Mystic Seaport, Brilliant Program, PO Box 6000, Mystic, CT 06355-0990 USA

Tel: 860-572-5323 **Fax:** 860-572-5355

Website: www.mysticseaport.org/brilliant

The *Brilliant* educational sailing program introduces teens and adults to life aboard a classic schooner while sailing the New England coast. On programs ranging from 2-day trips to 10-day voyages, teenagers and adults become full participants in the sailing of *Brilliant*: steering the vessel, raising the sails, standing watch and learning navigation. Participants are not passengers but are instead crew aboard our 61- foot wooden schooner. As the oldest sail education program in the country, *Brilliant* has taught teamwork, leadership, stewardship, and traditional seamanship for over 55 years to more than 9,000 teenagers and adults. Participants learn under the guidance of a professional crew and Coast Guard licensed Captain.

SPECIFICATIONS

Flag: Canada
Rig: Barquentine
Homeport: Halifax, Nova Scotia, Canada
Normal cruising waters: North American waters and the Caribbean
Sparred length: 245'
Draft: 15'
Beam: 30'
Rig height: 132'
Sail area: 17,000 square feet
Power: 1500 HP Deutz diesel
Hull: steel

CALEDONIA

Canadian Sailing Expeditions (CSE) has developed the concept of a traditional tall ship cruise product for Atlantic Canada and the Caribbean. The square-rigged *Caledonia* hosts corporate clients and leisure travelers in old world charm onboard a traditional tall ship, with new world amenities including local gourmet cuisine prepared by our onboard chefs and finely appointed cabins with queen size berths, ensuite toilet and shower, A/C, and heat. While onboard, guests enjoy a reading room, salon, and dining salon, as well as large open spaces on deck. Zodiacs, mountain bikes, and sea kayaks are available for the guests use. Become part of the crew of a traditional sailing ship and participate in the highly challenging and rewarding life on board a tall ship at sea. *Caledonia* is designed to enable guests to have a unique and personal experience with the ship, the crew, and the cruising destination. CSE's product offers a high level of education, accommodation, adventure and scenery.

Who sails: Groups and individuals of all ages
Program type: Sail training for paying trainees, day sails, overnight passages, adventure travel cruises
Season: Year-round
Built: 1947: Beverley, United Kingdom
Trainees-passengers: 40
Contact: Captain Doug Prothero, Canadian Sailing Expeditions, PO box 2613, Halifax, NS B3J 3N5 Canada
Tel: 902-429-1474 **Fax:** 902-429-1475
E-mail: doug@canadiansailingexpeditions.com
Website: www.canadiansailingexpeditions.com

SPECIFICATIONS

Flag: USA
Rig: Schooner, 3-masted
Homeport: San Francisco, California
Sparred length: 219'
LOD: 156'
Draft: 11' 3"
Beam: 36'
Rig height: 105'
Tons: 453 GRT
Hull: wood

Photo by Steve Danford

C. A. THAYER

Program type: Dockside sea education programs in maritime history
Designer: Hans Bendixsen
Built: 1895: Fairhaven, CA, Hans Bendixsen
Contact: Lynn Cullivan, Management Assistant, San Francisco Maritime National Historical Park, Building E, Fort Mason Center, San Francisco, CA 94123 USA
Tel: 415-561-7006 **Fax:** 415-556-1624
E-mail: lynn_cullivan@nps.gov
Website: http://www.nps.gov/safr/historyculture/c-a-thayer.htm

Built in 1895, the *C. A. Thayer* was part of a mighty Pacific Coast fleet of sailing schooners that carried lumber to San Francisco from Washington, Oregon and the California Redwood Coast. Later, the vessel supplied the Alaskan salt-salmon canneries, anchoring out during the summer and returning in September with the season's catch packed in her hold. From 1925 to 1950, *C. A. Thayer* carried men north to the Bering Sea cod fishing grounds. She was purchased by the State of California in 1957, and transferred to the National Park Service in 1977. Now a National Historic Landmark, the *C. A. Thayer* is a rare survivor from the days when strong canvas sails billowed over tall deckloads of freshly milled fir and redwood. Today, the *Thayer* is open to the public daily as a part of the San Francisco Maritime National Historical Park.

SPECIFICATIONS

Flag: USA
Rig: Topsail schooner
Homeport: San Diego, California
Normal cruising waters: Southern California and the California Coast
Sparred length: 145'
LOA: 93' 4"
LWL: 84'
Draft: 9' 5"
Beam: 24'
Rig height: 95'
Freeboard: 6'
Sail area: 7,000 square feet
Tons: 130 GRT
Power: 140 HP diesel
Hull: wood

CALIFORNIAN

Californian was launched in celebration of the 1984 Summer Olympics in Los Angeles. In 2003, *Californian* was designated the official tall ship of the State of California. She is the only ship to carry this prestigious title. A 145-foot topsail schooner, *Californian* is a replica of a mid-19th century revenue cutter. She has played host to thousands of adventure travelers, sailing enthusiasts, students and history buffs during her career. In 2003, she underwent an extensive refit including a haul out, re-stepping the masts, replacing the standing rigging, new sails and mechanical systems and a re-design and refurbishing of the areas below deck. The Maritime Museum of San Diego uses her for a variety of educational programs and public adventure sails. Her annual coastal tour offers residents and visitors an opportunity to enjoy the state of California's official tall ship.

Who sails: Groups and individuals of all ages
Program type: At sea and dockside education programs in maritime history and programs for at-risk youth in cooperation with area schools and social services agencies, passenger day sails and overnight passages
Season: Year-round
Designer: Melbourne Smith
Built: 1984: San Diego, CA, Nautical Heritage Society
Trainees-passengers: 60 daysails
Contact: Peter Durdaller, San Diego Maritime Museum, 1492 N. Harbor Drive, San Diego, CA 92101 USA
Tel: 619 234 9153 x 120
E-mail: pdurdaller@sdmaritime.org
Website: www.sdmaritime.org

SPECIFICATIONS

Flag: Uruguay
Rig: Staysail schooner
Homeport: Montevideo, Uruguay
Normal cruising waters: Worldwide
Sparred length: 205'
LOA: 198'
LOD: 172'
LWL: 147' 5"
Draft: 12'
Beam: 27'
Hull: steel

Photo by Thad Koza

CAPITAN MIRANDA

Who sails: Midshipmen, civilian students, foreign guests
Program type: Sail training vessel of the Uruguayan Navy.
Built: 1930: Cadiz, Spain, Astiueros Matagorda
Crew: 12 officers, 39 enlisted
Trainees-passengers: 35
Contact: Embassy of Uruguay, 1913 I Street, NW, Suite 419, Washington, DC 20006 USA
Tel: 202-331-1313 **Fax:** 202-331-8142
E-mail: navyofuruguay@yahoo.com
Website: www.armada.mil.uy

Built in 1930 in the Matagorda Shipyard and factory located in Cadiz, Spain, the *Capitan Miranda* originally served as a hydrographic vessel. As such, she carried out an outstanding and extensive career, performing countless cartographical surveys which were, and still are, highly useful to seamen. The ship honors the memory of Captain Francisco P. Miranda (1869 – 1925), who was not only a bright professional but also an exceptional teacher, particularly remembered for his research in sea subjects. In 1977, the vessel underwent a major refit and in 1978 was rededicated as a sail training vessel for the Uruguayan navy teaching newly graduated midshipmen to apply the knowledge acquired at the Naval Academy.

SPECIFICATIONS

Flag: United Kingdom
Rig: Bermudan Cutter
Homeport: Portsmouth, England
Normal cruising waters: UK, Europe, Mediterranean, Canaries, Caribbean, Azores
LOA: 72'
LWL: 61'
Draft: 10'
Beam: 18' 2"
Rig height: 95'
Sail area: 4,020 square feet (downwind)
Tons: 38 GRT
Power: 1 x Perkins 130 HP
Hull: steel

CHALLENGER FLEET

Tall Ships Youth Trust's fleet of four 72-foot Round-the-World Challenger Yachts were designed by the renowned yacht designer Rob Humphreys. They are 72-foot steel Bermudan Cutter rigged yachts which were built in 2000, and were originally designed to be sailed around the world – they now make fantastic sail training vessels.

The Tall Ships Youth Trust, incorporating the Sail Training Association, is a registered charity founded in 1956 and is dedicated to the personal development of young people aged 14-25 through the crewing of ocean-going vessels. Every year thousands of people ages 14 to 75 from all over the world sail on either the fleet of Challenger Yachts or the Trust's 200-foot tall ship, *Stavros S Niarchos*. The Challenger Yachts operate all year round and the fleet can be split to provide sail training in two locations at the same time, for example, in the UK and in the Caribbean. Youth voyages for 14-25 year olds last from 4 to 14 nights whereas 18+ voyages range from day sails to a 24-night Trans-Atlantic.

Who sails: Groups and individuals aged 14-75
Program type: Sail training for paying trainees
Season: Year-round
Designer: Rob Humphreys
Built: 2000
Crew: 18 including 12 trainees
Contact: Tall Ships Youth Trust, 2A The Hard, Portsmouth, Hampshire PO1 3PT England
Tel: +44 (0)23 9283 2055 **Fax:** +44 (0)23 9281 5769
E-mail: info@tallships.org
Website: www.tallships.org

SPECIFICATIONS

Flag: USA
Rig: Gaff-rigged cutter
Homeport: Traverse City, Michigan
Normal cruising waters: Great Lakes
Sparred length: 53'
LOA: 39'
LWL: 35'
Draft: 5' board up, 8' board down
Beam: 12'
Rig height: 68'
Freeboard: 4'
Sail area: 1,460 square feet
Tons: 18 GRT
Hull: wood (plank on frame)

CHAMPION

Who sails: MHA members, guests, and at-risk youth throughout Northern Michigan
Program type: Sail training, maritime history, and experiential education
Designer: Fenwick Williams
Built: 1968: Concordia Yachts, Massachusetts
Coast Guard certification: Uninspected Passenger Vessel
Crew: 3 **Trainees:** 5
Contact: Mark Thompson, Executive Director, Maritime Heritage Alliance, 322 Sixth Street, Traverse City, MI 49684
Tel: 231-946-2647 **Fax:** 231-946-6750
E-mail: mark@MaritimeHeritageAlliance.org
Website: www.MaritimeHeritageAlliance.org

Champion is a beautifully maintained, 1968 Concordia-built, Great Lakes cutter donated to the Maritime Heritage Alliance in 2008 by Mr. Henry Barkhausen of Harbor Springs, Michigan. Beginning in 2009, she will be utilized in a new sailing program for at-risk youth in Northern Michigan. Qualifying youth will spend four days aboard, learning to sail the boat and work together as a team, while building responsibility and self-esteem at the same time. The boat and new program will allow the MHA to further its mission of preserving, interpreting and sharing the maritime heritage of the Great Lakes. In addition, she will be made available for limited private charters and corporate outings on West Grand Traverse Bay, an arm of Lake Michigan. *Champion* will also attend local festivals to promote the MHA and the at-risk youth sailing program, and will be available for passengers.

SPECIFICATIONS

Flag: Norway
Rig: Full-rigged ship
Homeport: Oslo, Norway
Sparred Length: 205'
Draft: 15'
Beam: 36'
Hull: steel

Photo by Thad Koza

CHRISTIAN RADICH

Christian Radich was a successful businessman and shipowner of Danish descent who died childless in 1889. He stipulated in his will that 50,000 kroner should be donated for the purpose of building a sail training ship for the youth of Norway. The funds were to be released only after the death of his wife, who lived on for 27 years. by that time, the initial endowment had grown to 106,000 kroner, an amount large enough to provide much of the capital of the entire building fund. When the ship was finally christened in 1937, it was appropriate that it bear the name of its prescient donor, Christian Radich. The *Christian Radich* is owned and administered by Ostlandets Skoleskib, the East Coast Training Ship, although Norway's Ministry of Education is responsible for its operating expenses. For the past decade sail training has been integrated into the official Norwegian school system. Its basic curriculum is a full ten months of education for 50 cadets ranging in ages from 18 - 24; in addition, 18 cooks become part of the training class.

Who sails: Individuals ages 16 and older
Program type: Sail training for paying trainees
Built: 1937: Framnæs Mekaniske Værksted
Crew: 18 Trainees-passengers: 88
Contact: Stiftelsen Christian Radich, Box 666 Sentrum N - 0106 Oslo, Norway
Tel: +47 22 47 82 70 **Fax:** +47 22 47 82 71
E-mail: postmaster@radich.no
Website: http://radich.no/en/front-page/

SPECIFICATIONS

Flag: Brazil
Rig: Full-rigged ship
Homeport: Rio de Janeiro, Brazil
Normal Cruising Waters: Worldwide
Sparred Length: 254'
LOA: 249'
LOD: 205'
LWL: 183'
Draft: 15' 9"
Beam: 34' 6"
Rig Height: 152'
Freeboard: 5' 3"
Sail Area: 23,627 square feet
Tons: 703 GRT
Power: 1001 HP diesel
Hull: steel

Photo by Thad Koza

CISNE BRANCO

Who sails: Sail Training for Officers and Cadets from Brazilian Navy, Academy of Merchant Marine and other Naval schools.
Program type: Sail training, goodwill ship and representation for Brazilian Navy
Season: Year-round
Designer: Gerard Djikstra
Built: 2000: Amsterdam, Holland, Damen shipyards
Certification: Brazilian Naval Vessel
Crew: 52 **Trainees-passengers:** 31
Contact: Embassy of Brazil, 3006 Massachusetts Ave NW, Washington, DC USA
Tel: 202-238-2805 **Fax:** 202-238-2827
Website: www.brasilemb.org

The *Cisne Branco* (White Swan) is a Brazilian navy tall ship which was built in Amsterdam, Netherlands, by Damen Shipyard. The keel was laid on November 9th, 1998 and the ship launched and christened on August 4th, 1999. She was delivered to the Brazilian Navy on February 4th, 2000 and commissioned as a Brazilian Naval vessel on March 9th, 2000. *Cisne Branco* made its maiden voyage across the Atlantic Ocean to Brazil, celebrating the 500th anniversary of the discovery of Brazil by the Portuguese Admiral Pedro Alvares Cabral. The ship's project is inspired in the design of the 19th century clippers. The *Cisne Branco* is normally used in national and international activities as a representative of the Brazilian Navy and for Brazilian culture. Also, it is used as an instructional sailing ship to the cadets of the Brazilian Naval Academy, Academy of Merchant Marine and other naval schools.

SPECIFICATIONS

Flag: Barbados
Rig: Barquentine, 3-masted
Homeport: Bridgetown, Barbados
Normal cruising waters:
Worldwide
Sparred length: 188'
LOA: 154'
LOD: 152' 6"
Draft: 13' 1"
Beam: 31'
Rig height: 115'
Freeboard: 8'
Sail area: 10,000 square feet
Tons: 398 GRT
Power: 570 HP diesel
Hull: steel

Photo by Wojtek Wacowski

CONCORDIA

West Island College – Class Afloat is an international experiential education boarding school located in Lunenburg, Nova Scotia, Canada. Its mission is to broaden student understanding of international issues while preparing them for responsible global citizenship in the 21st century. The concept of "taking the classroom to the world" is intended to encourage self-sufficiency, cooperation, and a clear awareness of other cultures. Each academic year, 96 qualifying students spend one semester at the historic land-based boarding school and one semester working as crew and studying aboard the *Concordia*, a modern tall ship. A fully certified faculty instructs students in a full curriculum including social studies and global issues, anthropology, marine biology, maths, sciences and physical education. Optional non-credit enrichment courses are also offered in seamanship, celestial navigation, and the history and traditions of the sea. Over 1000 students have joined Class Afloat and sailed the world for an academic semester or full year program. Applications from 11th and 12th grade coeds are encouraged and accepted year-round.

Who sails: 11th and 12th grade students
Program type: Full-curriculum academics and marine biology for high school students
Season: Year-round
Built: 1992: Poland
Certification: Sailing School Vessel (Subchapter R), Lloyds 100A1 and LMC
Crew: 8 **Instructors:** 8 **Trainees-passengers:** 48
Contact: West Island College International – Class Afloat, 97 Kaulbach Street, PO Box 10, Lunenburg, Nova Scotia B0J 2C0 Canada
Tel: 902-634-1895 or 800-301-7245
Fax: 902-634-7155
E-mail: discovery@classafloat.com
Website: www.classafloat.com

SPECIFICATIONS

Flag: USA
Rig: Full-rigged ship
Homeport:
Baltimore, Maryland
Sparred length: 282'
LOA: 200'
LOD: 179'
LWL: 176'
Draft: 21'
Beam: 42'
Rig height: 165'
Freeboard: 16'
Sail area: 20,000 square feet
Tons: 398 GRT
Hull: wood

USS CONSTELLATION

Program type: Dockside interpretation, overnight and day education programming
Designer: John Lenthall
Built: 1854: Gosport Naval Shipyard, Portsmouth, VA, US Navy
Contact: Historic Ships in Baltimore, Pier 1, 301 East Pratt Street, Baltimore, MD 21202 USA
Tel: 410-539-1797 **Fax:** 410-539-6238
E-mail: administration@historicships.org
Website: www.historicships.org

The last all-sail warship built by the US Navy, USS *Constellation* served her country for nearly 100 years in both military and non-military roles. From 1859-1861, she was the flagship of the US African Squadron charged with the mission of intercepting vessels engaged in the illegal slave trade along the coast of West Africa. During the Civil War, *Constellation* saw duty in the Mediterranean Sea protecting American interests, and later was reassigned to the US as part of the Gulf Coast Blockading Squadron. During her later years, she sailed as a training ship for the US Naval Academy and then as a stationary training ship at the Naval War College in Newport, Rhode Island. She was last under sail in 1893. Her final role as a commissioned vessel came during World War II when she served as flagship of the US Atlantic Fleet. In 1955, *Constellation* was brought to Baltimore to be preserved as a national shrine. The ship underwent a massive restoration to return her to her original 1854 configuration. She is now open for public tours, offering a wide array of living history and educational programs under the management of the Living Classroom Foundation.

147

SPECIFICATIONS

Flag: USA
Rig: Full-rigged ship
Homeport: Charlestown, Massachusetts
Normal cruising waters: Boston Harbor
Sparred length: 306'
LOA: 204'
LOD: 174' 10" (gun deck)
LWL: 175'
Draft: 22'
Beam: 43' 6"
Rig height: 189' 2"
Freeboard: 15'
Sail area: 42,710 square feet
Tons: 2,200 GRT
Hull: wood

USS CONSTITUTION

"Old Ironsides" is the oldest commissioned warship afloat in the world. One of six ships ordered by President George Washington to protect America's growing maritime interests in the 1790s, *Constitution* earned widespread renown for her ability to punish French privateers in the Caribbean and thwart Barbary pirates of the Mediterranean. The ship's greatest glory came during the War of 1812 when she defeated four British frigates. During her first engagement against HMS *Guerriére* in 1812, seamen nicknamed her "Old Ironsides" when they saw British cannonballs glance off her 21-inch thick oak hull. In the 1830s, the ship was going to be to be disassembled, but the public outcry, sparked by the publication of an Oliver Wendell Holmes poem, saved her. Over the following century, the ship undertook many military assignments and served as a barracks and as a training ship. She was restored in 1927, and after a coast-to-coast tour, *Constitution* was moored in the Charlestown Navy yard in 1934 where she is now open year-round to the public for free tours.

Program type: Dockside interpretation
Built: 1797: Boston, MA, US Navy, Edmond Hartt Shipyard
Certification: Commissioned Naval Vessel
Crew: 75
Contact: Commanding Officer, USS Constitution, Charlestown Navy Yard, Charlestown, MA 02129-1797 USA
Tel: 617-242-5670 **Fax:** 617-242-2308
Website: www.ussconstitution.navy.mil

SPECIFICATIONS

Flag: USA
Rig: Brigantine
Homeport: Woods Hole, Massachusetts
Normal cruising waters: North Atlantic Ocean and Caribbean Sea
Sparred length: 134'
LOD: 98'
LWL: 87' 6"
Draft: 12' 6"
Beam: 26'
Rig height: 110'
Sail area: 7,500 square feet
Tons: 158 GRT
Power: Cummins KTA19, 500 HP
Hull: steel

CORWITH CRAMER

Who sails: College students admitted by competitive selection from over 150 colleges and universities worldwide. Also high school students participating in summer seminar programs.
Program type: SEA programs combine 6 weeks of academic study on campus in Woods Hole, MA with 6 weeks of oceanographic research at sea. Courses on shore include oceanography, nautical science, and maritime studies. Program offerings include SEA Semester (college level, 12 weeks, 17 credits), SEA Summer Session (college level, 8 weeks, 12 credits), and SEA seminars for high school students.
Designer: Woodin & Marean, Inc., Wiscasset, ME
Built: 1987
Coast Guard certification: Sailing School Vessel (Subchapter R) for Ocean service
Crew: 6 professional mariners and 4 scientists
Trainees-passengers: Up to 25 in all programs
Contact: Sea Education Association (SEA), PO Box 6, Woods Hole, MA 02543 USA
Tel: 508-540-3954 OR 800-552-3633
Fax: 508-540-0558
E-mail: admissions@sea.edu
Website: www.sea.edu

Along with the SSV *Robert C. Seamans*, the SSV *Corwith Cramer* is owned and operated by the Sea Education Association (SEA) of Woods Hole, Massachusetts. Built in 1987 and named for SEA's founder, the 134-foot steel brigantine was the first vessel built to the stringent safety requirements of the Sailing School Vessels Act. She is outfitted with an oceanographic laboratory, classroom, library, and computer laboratory. SEA students investigate and study the ocean from multiple perspectives ashore in Woods Hole and then at sea during open ocean passages. Our 12-week SEA Semesters are tailored to meet a wide variety of undergraduate majors and interests and offer 17 academic credits. SEA's traditional semester "Ocean Exploration" is open to students from all majors and takes an interdisciplinary approach to understanding the sea. SEA also offers a semester for advanced science students focused on "Oceans and Climate" as well as semesters focused on humanities and social sciences, "Documenting Change in the Caribbean" and "Sustainability in Polynesian Island Cultures and Ecosystems."

SPECIFICATIONS

Flag: Portugual
Rig: Schooner, 4-masted
Homeport: Lisbon, Portugal
Normal cruising waters:
Worldwide
Sparred length: 221'
Draft: 15' 6"
Beam: 32' 6"
Hull: steel

Photo by Thad Koza

CREOULA

Creoula is a 4-masted, steel-hulled schooner built in 1937 in a record 62 workdays. She was constructed for a Portuguese fishing company, Parceria Geral de Pescarias, and until her last trip in 1973, *Creoula* had wooden topmasts, booms, and gaffs. The standing rigging has always been steel, and the running rigging was originally made from sisal rope. Until 1973, this 4-masted schooner spent 37 consecutive years working the cold waters off Grand Banks, Newfoundland. The ship typically set sail from Lisbon in April for Nova Scotia, where she remained until the end of May. After renewing supplies in Sydney, Nova Scotia, or St. John's, Newfoundland, *Creoula* would sail to Greenland, where she fished until mid-September. In 1979, she was purchased from the Portuguese Department of Fisheries with the intention of converting her to a museum of fishery. A survey showed her hull to be in impeccable condition, however, and a decision was made to restore her as a sail training vessel. She is now owned by the Portuguese navy but carries only civilian cadets and trainees.

Program type: Sail training vessel
Season: Year-round
Built: 1937
Contact: Naval Attache of Portugal, Embassy of Portugal, 2010 Massachusetts Ave., NW Washington, DC 20008
Tel: 202-232-7632

SPECIFICATIONS

Flag: Mexico
Rig: Barque
Homeport: Puerto de Acapulco, Mexico
Normal cruising waters: Worldwide
Sparred length: 270'
LWL: 220' 4"
Draft: 17' 1"
Beam: 39' 4"
Sail area: 25,489 square feet
Power: 1,125 HP engine
Hull: steel

Photo by Thad Koza

CUAUHTEMOC

Who sails: Captains, officers, cadets, and sailors of the Mexican Navy
Program type: Sail training vessel
Season: Year-round
Built: 1982: Bilbao, Spain, Celaya Shipyards
Crew: 123 (officers and sailors)
Contact: Naval Attache of Mexico, Embassy of Mexico, 1911 Pennsylvania Avenue, NW, Washington, DC 20006 USA
Tel: 202-728-1760
E-mail: navalmx@msn.com or buquetemoc@hotmail.com

The sail training ship *Cuauhtemoc*, "tireless navigator", has covered 378,725 nautical miles and trained officers of the Mexican Navy for nearly 20 years. Through almost two decades, it's accomplishments have been acknowledged and praised by other navies in the world. The ship has participated in important regattas like the Colón Regatta, the Cutty Sark Tall Ship Races, and the Centenary of Osaka Port Modernization Regatta, among others. The sail training ship *Cuauhtemoc* is undoubtedly a living symbol of the sailor spirit that characterizes the personnel of the Mexican Navy, who are always ready to serve their country.

SPECIFICATIONS

Flag: USA
Rig: Gaff ketch
Homeport: Coupeville, Washington
Sparred length: 55'
LOA: 52'
LOD: 40'
LWL: 33' 4"
Draft: 6' 6"
Beam: 13' 6"
Rig height: 55'
Freeboard: 3' 6"
Sail area: 1,100 square feet
Tons: 19 GRT
Power: 225 HP diesel
Hull: wood

CUTTY SARK

Captain John Colby Stone is a world sailor and maintains the 52-foot classic ketch, *Cutty Sark*. In the summer you will commonly see the boat on the water in Penn Cove taking passengers on sailing tours. The *Cutty Sark* was built of teak by American Marine in Hong Kong in 1960. The first of 10 sister ships of the Mayflower class designed by Hugh Angleman and Charlie Davies, she wears the number 1 proudly on her mains'l. She is broad of beam, providing stable sailing and plenty of room for comfortable deck lounging. Her pilot house offers an alternate steering station and comfortable sitting area. She has a full galley with hot and cold pressure water, a propane stove and oven. You can charter this beautiful vessel for scenic sails throughout the waters surrounding Whidbey Island and the San Juan Islands. Relax. Let the wind pull the sails ahead, and Captain John Colby Stone assures you of a wonderful time.

Who sails: Families and individuals of all ages
Program type: Private charters
Designer: Hugh Angleman/Charlie Davies
Built: 1960: Hong Kong, American Marine
Contact: Captain John Colby Stone, Æolian Ventures, Inc, 2440 West Libbey Road, Coupeville, WA 98239 USA
Tel: 360-678-5567
E-mail: captjohn@whidbey.net
Website: www.svcuttysark.com

SPECIFICATIONS

Flag: Poland
Rig: Full-rigged ship
Homeport: Gdynia, Poland
Normal cruising waters:
Worldwide
Sparred length: 360'
LOD: 311'
Draft: 20' 7"
Beam: 45' 9"
Rig height: 162'
Sail area: 32,453 square feet
Tons: 2,385 GRT
Power: Cegielski - Sulzer type 8
AL 20/24, 2 * 750 PS (552 kW)
Hull: steel

Photo by Thad Koza

DAR MLODZIEZY

Who sails: Students of the Gdynia Maritime
University
Season: Year-round
Designer: Zygmunt Choren
Built: 1982: Gdansk, Poland
Crew: 40 **Trainees-passengers:** 150
Contact: Gdynia Maritime University, Morska
81-8, 81-225 Gdynia, Poland
Tel: 48 58 621-70-41
Fax: 48 58 620-67-01
Website: www.wsm.gdynia.pl/

Dar Mlodziezy, "gift of the children", is a full-rigged ship designed by the distinguished Polish Naval architect Zygmunt Choren and is the flagship of the Merchant Marine Academy in Gdynia, Poland. *Dar Mlodziezy* was funded in part by contributions of elementary school children during the 1960s and 1970s. Commissioned in 1982, she replaced the venerable *Dar Pomorza*, "gift of Pomoraze" (a reference to the coastal region of Poland), which served Poland for more than six decades before her retirement. *Dar Mlodziezy*'s distinctive design served as the prototype for a class of vessels (five in all) built in Gdansk for the Russian confederation of the 1980's. Four of the five vessels – *Mir, Druzhba, Pallada, and Nasheba* – now fly the Russian flag, while *Khersones* flies the flag of Ukraine. These are true sister ships and vary only slightly in dimensions and configuration.

153

SPECIFICATIONS

Flag: USA
Rig: Schooner, 3-masted
Homeport: Milwaukee, Wisconsin
Normal cruising waters:
Great Lakes, Florida, Bahamas
Sparred length: 137'
LOA: 99'
LOD: 98'
LWL: 88' 4"
Draft: 8' 9"
Beam: 24'
Rig height: 95'
Sail area: 5,916 square feet
Tons: 99 GRT
Power: twin 180 HP diesels
Hull: wood

DENIS SULLIVAN

The S/V *Denis Sullivan*, owned and operated by Discovery World Ltd., was completed by over 900 volunteers in 2000. This replica of a Great Lakes schooner, and Flagship of Wisconsin, operates as a floating classroom and goodwill ambassador for the State of Wisconsin. From her homeport in Milwaukee on Lake Michigan, the schooner offers educational day sails and private charters for people of all ages from May through September and is committed to re-establishing the historical, cultural and environmental bonds between the community and one of its most valuable resources, the Great Lakes. She winters in Florida, the Bahamas and Caribbean. Three hour LakeWatch Expeditions and Dockside Discovery educational programs are offered for 5th through 12th graders. High school and college students can partake in five to fourteen day Science Under Sail ™ programs in the Great Lakes, Bahamas and Caribbean.

Who sails: Students and the general public
Program type: Sail training for crew, volunteers, and paying trainees; sea education in maritime history, ecology, and marine science; professional development for educators; "themed" sails and passenger day sails; dockside interpretation while in port
Season: Year-round
Designer: Timothy Graul
Built: 2000: Milwaukee, WI, Rob Stevens
Coast Guard certification: Passenger Vessel (Subchapter T), Sailing School Vessel (Subchapter R)
Crew: 10 **Trainees-passengers:** 50 daysails, 16 overnight
Contact: Jeff Phillips, Marine Operations Manager, Discovery World, 500 North Harbor Drive, Milwaukee, WI 53202 USA
Tel: 414-765-8640 **Fax:** 414-765-0311
E-mail: JPhillips@discoveryworld.org
Website: www.discoveryworld.org

SPECIFICATIONS

Flag: Indonesia
Rig: Barquentine
Homeport: Surabaya, Indonesia
Normal cruising waters:
Indonesian waters, Indian Ocean,
Pacific Ocean
Sparred length: 191'
LOA: 165'
LOD: 163' 1"
LWL: 138' 4"
Draft: 13'
Beam: 31'
Rig height: 119' 7"
Freeboard: 15' 1"
Sail area: 11,738 square feet
Tons: 847 GRT
Power: 986 HP diesel
Hull: steel

Photo by Benson Lee

DEWARUCI

Who sails: Cadets of the Indonesian Naval
Academy
Program type: Sail training and sea education
for Indonesian Naval cadets
Season: Year-round
Built: 1952: Hamburg, Germany, H.C. Stulchen
& Sohn
Crew: 70 **Trainees-passengers:** 80
Contact: Indonesian Naval Attaché, Defense
Attaché Office, 2020 Massachusetts Avenue
NW, Washington, DC 20036 USA

KRI *Dewaruci,* the beautiful barquentine flying the red
and white Indonesian flag, is the largest tall ship in the
Indonesian Navy. She was built in 1952 by H. C. Stulchen
and Son of Hamburg, Germany and launched in 1953.
Since then, the ship has served the Indonesian Navy as
a sail training vessel and as a successful ambassador of
goodwill for the people of Indonesia. *Dewaruci's* name and
figurehead represent the mythological Indonesian god of
truth and courage.

SPECIFICATIONS

Flag: USA
Rig: Schooner
Homeport: Key West, Florida
Normal cruising waters:
Florida Keys, Bahamas
Sparred length: 75'
LOA: 69'
LOD: 65'
LWL: 62'
Draft: 5'
Beam: 20'
Rig height: 73'
Freeboard: 5'
Sail area: 1,700 square feet
Tons: 49 GRT
Power: 130 John Deere
Hull: steel

DREAM CATCHER

Designed by marine architects Woodin and Marean from Maine, and built by Treworgy Yachts in Palm Coast, Florida in 1996, *Dream Catcher's* conception, design factors, and interior design came from Captain John Duke. John grew up on the waters of Biscayne Bay in Miami, Florida, has been USCG licensed since 1979, and has been sailing the waters of the lower Florida Keys, South Florida and the Bahamas for 30 years. During this time, he has worked with scientific research groups, environmental groups, and has introduced hundreds of marine enthusiasts to the many wonders of the sea. The *Dream Catcher* provides sailing adventures designed to be informative for both environmental professionals and individuals interested in marine habitat. Ideal for large families and groups interested in participating in and learning all aspects of sailing and navigation, *Dream Catcher* is looking for groups that want to be part of an adventure!

Who sails: Students, families, groups and individuals of all ages
Program type: Sail training for volunteer crew and paying trainees; sea education in cooperation with accredited institutions and other organized groups; longboat rowing aboard *Aida*, a 32' longboat that is used on *Dream Catcher's* extended voyages
Designer: Woodin and Marean
Built: 1996: Hammocks, FL, Treworgy Yachts
Coast Guard certification: Passenger Vessel (Subchapter T)
Trainees-passengers: 49 daysails, 19 overnight
Contact: Captain John Duke, Coastal Sailing Adventures, Inc., 28555 Jolly Roger Drive, Little Torch Key, FL 33042 USA
Tel: 305-304-5100
E-mail: saildreamcatcher@mindspring.com
Website: http://www.sailingkeywestflorida.com

SPECIFICATIONS

Flag: USA
Rig: Barque, 3-masted
Homeport: New London, Connecticut
Normal cruising waters: Atlantic Ocean, Pacific Ocean, Caribbean
Sparred length: 295'
LOA: 266' 8"
LWL: 231'
Draft: 17'
Beam: 40'
Rig height: 147' 4"
Sail area: 22,245 square feet
Tons: 2,186 GRT
Power: 1,000 HP diesel
Hull: steel

Photo by Thad Koza

EAGLE (WIX 327)

Who sails: US Coast Guard Academy cadets, US Coast Guard Officer candidates, and other USCG personnel
Program type: Seamanship training
Season: Year-round
Built: 1936: Hamburg, Germany, Blohm & Voss
Contact: Commanding Officer, USCGC EAGLE (WIX-327), 45 Mohegan Ave., New London, CT 06320 USA
Tel: 860-625-0831 **Fax:** 860-436-1659
Website: www.uscga.edu

One of five sister ships built for sail training in Germany in the 1930s, *Eagle* was included in reparations paid to the United States following World War II and the Coast Guard took her over as a training ship. Aboard the *Eagle*, cadets have a chance to put into practice the navigation, engineering, and other skills they are taught at the Coast Guard Academy. As underclassmen, they fill positions normally taken by the enlisted crew of a ship, including watches. They handle the more than 20,000 square feet of sail and more than 20 miles of rigging. Over 200 lines must be coordinated during a major ship maneuver, and the cadets must learn the name and function of each. As upperclassmen, they perform officer-level functions. For many, their tour of duty aboard the *Eagle* is their first experience of life at sea and it is here that they learn to serve as the leaders they will one day become in the Coast Guard. *Eagle* is safely maintained and operated by six officers and 49 crew who are stationed on board for two to three years at a time. This experienced core provides leadership and coaching to over 700 trainees and 60 short term temporary crew each year.

157

SPECIFICATIONS

Flag: USA
Rig: Barque, 3-masted
Homeport: Galveston, Texas
Normal cruising waters: Coastal waters near Galveston
Sparred length: 205'
LOA: 155'
LOD: 150'
Draft: 10'
Beam: 28'
Rig height: 110'
Freeboard: 10'
Sail area: 12,000 square feet
Tons: 411 GRT
Power: 450 HP diesel
Hull: iron

ELISSA

In 1975, a rusted iron hulk lay in the waters of Piraeus, Greece. Nearly 100 years earlier, she had sailed the world's oceans as a proud square-rigged sailing ship. Cut down, leaking and decrepit, she waited a cable's length from the scrap yard. Today, *Elissa* remains one of the hallmarks of maritime preservation. Lovingly restored and maintained, she sails again, continuing a far longer life than most ships are ever granted. She tests her readiness annually in a series of sea trials amid the oil rigs and shrimpers off Galveston Island. Working under professional officers, her volunteer crew completes an extensive dockside-training program. As funds allow, she makes longer voyages.

Who sails: School groups from middle school through college; individuals of all ages
Program type: Sail training for crew and apprentices; sea education in maritime history based on informal, in-house training; dockside interpretation
Season: April to November
Built: 1877: Aberdeen, Scotland, Alexander Hall and Sons Yard
Coast Guard certification: Cargo and Miscellaneous Goods (Subchapter I)
Crew: 40 **Trainees-passengers:** 85 daysails
Contact: Texas Seaport Museum/Galveston Historical Foundation, Pier 21, No. 8, Galveston, TX 77550 USA
Tel: 409-763-1877 **Fax:** 409-763-3037
E-mail: elissa@galvestonhistory.org
Website: www.tsm-elissa.org

SPECIFICATIONS

Flag: USA
Rig: Barque, 3-masted
(lateen mizzen)
Homeport: Manteo, North Carolina
Normal cruising waters:
Inland sounds of North Carolina
Sparred length: 78'
LOA: 68' 6"
LOD: 55'
LWL: 59'
Draft: 8'
Beam: 16' 6"
Rig height: 65'
Sail area: 1,920 square feet
Tons: 97 GRT
Hull: wood

ELIZABETH II

Who sails: Volunteer crew
Program type: Sail training for volunteer crew and apprentices; dockside interpretation
Season: Spring and fall
Designer: W. A. Baker and Stanley Potter
Built: 1983: Manteo, North Carolina, O. Lie-Nielsen, Creef-Davis Shipyard
Contact: Scott Stroh, Executive Director, Roanoke Island Festival Park, One Festival Park, Manteo, NC 27954 USA
Tel: 252-475-1500 **Fax:** 252-475-1507
E-mail: scott.stroh@ncmail.net
Website: www.roanokeisland.com

Built with private funds to commemorate the 400th Anniversary of the English colonization of the America's, *Elizabeth II* is named for a vessel that sailed from Plymouth, England on the second of the three Roanoke voyages sponsored by Sir Walter Raleigh between 1584 and 1587. She probably carried marines, colonists and supplies to establish a military garrison to support England's claim to the New World. *Elizabeth II's* sail training program teaches volunteer crew about America's 16th century maritime heritage. In addition to classroom instruction and dockside training, crewmembers participate in the care and maintenance of the vessel. Voyages are scheduled during the spring and fall seasons. Sponsorship for the volunteer crew program is provided by the nonprofit Friends of *Elizabeth II*, Inc.

SPECIFICATIONS

Flag: USA
Rig: Gaff topsail schooner, 2-masted
Homeport: New Bedford, Massachusetts
Sparred length: 156'
LOA: 112'
LOD: 106'
LWL: 93'
Draft: 13'
Beam: 24' 3"
Rig height: 115'
Freeboard: 4'
Sail area: 8,323 square feet
Tons: 98 GRT
Power: 350 HP Cummins diesel
Hull: wood

ERNESTINA

Launched on February 1, 1894 in Essex, MA as the *Effie M. Morrissey,* the schooner became famous as a Gloucester Grand Banks fisherman, as an Arctic expeditionary vessel under the command of Captain Robert Abrams Bartlett, and as a World War II survey and supply vessel under Commander Alexander Forbes. After a fire in 1946, the *Morrissey* was raised and then purchased by Capt. Henrique Mendes who renamed her *Ernestina* to serve in the transatlantic Cape Verdean packet trade. In 1982 she was gifted by the Republic of Cape Verde to the U.S. The essence of *Ernestina's* educational mission today extends from the vessel's phenomenal and unique history. Aboard *Ernestina*, students of all ages use the ship as a platform to study the marine environment and human impacts during structured dockside programs.

Who sails: School groups from elementary through college and individuals of all ages
Program type: Dockside interpretation and educational programs and restoration projects
Designer: George M. McClain
Built: 1894: Essex, MA, James and Tarr Shipyard
Crew: 11 **Trainees-passengers:** 65 - 80 daysails, 24 overnight
Coast Guard certification: Moored Attraction Vessel (while under restoration)
Contact: Paul J. Brawley, Executive Director, Schooner Ernestina Commission, State Pier, P.O. Box 2010, New Bedford, MA 02741-2010 USA
Tel: 508-992-4900 **Fax:** 508-984-7719
E-mail: Paul.Brawley@state.ma.us
Website: www.ernestina.org

SPECIFICATIONS

Flag: Chile
Rig: Barquentine, 4-masted
Homeport: Valparaiso, Chile
Normal cruising waters:
Worldwide
Sparred length: 371'
Draft: 19' 8"
Beam: 42' 8"
Hull: steel

Photo by Thad Koza

ESMERALDA

Program type: Sail training vessel of the Chilean Navy
Design: Camper & Nicholson
Built: 1952 – 1954, Cadiz, Spain
Contact: Embassy of the Republic of Chile, 1732 Massachusetts Avenue, NW, Washington, DC 20036 USA
Tel: 202-785-1746 **Fax:** 202-887-5579

The pride of the Chilean Navy, *Esmeralda* was built in Cadiz, Spain from plans used to build Spain's *Juan Sebastian de Elcano*. Both vessels were constructed from Camper & Nicholson design at the same yard, though some 27 years apart. The only difference between these two elegant 4-masters are the additional fore-and-aft sail on the *Sebastian's* foremast, designating her as a topsail schooner, and the slightly flatter angle of *Esmeralda's* bowsprit. Esmeralda was completed in 1954. Her distinctive figurehead represents a giant Andes condor, the national bird of Chile.

SPECIFICATIONS

Flag: France
Rig: Topsail schooner
Homeport: Brest, France
Sparred length: 124'
Draft: 12'
Beam: 24'
Hull: wood

Photo by Thad Koza

ETOILE

Along with her sister ship *La Belle Poule*, the schooner *Etoile* serves the French Navy in the training of future officers. Designed with the hull shape and the rigging of fishing vessels from Breton, *La Belle Poule* and *Etoile* were built in 1932 in the fishing port of Fecamp in northern Normandy, France. During World War II, both vessels relocated to Portsmouth, England, where they served the Free France Forces. They are permitted to fly the French ensign with the imposed Cross of Lorraine in recognition of their service during the war.

Program type: Sail training vessel of the French Navy
Built: 1932: Fecamp, Normandy, France
Contact: Embassy of France, 4101 Resevoir Road, NW, Washington, DC 20007 USA
Tel: 202-944-6000 **Fax:** 202-944-6166

SPECIFICATIONS

Flag: The Netherlands
Rig: Barque
Homeport: The Hague, The Netherlands
Normal cruising waters: Worldwide
Sparred length: 185'
LOA: 159'
LOD: 143'
LWL: 132'
Draft: 12'
Beam: 24'
Rig height: 109'
Freeboard: 4'
Sail area: 11,000 square feet
Tons: 303 GRT
Hull: steel

EUROPA

Who sails: Youth trainees, individuals, families, and groups of all ages
Program type: Sail training for paying trainees; fully accredited sea education in maritime history; special expeditions to Antarctica; dockside interpretation during port visits
Season: Year-round
Built: 1911: Hamburg, Germany, Stülcken
Crew: 12 **Trainees-voyage crew:** 100 daysails, 50 overnight
Contact: Rederij Bark EUROPA, PO Box 23183, 3001 KD Rotterdam The Netherlands
Tel: +31 (0) 10 281 0990
Fax: +31 (0) 10 281 0991
E-mail: info@barkeuropa.com
Website: www.barkeuropa.com

Europa was launched in Hamburg in 1911. Her construction had been ordered by the city of Hamburg for use as a lightship in the entrance of the river Elbe. In her second life, which started after an 8 year refit in 1994, the *Europa* recommenced sailing as a sail-training vessel. *Europa* has since become famous among tall ship lovers as a ship which really sails. The professional crew of 14 seafarers involve the voyage crew/trainees as much as possible in running and sailing this traditionally rigged barque. The "guest crew" sail the ship in accordance to their individual abilities and ambition and no former sailing experience is needed. They learn how to stand watches, take turns at steering or as lookout, take in or set sails, scrub the decks and practice traditional seafaring/ seamanship skills. Following her annual Antarctic voyages, the *Europa* "follows the sun" in the wake of the old sailing routes into the Northern Hemisphere. In 2010 she will take part in the TALL SHIPS CHALLENGE® Series in the Great Lakes. In the summer of 2011 she will have her Centennial Birthday in Northern European Waters and will take part in the "Sail Training International" races.

SPECIFICATIONS

Flag: USA
Rig: Brigantine
Homeport: Los Angeles, California
Normal cruising waters:
Southern California and offshore
islands
Sparred length: 110' 8"
LOA: 90'
LOD: 81' 7"
LWL: 72' 6"
Draft: 11'
Beam: 21' 9"
Rig height: 87' 8"
Sail area: 4,540 square feet
Tons: 99 GRT
Power: 315 HP diesel
Hull: wood

Photo by Lee Uran

EXY JOHNSON

The Los Angeles Maritime Institute (LAMI) launched the twin brigantines, *Exy Johnson* and *Irving Johnson,* in 2002 for the TopSail Youth Program. With ships named in honor of sail training pioneers and seven-time circumnavigators with youth crew aboard their ship, *Yankee,* TopSail recognizes that the shipboard environment is challenging yet nurturing, encouraging exploration and self-reliance. TopSail is notably effective with youth who are not coping well with the demands of society and are at risk of dropping out of school and giving up. The 2007 research findings from the University of Edinburgh-Sail Training International study describe TopSail as "highly successful, developing personal and social confidence, and the ability to work together with others." With the premise that 'school is where the kids are...' , TopSail youth engage in building cooperation, courage, confidence and character in the real-world classroom of the sea. LAMI is a volunteer-driven, youth-focused, educational 'family' organization. We welcome the skills and enthusiasm of people of all ages and all walks of life to sail with youth, maintain the tall ships, and be involved in many other ways.

Who sails: Youth/school groups from diverse communities, mostly from middle schools in urban areas
Program type: Educational sailing adventures for youth and adult groups
Season: Year-round
Coast Guard certification: Sailing School Vessel (Subchapter R), Passenger vessel (Subchapter T)
Contact: Captain Jim Gladson, President, Los Angeles Maritime Institute, Berth 84, Foot of Sixth Street, San Pedro, CA 90731 USA
Tel: 310-833-6055 **Fax:** 310-548-2055
Website: www.LAMITopSail.org

164

SPECIFICATIONS

Flag: Canada
Rig: Brigantine
Homeport: Ottawa, Ontario, Canada
Normal cruising waters:
Great Lakes and East Coast
(summer), Caribbean (winter)
Sparred length: 110'
LOD: 82'
LOA: 62'
Draft: 6'
Beam: 24' 6"
Rig height: 80'
Freeboard: 8'
Sail area: 4,000 square feet
Tons: 124 GRT
Power: 235 HP diesel
Hull: fiberglass on steel

FAIR JEANNE

Who sails: Middle school, high school, college, adults, Elderhostel
Program type: Sail training for paying trainees; overnight voyages; sea education in maritime history with formal organizations and as informal; in-house programming; dockside interpretation; bursary programs available
Season: Spring, summer and fall
Designer: Captain Thomas G. Fuller
Built: 1982: Ottawa, Ontario, Canada, T. G. Fuller
Certification: Sailing School Vessel, inland/near coastal
Crew: 6 high school and university officers
Trainees-passengers: 36 daysails; 24 overnight
Contact: Bytown Brigantine, Inc., 2700 Queensview Drive, Ottawa, Ontario K2B 8H6 Canada
Tel: 613-596-6258 **Fax:** 613-596-5947
E-mail: tallshipinfo@tallshipsadventure.org
Website: www.tallshipsadventure.org

Designed and built in 1982 by the late Captain Thomas G. Fuller, *Fair Jeanne* was first sailed as a private yacht. Captain Fuller was one of Canada's most decorated WWII naval war heroes, earning the name "Pirate of the Adriatic". His wartime experience taught him the value of instilling confidence and resourcefulness in our youth while at sea. More than 100,000 nautical miles and, 22 years later, *Fair Jeanne* is now in service as a sail training vessel for Bytown Brigantine, a non-profit charitable organization dedicated to providing adventure through the time honored traditions inherent in square rigged sailing. During the summer months she provides programs for youth 14-19 years old, and during the spring and fall she also provides programs for school groups, adults, and Elderhostel.

SPECIFICATIONS

Flag: Sweden
Rig: Schooner
Homeport: Karlskrona, Sweden
Sparred length: 129'
Draft: 13' 9"
Beam: 23'
Hull: steel

Photo by Thad Koza

FALKEN

Falken and her sister ship *Gladan* are twin schooners built in 1947, in the same yard and according to the same plans. Differentiated only by their sail numbers, these two vessels train future officers of the Swedish Royal Navy, as they have since their commissioning.

Program type: Sail training vessel of the Swedish Royal Navy
Built: 1947
Contact: Embassy of Sweden, 1501 M Street, NW, Suite 900, Washington, DC 20005-1702 USA
Tel: 202-467-2600 **Fax:** 202-467-2699

SPECIFICATIONS

Flag: USA
Rig: Chebacco schooner
Homeport: Salem, Massachusetts
Sparred Length: 70'
LOA: 60'
LOD: 52'
LWL: 49'
Draft: 6'4"
Beam: 15'
Rig Height: 70'
Freeboard: 5'
Sail Area: 1200 square feet
Tons: 29 GRT
Power: 160 HP diesel
Hull: white oak

FAME

Who sails: Everyone
Program Type: Public day sails; private charters; summer day camp for children; sail training; sea education in maritime history; dockside interpretation
Season: May through October
Designer: H. A. Burnham
Built 2003: Essex, MA, H.A. Burnham
Coast Guard certification: Passenger Vessel (Subchapter T)
Crew: 2 **Trainees-passengers:** 40 daysails
Contact: Captain Mike Rutstein, Pennant Enterprises, 73 Middleton Road, Boxford, MA 01921 USA
Tel: 978-729-7600 **Fax:** 978-561-3021
E-mail: SchoonerFame@aol.com
Website: www.SchoonerFame.com

Fame is a replica of a successful Salem privateer from the War of 1812. The original *Fame* was a Chebacco-style fishing schooner that was converted to privateering at the outbreak of war. She was one of the first American privateers to put to sea, and one of the first to bring back a prize. She captured 21 vessels — both British merchantmen and American smugglers — before being lost in the Bay of Fundy in 1814. Her captured crew was involved in the infamous Dartmoor prison riot of 1815. Our *Fame* is a traditional double-sawn-frame vessel, framed and planked in native white oak by Harold Burnham of Essex, MA in 2003. *Fame* is now based at Pickering Wharf in Salem, where she carries the paying public on 90-minute cruises around historic Salem Sound. For much more information on *Fame*, please visit our website at www. SchoonerFame.com.

SPECIFICATIONS

Flag: USA
Rig: Topsail schooner
Homeport: Dundalk, Maryland
Normal cruising waters:
Chesapeake Bay, East Coast of US
Sparred length: 47'
LOD: 40'
LWL: 30'
Draft: 4' 9"
Beam: 10' 6"
Sail area: 1,000 square feet
Tons: 9 GRT
Power: 25 HP diesel
Hull: fiberglass

FAREWELL

Peter Van Dine designed *Farewell* and traded the design with Andy Merrill for guitar lessons for he and his wife. Over a two year period, Andy built *Farewell* in his backyard in Annapolis, MD and launched her in 1972. *Farewell* was home to Andy and his family until 1982. The second owner purchased *Farewell* in 1994 to use as a coastal sail training vessel for three pre-teen sons. In 1996, the owner and the three boys cruised from Annapolis, MD to Camden, ME. The ship competed in the Great Chesapeake Bay Schooner Race each year from 1994 to 1998. In early 1999, her present owner, Captain Linda Meakes, purchased *Farewell*. During the past several years, *Farewell* has participated in ASTA events and several maritime festivals and celebrations, including the homecoming of the USS *Constellation*, the Baltimore Preakness Schooner Race, and the Leukemia & Lymphoma Society Bridge to Bridge race. *Farewell* has also continued the tradition of competing in the Great Chesapeake Bay Schooner Race.

Who sails: Groups and individuals of all ages
Program type: Sail training for paying trainees; sea education in maritime history; passenger day sails and overnight passages; dockside interpretation
Season: April through November
Designer: P. Van Dine
Built: 1972: Andy Merrill
Crew: 6
Contact: Captain Linda Meakes, 8500 Cove Road, Dundalk, MD 21222 USA
Tel: 410-961-4054
E-mail: schoonergirl@comcast.net
Website: www.geocities.com/schoonerfarewell

SPECIFICATIONS

Flag: USA
Rig: Square topsail sloop
Homeport: South Haven, Michigan
Normal cruising waters: Upper Great Lakes
Sparred Length: 101'
LOD: 56' 3"
Draft: 8' 9"
Beam: 16' 10"
Rig Height: 82'
Sail area: 3,180 square feet
Tons: 49.2 GRT
Power: diesel
Hull: wood

FRIENDS GOOD WILL

Who sails: Museum members, school groups, individuals and families
Program Type: Sail Training for museum members and crew; passenger day sails; dockside interpretation, historical reenactment at home port and during port visits; education in history, geography, navigation, marine science for school groups of all ages. Affiliated with Sea Scout Ship #5191, South Haven, Michigan.
Designer: Scarano Boatbuilding, Inc.
Built: 2004: Albany, NY, Scarano Boatbuilding, Inc.
Coast Guard certification: Passenger Vessel (Subchapter T)
Crew: 13 **Trainees-passengers:** 28 daysails
Contact: Michigan Maritime Museum, 260 Dyckman Avenue, South Haven, Michigan 49090 USA
Tel: 269-637-8078 **Fax:** 269-637-1594
E-mail: info@michiganmaritimemuseum.org
Website: www.MichiganMaritimeMuseum.org

"We have met the enemy and they are ours...", Commander Oliver Hazard Perry, U.S.N., Battle of Lake Erie, September 10, 1813. This famous dispatch, dashed off within an hour after the great guns fell silent, went on to reference a merchant sloop turned man-o-war. That sloop was *Friends Good Will*. The Michigan Maritime Museum launched a replica of this fateful vessel in 2004. Scarano Boatbuilding, Inc. of Albany, New York, designed and built *Friends Good Will*, to be rigged and sailed by Museum volunteers. The vessel serves as an historic flagship for the preservation of traditional maritime skills. The Michigan Maritime Museum is developing programs and curriculum, utilizing its Padnos Boat Shed as a rig shop and its ample exhibit space to assist in educating members, visitors, school groups of all ages and special tours about Michigan's maritime history and culture. Combining these resources with dockside interpretation and a day sail program throughout the summer, *Friends Good Will* employs traditional materials and skills to keep Michigan's rich maritime heritage alive.

SPECIFICATIONS

Flag: USA
Rig: Full-rigged ship
Homeport: Salem, Massachusetts
Normal cruising waters:
Massachusetts Bay, Buzzards Bay
Sparred length: 171'
LOA: 116'
LOD: 104'
LWL: 99'
Draft: 11' 3"
Beam: 30'
Rig height: 125'
Freeboard: 10'
Sail area: 9,409 square feet
Tons: 99 GRT
Power: twin 300 HP diesels
Hull: wood

Photo by Leighton O'Connor

FRIENDSHIP OF SALEM

Friendship, a full size replica of a Salem East Indiaman, built for the National Park Service and berthed at Salem Maritime National Historic Site in Salem, Massachusetts, was launched in August 1998. Although she represents a specific vessel built in Salem in 1797, she is typical of a class of commercial carriers commonly employed in both the East India and transatlantic trades during the early years of the new American republic. Her historic predecessor is credited with 15 voyages to the Far East, South America, Mediterranean, and northern Europe. She had the misfortune of being taken as a prize of war by the British Royal Navy on a return voyage from Archangel, Russia, in 1812. Sold by the British government in 1813, her ultimate fate remains a mystery. Today's *Friendship* is built from wood laminates and solid timbers and was designed as a passenger carrying and sail training vessel while exhibiting the look and function of an historic vessel. *Friendship* is accessible to the public for dockside tours.

Who sails: When fully certified, *Friendship* will welcome all age groups through school programs as well as general public on day sails and weekly programmed trips.
Program type: Dockside programs and hands on interpretation as an historic site exhibit; informal sea education in maritime history. Special events at other ports and dockside leasing for special events at Salem.
Season: Open for tours all year
Designer: Bay Marine, Inc., Barrington, RI
Built: 1998: Scarano Boats, Albany, NY; 1999-2002: Salem, MA., Dion Yacht Yard, NPS & USS Constitution Naval Detachment
Coast Guard certification: Passenger Vessel (Subchapter T) pending
Crew: 5 **Trainees-passengers:** 30 daysails
Contact: Colleen Bruce, Chief, Marine and Special Programs, Salem Maritime National Historic Site, 160 Derby Street, Salem, MA 01915 USA
Tel: 978-740-1694 **Fax:** 978-740-1685
E-mail: colleen_bruce@nps.gov
Website: www.nps.gov/sama and www.salem-web.com/frndship

SPECIFICATIONS

Flag: USA
Rig: Brigantine
Homeport: Fairhaven, Massachusetts
Normal cruising waters: Southern New England
Sparred length: 74'
LOD: 54'
LWL: 47'
Draft: 7'
Beam: 15'
Rig height: 65'
Freeboard: 5'
Sail area: 9,409 square feet
Tons: 39 GRT
Power: Detroit 4-71 175 BHP
Hull: wood

Photo by Thad Koza

FRITHA

Who sails: Students of the Northeast Maritime Institute
Program type: Sail training
Designer: Murray Peterson
Built: 1985: New Zealand, McMullan and Wing
Coast Guard certification: Uninspected Passenger Vessel (Subchapter C)
Crew: 2 **Trainees-passengers:** 6 daysails, 6 overnight
Contact: Northeast Maritime Institue, 32 Washington Street, Fairhaven, MA 02719 USA
Tel: 508-992-4025 **Fax:** 508-992-1236
E-mail: fritha@northeastmaritime.com
Website: www.northeastmaritime.com

The S/V *Fritha*, is a 74-foot tall ship used for training purposes at Northeast Maritime Institute and is widely available for charters to the public. Launched in 1986 in New Zealand and named for the heroine in Paul Gallico's book, The Snow Goose, the brigantine *Fritha* was built by traditional methods to unparalleled standards of excellence in materials and craftsmanship. The *Fritha's* home waters of Southern New England offer some of the most beautiful scenery and the best sailing in the world. Interesting ports and anchorages include Buzzard's Bay, Elizabeth Islands, Martha's Vineyard and Nantucket, and are only a few hours' sail from *Fritha's* home port of Fairhaven, Massachusetts. The *Fritha* can also meet you in places outside of her home waters as well. With a licensed captain and professional crew, your sailing adventure aboard the brigantine *Fritha* will create memories that last a lifetime. Fritha can accommodate up to six passengers and is ready to take family and friends on an exciting and educational adventure. Learn navigation, knot tying and the art of square rigged sailing. The crew encourages guests to help haul the sails during your time aboard. *Fritha* is owned and operated by Northeast Maritime Institute.

171

SPECIFICATIONS

Flag: USA
Rig: Barquentine, 3-masted
Homeport: Philadelphia, Pennsylvania
Normal cruising waters: Delaware River and the Atlantic Coast
Sparred length: 177'
LOA: 150'
LOD: 140'
LWL: 133'
Draft: 17'
Beam: 26"
Rig height: 100'
Sail area: 8,910 square feet
Tons: 299 GRT
Power: diesel
Hull: wood, copper clad

GAZELA

The wooden barkentine, *Gazela Primeiro*, was originally built to fish for cod in the Grand Banks. Now owned and operated by the Philadelphia Ship Preservation Guild, a nonprofit volunteer organization, the *Gazela* sails as a goodwill ambassador for the Commonwealth of Pennsylvania and the Ports of Philadelphia, Pennsylvania and Camden, New Jersey. Our mission extends beyond historic preservation to community outreach through such activities as maritime education of disadvantaged youth. *Gazela* has been featured in several major motion pictures including "Interview with the Vampire" and "The Widow of St. Pierre", as well as several documentaries including "The Irish in America".

Who sails: Volunteers who support the Philadelphia Ship Preservation Guild
Program type: Sail training for crew and apprentices; sea education based on informal in-house programming; dockside interpretation both in homeport and on out-port visits
Built: 1883: Cacihas, Portugal, major rebuild 1901: Setubal, Portugal
Crew: 35 (volunteer)
Contact: Philadelphia Ship Preservation Guild, 301 S.Columbus Blvd., Philadelphia, PA 19106 USA
Tel: 215-238-0280 **Fax:** 215-238-0281
E-mail: office@gazela.org
Website: www.gazela.org

SPECIFICATIONS

Flag: USA
Rig: Sloop
Homeport: Newport, Rhode Island
Normal cruising waters:
North Atlantic and Caribbean
Sparred length: 69' 8"
LOA: 69' 8"
LOD: 68'
LWL: 53' 11"
Draft: 6' 8" – 13' 5"
Beam: 18' 7"
Rig height: 85' 6"
Freeboard: 5'
Sail area: 2,091 square feet
Tons: 53 GRT
Power: diesel
Hull: fiberglass

GERONIMO

Who sails: High school students through adults
Program type: Marine/nautical science
Season: Year-round
Designer: Ted Hood Design Group
Built: 1998: Portsmouth, RI, New England Boatworks
Coast Guard certification: Sailing School Vessel (Subchapter R)
Crew: 3 **Trainees-passengers:** 8
Contact: Captain Deborah Hayes, Program Director, St. George's School, 372 Purgatory Road, PO Box 1910, Newport, RI 02840 USA
Tel: 401-842-6747 **Fax:** 401-842-6696
E-mail: Deborah_Hayes@stgeorges.edu
Website: www.sailgeronimo.org

The sailing vessel *Geronimo* sails year round between the Canadian maritime and the greater Carribean. Trainees are taught Nautical Science and Oceanography/Marine Biology while on board. During the academic year, *Geronimo* carries students from St. George's School on 6-week long voyages. During these trips, the students stand watch, learn the intricacies of handling a modern sailing vessel and conduct research on sea turtles working in conjunction with the Archie Carr Center for Sea Turtle Research University of Florida, Gainsville. In the summer months, the vessel makes three shorter trips along the east coast. Summer trainees range in age from high school to adult.

SPECIFICATIONS

Flag: Sweden
Rig: Schooner
Homeport: Karlskrona, Sweden
Sparred length: 129'
Draft: 13' 9"
Beam: 23'
Hull: steel

Photo by Thad Koza

GLADAN

Gladan and her sister ship *Falken* are twin schooners built in 1947, in the same yard and according to the same plans. Differentiated only by their sail numbers, these two vessels train future officers of the Swedish Royal Navy as they have since their commissioning.

Program type: Sail training vessel of the Swedish Royal Navy
Built: 1947
Contact: Embassy of Sweden, 1501 M Street, NW, Suite 900, Washington, DC 20005-1702
Tel: 202-467-2600 **Fax:** 202-467-2699

SPECIFICATIONS

Flag: USA
Rig: Gaff topsail schooner
Homeport: Biloxi, Mississippi
Normal cruising waters:
Coastwise Gulf of Mexico
Sparred length: 76'
LOA: 65'
LOD: 50'
LWL: 47'
Draft: 4' 10"
Beam: 17'
Freeboard: 4' 6"
Sail area: 2,400 square feet
Tons: 21 GRT
Power: 4-71 Detroit diesel
Hull: wood, Juniper

GLENN L. SWETMAN

Who sails: Groups and individuals of all ages
Program type: Sail training for volunteer and paying trainees; sea education in maritime history, marine science, and ecology for college students and adults in cooperation with accredited institutions, organized groups, and as informal in-house programming; children's summer camp; private charters
Season: Year-round
Designer: William Holland
Built: 1989: Biloxi, Mississippi, William T. Holland
Coast Guard certification: Passenger Vessel (Subchapter T)
Crew: 3 **Trainees-passengers:** 49 daysails
Contact: Maritime and Seafood Industry Museum of Biloxi, PO Box 1907, Biloxi, MS 39533 USA
Tel: 228-435-6320 **Fax:** 228-435-6309
E-mail: schooner@maritimemuseum.org
Website: www.maritimemuseum.org

The *Glenn L. Swetman* is the first of two replica Biloxi oyster schooners built by the Biloxi Schooner Project under the auspices of the Maritime and Seafood Industry Museum. She is available for charter trips in the Mississippi Sound and to the barrier islands, Cat Island, Horn Island, and Ship Island. Walk-up day sailing trips are made when she is not under charter. Groups can learn about the maritime and seafood heritage of the Gulf Coast, and about the vessels that began Biloxi's seafood industry. The *Glenn L. Swetman* is an integral part of the museum's Sea and Sail Summer Camp, and sailing classes are also offered through local colleges. *Glenn L. Swetman* also accommodates weddings, parties, and Elderhostel and school groups.

SPECIFICATIONS

Flag: Colombia
Rig: Barque, 3-masted
Homeport: Cartegena, Colombia
Normal cruising waters:
Worldwide
Sparred length: 249' 4"
LOA: 212'
LOD: 189'
LWL: 184'
Draft: 14' 9"
Beam: 34' 9"
Rig height: 126' 4"
Freeboard: 21' 7"
Sail area: 15,075 square feet
Tons: 934 GRT
Power: twin 256 HP KV
Hull: steel

GLORIA

Built in Bilbao, Spain for the Colombian Navy in 1966, the 3-masted barque *Gloria* is used as a school ship for the cadets of the Colombian Naval Academy. She carries a compliment of 150 men and women, ranging from enlisted to midshipmen and officers. The cruises are aimed at training officers in their third year at the Naval Academy, to implement their academic knowledge in the areas of star navigation, seamanship, leadership and teambuilding. *Gloria* is a proud goodwill ambassador of the Colombian Navy. During her service she has made 46 cruises, navigating over 500,000 nautical miles and visiting 143 different ports around the world.

Who sails: Midshipmen, enlisted and officers of the Colombian Navy
Program type: Sail training vessel of the Colombian Navy
Season: Year-round
Designer: Sener
Built: 1969: Bilbao, Spain, A. T. Celaya
Certification: Colombian Naval Vessel
Crew: 69 **Trainees-passengers:** 80 students
Contact: Embassy of Colombia, 2118 Leroy Place, NW, Washington, DC 20008
Tel: 202-387-8338 **Fax:** 202-232-8643
E-mail: embassyofcolombia@colombiaemb.org
Website: www.colombiaemb.org

SPECIFICATIONS

Flag: USA
Rig: Bark, 3-masted (lateen mizzen)
Homeport: Jamestown Settlement, Virginia
Normal cruising waters: Chesapeake Bay, US East Coast
Sparred length: 88'
LOA: 74'
LOD: 65'
LWL: 56'
Draft: 7'
Beam: 17'
Rig height: 72'
Freeboard: 7' 6"
Sail area: 2,420 square feet
Power: twin 115 HP diesel
Hull: wood

GODSPEED

Who sails: Crew consisting of Jamestown Settlement staff and volunteers. Age 18 years and older
Program type: Sail training and dockside interpretation
Season: Year-round
Designer: Tri-Coastal Marine
Built: 2006: Rockport Marine, Inc., Rockport, Maine
Coast Guard certification: Moored Attraction Vessel
Crew: 12 **Trainees-passengers:** 20
Contact: Capt. Eric Speth, Maritime Program Manager, Jamestown Settlement, PO Box 1607, Williamsburg, VA 23187 USA
Tel: 757-253-4838 **Fax:** 757-253-7350
Website: www.historyisfun.org

Godspeed is a full-scale re-creation of one of the three ships that brought America's first permanent English colonists to Virginia in 1607. Together with the *Susan Constant* and *Discovery*, *Godspeed* is on exhibit at Jamestown Settlement, a living-history museum of 17th-century Virginia, and hosts about a half-million visitors every year. Jamestown Settlement is administered by the Jamestown-Yorktown Foundation, a Virginia state agency. Built at Rockport Marine in Maine and commissioned at Jamestown Settlement in 2006, *Godspeed* is a third-generation re-creation. The first was built for the 1957 350th-anniversary commemoration of the founding of Jamestown. *Godspeed, Susan Constant* and *Discovery* are based on the historically documented tonnages of the original ships and 17th-century principles of tonnage measurement. With a crew of staff and volunteers, *Godspeed* and *Susan Constant* periodically sail to other ports in the Chesapeake Bay region to participate in commemorative and community events and host educational programs. A volunteer sail-training program is offered to individuals 18 and older.

SPECIFICATIONS

Flag: Germany
Rig: Barque
Homeport: Kiel, Germany
Normal cruising waters:
Worldwide
Sparred length: 293'
Draft: 15' 6"
Beam: 39'
Sail Area: 21,140 square feet
Hull: steel

GORCH FOCK II

Built from the same plans and in the same shipyard (Blohm & Voss in Hamburg, Germany) as the original, *Gorch Fock II* boasts contemporary safety features and the latest navigational equipment. She is an eminent replacement for her namesake (now the training vessel *Tovarishch* from Ukraine). Since her launch in 1958, *Gorch Fock II* has logged thousands of nautical miles in her twice-yearly voyages and has hosted more than ten thousand cadets for training cruises. The barque is named for a popular German writer of sea stories, Hans Kinau (1880 – 1916), who used the pseudonym Gorch Fock (fock means "foresail" in German). Kinau became part of the romantic mythology of the sea when he perished aboard the cruiser *Weisbaden*, which was sunk during the Battle of Jutland on 31 May 1916. The training vessel of the German Navy, *Gorch Fock II* is a proud symbol of Germany's distinguished sailing and shipbuilding traditions.

Program type: Sail training vessel of the German Navy.
Built: 1958: Hamburg, Germany, Blohm & Voss
Crew: 73 **Trainees-passengers:** 200
Contact: Embassy of the Federal Republic of Germany, 4645 Reservoir Road, NW, Washington, DC 20007 USA
Tel: 202-298-8140 **Fax:** 202-298-4249

SPECIFICATIONS

Flag: USA
Rig: Gaff schooner
Homeport: Camden, Maine
Normal cruising waters: Penobscot Bay/mid-coast Maine
Sparred length: 123'
LOD: 81'
LWL: 72'
Draft: 6' board up,16' board down
Beam: 24'
Rig height: 70'
Freeboard: 4'
Sail area: 4,985 square feet
Tons: 58 GRT
Power: carries neither inboard engines nor powered deck machinery, propulsion when needed by 14' yawl boat w/diesel motor.
Hull: wood

GRACE BAILEY

Who sails: 16 and up (any age with full boat charter)
Program type: cruising
Season: End of May thru early October
Designer: Smith
Built: 1882: Oliver Perry Smith, Patchoque, New York
Coast Guard certification: Passenger Vessel (Subchapter T)
Crew: 5 **Passengers-trainees:** 49 daysails, 29 overnight
Contact: Captain Ray and Ann Williamson, owners, Maine Windjammer Cruises®, PO Box 617, Camden, Maine 04843 USA
Tel: 207-236-2938 – Reservations 800-736-7981
E-mail: sail@MaineWindjammerCruises.com
Website: www.MaineWindjammerCruises.com

The *Grace Bailey* was built in 1882 by Oliver Perry Smith in Patchoque, New York. Her work included carrying lumber from South Carolina and Georgia and in the mid 1800s was registered for foreign trade and made voyages to the West Indies. In 1906 she was renamed the *Mattie* and sailed as a bay coaster in Maine waters carrying general cargo. She also carried granite to New York City to be used in the construction of the Post Office Building and Grand Central Station. Capt. Frank Swift chartered her in 1939 to be used as a cruise schooner and soon was purchased and chosen as the flagship of his growing Windjammer Cruise fleet. The *Grace Bailey* was totally restored in 1990 by present owners Capt. Ray & Ann Williamson, rechristened with her original name and designated a National Historic Landmark. She carries 29 passengers and does five day and weekend cruises off the coast of Maine and is one of five surviving two-masted coasting schooners in the USA. She is a pure sailing vessel with cotton sails and all natural fiber running rigging.

SPECIFICATIONS

Flag: Ecuador
Rig: Barque
Homeport: Guayquil, Ecuador
Normal cruising waters:
Worldwide
Sparred length: 257'
LOA: 221'
LOD: 218'
LWL: 184'
Draft: 15' 4"
Beam: 34' 9"
Sail area: 15,784 square feet
Power: diesel
Hull: steel

GUAYAS

Guayas was built in the Celaya Shipyard in Bilbao, Spain. She is named after the Chief of Huancavilcas, a native culture in the Ecuadorian coastal region.   Commissioned in 1977, the *Guayas* is proud to serve as a goodwill ambassador for the Ecuadorian Navy. The ship carries a complement of 16 officers, 43 midshipmen, and 94 enlisted men, including the ship's band. During a cruise, considered one semester at the Ecuadorian Naval Academy, midshipmen apply, in a very challenging environment, theoretical principals of navigation, seamanship and other subjects learned in the classroom.

Who sails: Ecuadorian Naval Academy cadets
Program type: Sail training for Ecuadorian Naval Academy cadets
Season: Year-round
Designer: Celaya
Built: 1976: Bilbao, Spain, Celaya Shipyard
Certification: Ecuadorian Naval Vessel
Crew: 76
Contact: Naval Attaché, Embassy of Ecuador, 2535 15th Street NW, Washington, DC 20009 USA
Tel: 202-265-7674 **Fax:** 202-667-3482

SPECIFICATIONS

Flag: USA
Rig: Gaff topsail schooner, 2-masted
Homeport: Islesboro, Maine
Normal cruising waters: North Atlantic Ocean and Caribbean Sea, Canada to South America
Sparred length: 131'
LOA: 95'
LOD: 90'
LWL: 85'
Draft: 9' 7"
Beam: 24'
Rig height: 91'
Freeboard: 5'
Sail area: 4,200 square feet
Tons: 94 GRT
Power: 220 HP diesel
Hull: wood

HARVEY GAMAGE

Who sails: Individuals and school groups from middle school through college; affiliated institutions include Proctor Academy, University of Maine, Center for Coastal Studies, Outward Bound, and other schools
Program type: Traditional seamanship training combined with accredited academic studies
Season: Year-round
Designer: McCurdy & Rhodes
Built: 1973: South Bristol, Maine, Harvey F. Gamage Shipyard
Coast Guard certification: Sailing School Vessel (Subchapter R), Passenger Vessel (Subchapter T)
Crew: 8 - 11 including instructors **Student-trainees:** 24 overnight
Contact: Executive Director, Ocean Classroom Foundation, 29 McKown Street, Boothbay Harbor, Maine 04538 USA
Tel: 800-724-7245
E-mail: mail@oceanclassroom.org
Website: www.oceanclassroom.org

Owned by the Ocean Classroom Foundation, the schooner *Harvey Gamage* offers programs of education under sail to the youth of America. Programs range from four month semesters-at-sea to week-long programs with schools and youth groups. Trainees sail the ship and learn traditional seamanship skills under the captain and crew, and they explore maritime subjects with the onboard academic staff. Ocean Classroom's Discovery™ program is a semester-at-sea for qualified high school students, fully accredited by Proctor Academy. The voyage covers more than 6,000 nautical miles, connecting South American shores to the Canadian Maritimes. Students live and work as sailors on a true voyage of discovery, while they study maritime history, maritime literature, marine science, applied mathematics, and navigation. Discovery™ is offered Fall and Spring Terms. Other programs include SEAmester™, OceanBound and Summer Seafaring Camps. The Ocean Classroom Foundation also owns and operates the schooners *Spirit of Massachusetts* and *Westward*.

SPECIFICATIONS

Flag: USA
Rig: Square topsail ketch
Homeport: Grays Harbor, Aberdeen,Washington
Normal cruising waters: West Coast of North America
Sparred length: 103'
LOD: 65'
LWL: 62'
Draft: 6'
Beam: 22'
Rig height: 75'
Freeboard: 3'
Sail area: 4,200 square feet
Tons: 64 GRT
Power: twin diesels
Hull: wood

HAWAIIAN CHIEFTAIN

Hawaiian Chieftain is a 103-foot square-rigged topsail ketch owned and operated by Grays Harbor Historical Seaport Authority. Built in Lahaina, Hawaii in 1988, she is a contemporary interpretation of a traditional design based on the European trading vessels that called in Hawaii during the 18th-century. Each year, *Hawaiian Chieftain* sails the Pacific Coast from British Columbia to San Diego in company with the *Lady Washington* providing "Voyages of Discovery" sailing and dockside educational programs. This hands-on history program teaches 4th & 5th grade students about the exploration of the Pacific Coast during the 1790s. The ships offer dockside tours and sea battle reenactment, sails for the public, as well as a crew training program, "Two Weeks Before the Mast." Summer programs include "Family Camp" and "Youth Camp" for ages 12 to 16. *Hawaiian Chieftain* programs are designed to educate, excite, inspire and empower students and the general public. *Hawaiian Chieftain* also offers sail training and team building for adults, private charters, and natural history cruises.

Who sails: Individuals and groups
Program type: Sail training for apprentices and paying trainees; maritime heritage programs for schools, homeschools and youth organizations; public programs include summer camps, three-hour sails, dockside tours and passages
Season: Year-round
Designer: Raymond R. Richards
Built: 1988: Lahaina, Maui, Hawaii, Lahaina Welding Co.
Coast Guard certification: Passenger Vessel (Subchapter T)
Crew: 8 **Trainees-passengers:** 45 overnight
Contact: Capt. Les Bolton, Executive Director, Grays Harbor Historical Seaport Authority, PO Box 2019, Aberdeen, WA 98520 USA
Tel: 800-200-5239 **Fax:** 360-533-9384
E-mail: les@historicalseaport.org
Website: www.historicalseaport.org

SPECIFICATIONS

Flag: USA
Rig: Dipping lug
Homeport: Grays Harbor, Aberdeen, Washington
Normal cruising waters: Grays Harbor, Puget Sound, Western Washington
Sparred length: 26'
LOA: 25'
LOD: 25'
LWL: 25'
Draft: 20"
Beam: 7'
Rig height: 16'
Sail area: 316 square feet
Tons: 3,800 LBS
Hull: wood

HEWITT R. JACKSON

Who sails: Students in grades elementary through college and groups and individuals of all ages
Program type: Sail training for volunteer and paying crew and trainees in cooperation with accredited institutions and other organized groups; sea education in maritime history, marine science, and ecology; passenger day sails; dockside interpretation
Designer: Stewart Hoagland, Hewitt Jackson
Built: 1993: Aberdeen, WA, Grays Harbor Historical Seaport Authority
Coast Guard certification: Sailing School Vessel (Subchapter R)
Crew: 2 **Trainees-passengers:** 8 – 13 day sails
Contact: Capt. Les Bolton, Executive Director, Grays Harbor Historical Seaport Authority, PO Box 2019, Aberdeen, WA 98520 USA
Tel: 800-200-5239 **Fax:** 360-533-9384
E-mail: les@historicalseaport.org
Website: www.historicalseaport.org

On May 12, 1792 Captain Robert Gray sailed his ship, *Columbia Rediviva*, over the bar of the "Great River of the West" and named it Columbia's River in honor of his ship. Captain Gray never would have entered that river had it not been for the information he received from the first American vessel to enter the river, *Columbia's* longboat. Unnamed and unheralded, ship's longboats were the workhorses of the 16th- to 19th-century. Powered by either oars or sails, these versatile seaworthy craft carried all manner of cargo from ship to shore and back again. Grays Harbor Historical Seaport Authority built two 18th-century ship's longboat reproductions in 1993. Noted maritime historian and artist Hewitt R. Jackson, who worked closely with naval architect Stewart Hoagland and Seaport Director Les Bolton to ensure both historical accuracy and the meeting of specific program needs, painstakingly researched the design for the Seaport longboats. Powered by ten oars, or up to a 3-masted dipping lugsail rig, these versatile vessels are ideal for exploring the protected inland waterways of Washington. Programs are customized to the needs and interests of specific groups.

SPECIFICATIONS

Flag: USA
Rig: Gaff topsail schooner
Homeport: Port Huron, Michigan
Normal cruising waters: Great Lakes and Eastern Seaboard
Sparred length: 154'
LOA: 126'
LOD: 119'
LWL: 100'
Draft: 14'
Beam: 25' 6"
Rig height: 125'
Sail area: 9,728 square feet
Freeboard: 4' 8"
Tons: 135 GRT
Power: twin Detroit diesel, 8V-92, 350 HP each
Hull: white oak

HIGHLANDER SEA

Dedicated to showcasing the marine lore of Port Huron, Michigan and the Great Lakes region, Acheson Ventures, LLC purchased *Highlander Sea* for her new role as Port Huron's flagship ambassador. The ship was repatriated to the US in April 2002. Originally christened *Pilot*, she served 47 years as a Boston Harbor pilot ship. In the 1970s, she was purchased to circumnavigate the globe, got as far as Fiji and was sold. Her next owner renamed her *Star Pilot* and obtained US Coast Guard Certification as a school-ship. In 1998 Secunda Marine Services acquired the ship in San Diego, sailed her to Nova Scotia, Canada, renamed her *Highlander Sea* and refit her extensively to train young seafarers. Today, *Highlander Sea* offers opportunities for character development, teamwork, and community citizenship for the people of Port Huron, in particular its youth, through leadership and training. The ship rests in Port Huron, sails the Great Lakes and Eastern Seaboard, and is available for public tours, educational programs, and special events.

Who sails: Enthusiastic individuals age 16 and up
Program type: Sail training opportunities for volunteer crew or trainees; sea education in maritime history and ecology in cooperation with accredited institutions and other organized groups; overnight passages and passenger day sails; dockside interpretation
Season: April to November
Designer: W. Starling Burgess
Built: 1924: Essex, MA, J. F. James and Son
Coast Guard certification: Passenger Vessel (Subchapter T)
Crew: 12 **Trainees-passengers:** 12 daysails, 12 overnight
Contact: Captain Ben Hale, Highlander Sea, 2336 Military Street, Port Huron, MI 48060 USA
Tel: 810-966-3488 **Fax:** 810-982-1900
E-mail: caphighlandersea@achesonventures.com
Website: www.highlandersea.com

SPECIFICATIONS

Flag: USA
Rig: Sharpie schooner
Homeport: Wheeler's Bay, Maine
Normal cruising waters:
Maine Coast, Florida Keys
Sparred length: 30'
LWL: 27' 6"
Draft: 12" board up, 5' board down
Beam: 8' 6"
Rig height: 30'
Freeboard: 2'
Sail area: 340 square feet
Hull: fiberglass

HURRICANE (I - 22)

Who sails: Individuals and groups 14 and older, coed; corporations and organizations
Program type: Sail training and seamanship, taught to encourage growth, discovery and life enhancement
Designer: Rodger Martin Design, Newport, R.I.
Built: 2007: Union River Boat/Southport Island Marine, Maine
Crew: 2 **Trainees-passengers:** 6
Contact: Outward Bound Wilderness, 910 Jackson St., Golden, CO 80401 USA
Tel: 800-477-2627 **Fax:** 720-497-2441
E-mail: contactus@outwardbound.org
Website: www.outwardbound.org

Built exclusively for Outward Bound's second school in the United States and modeled after traditional whaling vessels and Coast Guard rescue boats, the Hurricane Island ketch-rigged pulling boat has served since 1965. The fleet is being replaced by a new design based on the New Haven Sharpie. Outward Bound has built its reputation teaching sailing on the East Coast and internationally for 40 years, primarily using its small open boats, as well as historic schooners such as *Westward, Harvey Gamage*, and *Spirit of Massachusetts*. Students experience open ocean adventure and island living, sailing the coast of Maine, the Canadian Maritimes, or the Caribbean. Living as student-crew, participants rotate responsibilities, learning to sail and navigate, as well as developing teamwork and leadership skills. Outward Bound is a nonprofit educational organization that offers more than 750 Wilderness courses throughout the US as well as internationally. To learn about our range of activities, locations and course types, visit www.outwardbound.org or call 1-888-88BOUND.

IMAGINE

The schooner *Imagine* was launched in 1997. She is the fifth of a series of series of schooners designed and built by Scarano Boat in the 1990s. Although dimensionally very similar to the other four vessels, she has an interior layout more suitable for sail training and can accommodate up to 14 trainees and crew for extended sailing adventures.

Who sails: School groups from elementary through college, private and corporate charters, families, and individuals of all ages
Program type: Sail training with paying trainees, passenger day sails
Built: 1997; Albany, NY, Scarano Boat
Coast Guard certification: Passenger Vessel (Subchapter T)
Crew: 3 **Trainees-passengers:** 49 daysails, 14 overnight
Contact: Classic Harbor Line, Chelsea Piers Suite 5912, 23rd St. at Hudson River, NY, NY 10011 USA
Tel: 212-827-1825 **Fax:** 646-349-5963
E-mail: info@Sail-NYC.com
Website: www.Sail-NYC.com

SPECIFICATIONS

Flag: USA
Rig: Gaff schooner, 2-masted
Homeport: Suttons Bay, Michigan
Normal cruising waters: Grand Traverse Bay, Lake Michigan
Sparred length: 77'
LOA: 61' 6"
LOD: 61' 6"
LWL: 53'
Draft: 7'
Beam: 17'
Rig height: 66'
Freeboard: 4'
Sail area: 1,800 square feet
Tons: 41 GRT
Power: 130 HP diesel
Hull: steel

INLAND SEAS

Who sails: School groups and individuals of all ages
Program type: Sail training for volunteer and paying trainees; sea education in marine science, maritime history, and ecology for students from elementary through college, adults, and at-risk youth; dockside interpretation during port visits
Season: May through early October
Designer: Charles W. Wittholz, Woodin & Marean
Built: 1994: Palm Coast, FL, Treworgy Yachts
Coast Guard certification: Passenger Vessel (Subchapter T)
Crew: 5 **Trainees-passengers:** 32 daysails, 10 overnight
Contact: Thomas M. Kelly, Executive Director, Inland Seas Education Association, PO Box 218, Suttons Bay, MI 49682 USA
Tel: 231-271-3077 **Fax:** 231-271-3088
E-mail: isea@schoolship.org
Website: www.schoolship.org

The *Inland Seas* Education Association (ISEA) was created in 1989 to teach culturally diverse students from throughout the state of Michigan, the Midwest and beyond about the science and heritage of the Great Lakes. ISEA's award-winning experiential educational programs are designed for students in grades 5 – 12 and are modified for learners of all ages. More than 80,000 participants have experienced the Great Lakes Schoolship Program, including students from over 140 Michigan communities. Summer shipboard experiences for all ages include astronomy, history, and science programs on Grand Traverse Bay and Lake Michigan. The goal of every ISEA program is to encourage young people to pursue academic interests related to the Great Lakes, particularly the sciences, and to provide enhanced public understanding and stewardship of the Great Lakes for future generations. The heart of the Schoolship Program is the work of 200 dedicated and professionally trained volunteers who donate nearly 8,000 hours annually aboard the Schoolship.

SPECIFICATIONS

Flag: USA
Rig: Brigantine
Homeport: Los Angeles, California
Normal cruising waters: Southern California and offshore islands
Sparred length: 110' 8"
LOA: 90'
LOD: 81' 7"
LWL: 72' 6"
Draft: 11'
Beam: 21' 9"
Rig height: 87' 8"
Sail area: 4,540 square feet
Tons: 99 GRT
Power: 315 HP diesel
Hull: wood

Photo by Volker Correll

IRVING JOHNSON

In April of 2002, the Los Angeles Maritime Institute launched the twin brigantines *Exy Johnson* and *Irving Johnson*. Named in honor of the Johnsons and their lifelong commitment to character-building sailing adventures, the brigantines were constructed on the waterfront in San Pedro, California. Designed for LAMI's TopSail Youth Program, the brigantines were built especially to meet the needs of middle school youth. The TopSail Youth Program uses sail training to provide youth with real-life challenges that develop the knowledge, skills and attitudes needed to live healthy, productive lives. TopSail enriches, validates and challenges conventional school curricula by bringing biology, history, mathematics, physics, geography, literature and the environment to life in the real world classroom of the sea. Irving McClure Johnson began training for a sailor's life as a teenager. In 1929 he sailed around Cape Horn on the barque *Peking*. Captain Johnson met his wife Electa, "Exy", sailing trans-Atlantic aboard *Wanderbird*. The Johnsons sailed around the world seven times with youth crew on two different *Yankees,* then cruised European and African waters in their third *Yankee*, a ketch.

Who sails: Youth/school groups from diverse communities, mostly middle schoolers from 'at-risk' urban areas
Program type: Educational sailing adventures for youth and adult groups
Season: Year-round
Coast Guard certification: Sailing School Vessel (Subchapter R), Passenger Vessel (Subchapter T)
Contact: Captain Jim Gladson, President, Los Angeles Maritime Institute, Berth 84, Foot of Sixth Street, San Pedro, CA 90731 USA
Tel: 310-833-6055 **Fax:** 310-548-2055
Website: www.LAMITopSail.org

SPECIFICATIONS

Flag: Poland
Rig: Barquentine
Homeport: Gdynia, Poland
Normal cruising waters: Baltic Sea
Sparred length: 161'
LOA: 140'
LOD: 137'
LWL: 121'
Draft: 13' 9'
Beam: 26'
Rig height: 115'
Freeboard: 5'
Sail area: 377 square feet
Hull: steel

Photo by Thad Koza

ISKRA

Who sails: Cadets of the Polish Naval Academy
Program type: Training vessel
Designer: Zygmunt Choren
Built: 1982: Gdanska Shipyard
Contact: Commanding Officer, ORP Iskra, JW 1449 ORP ISKRA, Gdynia, Wojewodztwo Pomorskie, 81-103 Gdynia 3 Poland
Tel: 48-58-626-25-54
Fax: 48-58-626-25-54
E-mail: iskra2@poczta.fm

The ship took her name after a 3-masted gaff schooner, *Iskra*, which sailed under the Polish navy ensign for 50 years between 1927 and 1977. ORP *Iskra* was built in 1982 in Gdanska Shipyard. She is a 3-masted barquentine with different rigging on all three masts. The foremast has five square sails; main sail is gaff-rigged; and mizzen is Bermudian. The main purpose of the ship is to train Polish Naval Academy cadets on their summer practices. Every year since 1987, she has participated in the Cutty Sark Tall Ships' Races. During her years of sailing, the ship has won numerous prizes including the United Nations Peace Medal in 1990, the Cutty Sark Trophy in 1989, the Fair Play Prize in the 1999 Cutty Sark Tall Ships Race, and the Polish Navy's Best Ship Prize (five times). The letters ORP in front of her name are the abbreviation for "Ship of the Republic of Poland" and indicate that the ship belongs to the Polish Navy. The name *Iskra* means "spark".

SPECIFICATIONS

Flag: USA
Rig: Gaff schooner
Homeport: Key West, Florida
Normal cruising waters: Key West, middle and lower Keys to the Dry Tortugas
Sparred length: 80'
LOD: 65'
Draft: 5' 11"
Beam: 16' 6"
Rig height: 62'
Sail area: 1,896 square feet
Tons: 34 GRT
Power: American Diesel 135 HP
Hull: steel

JOLLY II ROVER

The *Jolly II Rover* is the only square rigged, topsail schooner sailing out of the Historic Seaport of Key West. This beautiful, 80-foot, 1800s style coastal schooner has been sailing the crystal waters of Key West since 2005, when hurricane Katrina blew us from New Orleans' Lake Pontchartrian to our natural home in the Florida Keys. The *Rover* has impressed thousands of Key West visitors and locals, and is beginning to attract a large number of impassioned regulars who keep sailing the *Rover* again and again. Many Key West regulars and visitors alike consider multiple trips aboard the schooner to be a regular and much anticipated part of their Key West vacation. The *Rover* features plenty of seating, amazing crew, and of course our signature red sails. Ignite your passion for sailing and for life on board this traditional sailing ship, and experience the best in Key West sailing adventure and romance.

Who sails: Students ages middle school through college; individuals and groups
Program type: Sail traiing for paying crew and trainees; daysails and overnight passages
Designer: Merritt Walter
Built: 1994: Bock Marine
Coast Guard certification: Passenger Vessel (Subchapter T)
Crew: 3 **Trainees-passengers:** 49 daysails, 20 overnight
Contact: Bill Malone, Schooner Jolly II Rover, PO box 4053 Key West, Florida 33041 USA
Tel: 305-304-2235
E-mail: jollyrover@cox.net
Website: www.schoonerjollyrover.com

SPECIFICATIONS

Flag: USA
Rig: Ship, 3-masted
Homeport: Mystic, Connecticut
Sparred length: 118' 6"
LOA: 100' 8"
Draft: 12'
Beam: 25' 3"
Rig height: 98' 6"
Tons: 213 GRT
Hull: iron

JOSEPH CONRAD

Who sails: Individuals and organized groups ages 10 – 15
Program type: Sail training; dockside visitation for school groups and individuals
Season: June – August
Designer: Burmeister and Wain
Built: 1882: Copenhagen, Denmark, Burmeister & Wain
Contact: Mystic Seaport Watercraft Department, PO Box 6000, Mystic, CT 06355-0990 USA
Tel: 860-572-5322 **Fax:** 860-572-5355
Website: www.mysticseaport.org

For over 60 years, young people have come to Mystic Seaport, our nation's leading maritime museum, to learn to sail and live on board the tall ship *Joseph Conrad*. Each morning, campers tackle the wind and current of the Mystic River and then set off for an active afternoon investigating the Museum's unique exhibitions. After a late-day sail session, some "R and R" and dinner, campers spend their evenings with new friends, stargazing in a planetarium, climbing the rigging of the *Conrad* or enjoying a lively sea music sing-a-long. The *Joseph Conrad* program is open to individual boys and girls and organized groups ages 10 – 15. No prior experience is required for beginner sessions, only a desire to participate and learn. Intermediate sessions are for those who have attended a previous beginner session or have had sailing experience. All must hold current Red Cross swimmers certification or its equivalent.

SPECIFICATIONS

Flag: Spain
Rig: Topsail schooner, 4-masted
Homeport: Cadiz, Spain
LOA: 305' 6"
Draft: 23' 7"
Beam: 42' 7"
Rig height: 164'
Power: GM358 diesel
Hull: iron

JUAN SEBASTIAN DE ELCANO

The official training vessel for the midshipmen and ensigns of the Spanish Navy, *Juan Sebastian de Elcano* was launched in 1927 and delivered to the Spanish navy in 1928. Her hull is made of iron and she has four masts, each named after other training ships which preceded her (*Blanca*, *Almansa*, *Asturias*, and *Nautilus*). She is named in honor of *Juan Sebastion de Elcano*, captain of Ferdinand Magellan's last exploratory fleet. The ship also carries the *de Elcano* coat of arms–a terraqueous globe and the motto "Primus Circumdedisti Me" (first to circumnavigate me) which emperor Charles I conferred on *de Elcano* after he returned to Spain having completed Magellan's global expedition. She has sailed in more than 50 training voyages, including six circumnavigations of the globe.

Who sails: Midshipmen of the Spanish Navy
Program type: Training vessel of the Spanish Naval Academy
Designer: Nicholson, England
Built: 1927: Cadiz, Spain, Shipyard Echevarrieta y Larrinaga
Certification: Spanish Naval Vessel
Crew: 250 – 270 including midshipmen
Contact: Office of the Naval Attache, Embassy of Spain, 4801 Wisconsin Avenue, NW, 3rd floor, Washington, DC 20016 USA
Tel: 202-244-2166 **Fax:** 202-362-3993

SPECIFICATIONS

Flag: Japan
Rig: Brigantine
Homeport: Sausalito, California
LOA: 151'
Draft: 11' 2"
Beam: 25'
Hull: steel

KAISEI

Program type: To study the North Pacific Gyre and the marine debris that has collected in this oceanic region, to determine how to capture the debris and to study the possible retrieval and processing techniques that could be potentially employed to detoxify and recycle these materials into diesel fuel. The first research expedition, scheduled for the summer of 2009, will be critical to understanding the logistics that would be needed to launch future clean-up operations and testing existing technologies that have never been utilized under oceanic conditions.

Built: 1990

Contact: Ocean Voyages Institute, 1709 Bridgeway, Sausalito CA 94965 USA

Tel: 415-332-4681 **Fax:** 415-332-7460

E-mail: sail@oceanvoyages.com

Website: www.oceanvoyages.com

Launched in 1990, *Kaisei* has already traversed the globe and sailed thousands of people to far reaching ports. *Kaisei* has visited over 15 countries, crewed by volunteers from over 26 nations. Her voyages have created a powerfully diverse network of supporters; dissolving racial, ethnic, religious, political, and age barriers around the world. *Kaisei* has sailed International Peace Missions with citizens of political "hot spots" such as joint crews made up of Japanese and Korean citizens. *Kaisei* is now operated by Ocean Voyages Institute, a non-profit organization (501-c-3) founded in 1979 by a group of international sailors, educators, and conservationists with a mission of teaching the maritime arts and sciences, and researching and preserving the world's oceans. Selective partnerships with leading international youth and environmental organizations have paved the way for innovative programs rich with challenge, service, and humble appreciation of the interconnectedness of humanity and the resources that sustain us.

SPECIFICATIONS

Flag: Bulgaria
Rig: Barquentine
Homeport: Varna, Bulgaria
Sparred length: 159'
Draft: 11'
Beam: 27'
Hull: steel

Photo by Thad Koza

KALIAKRA

Completed in 1984, *Kaliakra* trains future officers for the Bulgarian Navy and is a sister ship to *Iskra*. Her home port is Varna on the Black Sea, although she has been a frequent participant in European and American tall ship gatherings. As initially rigged, only four yardarms crossed her foremast because of variations in deck thickness that affected the height of the foremast. Since her refitting in 1992, however, she carries five yardarms in her barquentine configuration. Her figurehead is a stylized version of a Bulgarian mythological figure.

Program type: Training vessel of the Bulgarian Navy
Built: 1984
Contact: Embassy of the Republic of Bulgaria, 1621 22nd Street NW, Washington, DC 20008 USA
Tel: 202-387-7969 **Fax:** 202-234-7973

SPECIFICATIONS

Flag: USA
Rig: Full-rigged ship
Homeport: Wilmington, Delaware
Normal cruising waters:
Mid-Atlantic and Northeast
Sparred length: 141'
LOA: 93'
LOD: 91'
LWL: 89' 2"
Draft: 12' 5"
Beam: 24' 11"
Rig height: 105'
Freeboard: 8'
Sail area: 7,600 square feet
Tons: 168 GRT
Power: 2 Caterpillar 3208 180 HP ea
Hull: wood

KALMAR NYCKEL

Who sails: School groups from elementary through college, as well as individuals and families
Program type: Sail training for volunteers; education programs for school children, dockside interpretation during port visits
Season: May through October
Designer: Tom Gillmer
Built: 1997: Wilmington, Delaware, Allen C. Rawl
Coast Guard certification: Passenger Vessel (Subchapter T)
Crew: 8 **Trainees-passengers:** 49 daysails
Contact: Kalmar Nyckel Foundation, 1124 East Seventh Street, Wilmington, DE 19801 USA
Tel: 302-429-7447 **Fax:** 302-429-0350
E-mail: officemanager@kalmarnyckel.org
Website: www.kalmarnyckel.org

The *Kalmar Nyckel*, the tall ship of Delaware, is a re-creation of the first Swedish colonial settlement ship to arrive in America in 1638, which established the colony of New Sweden in what is now Wilmington, Delaware. Launched in the fall of 1997, commissioned in May of 1998, and USCG certified in June of 2000, this ornately carved 17th Century Dutch pinnace sails the Northeast and Mid-Atlantic regions seasonally, carrying out her mission of education and goodwill. She transforms Delaware's history into hands-on educational opportunities for children through adults, from teaching fourth and sixth graders history and physics to conducting her bi-annual volunteer crew sail training. She provides economic development opportunities, private charters both underway and dockside, public sails and public tours, and statewide marketing initiatives on a national scale, serving as Delaware's tall ship ambassador. A professional captain, mates and a volunteer crew man the *Kalmar Nyckel*.

SPECIFICATIONS

Flag: Russia
Rig: Barque, 4-masted
Homeport: Kalingrad, Russia
Normal cruising waters:
Western European waters (summer)
Southern European waters (winter)
Sparred length: 376'
LOA: 346'
LOD: 329'
LWL: 311' 6"
Draft: 19'
Beam: 46'
Rig height: 176'
Freeboard: 27' 9"
Sail area: 36,380 square feet
Power: twin 600 HP diesels
Hull: steel

KRUZENSHTERN

Kruzenshtern was built as *Padua* in 1927 in Bremerhaven, Germany. The sister ship to *Peking*, she is the last of the "Flying P" liners still under sail. These vessels were engaged in the grain trade from Australia to Europe. In 1933, *Kruzenshtern* sailed from her homeport of Hamburg to Port Lincoln in Australia in only 67 days. At the end of World War II she was handed over to the USSR and converted into a sail training ship. Since 1990, up to 40 trainees of all ages have been welcomed onboard to sail along with the Russian students of the Baltic Academy in Kalingrad, Russia, learning the ropes, manning the helm, or climbing the rigging to set more than 30,000 square feet of sail. No previous experience is necessary. *Kruzenshtern* is supported by Tall Ship Friends, a nonprofit organization in Hamburg, Germany. The goals of Tall Ship Friends are to promote sail training on square-riggers, to contribute to the further existence of these beautiful ships, and to provide an unforgettable experience for the participants. Members of Tall Ship Friends receive the quarterly Tall Ships News (English/German) and a personal sailing log.

Who sails: Groups and individuals of all ages
Program type: Sail training for paying trainees; fully accredited sea education in traditional seamanship
Built: 1927: Bremerhaven, Germany, J.C. Tecklenborg
Certification: Special Purpose (School Vessel), Russia
Crew: 45-70 **Trainees-passengers:** 250 day-sails, 60 overnight
Contact: Wulf Marquard, Managing Director, Tall Ship Friends Germany, Schweriner Sir. 17, Hamburg, D22143 Germany
Tel: 49-40-675 635 97 **Fax:** 49-40-675 635 99
E-mail: tallshipl@aol.com
Website: www.tallship-friends.de

SPECIFICATIONS

Flag: Cook Islands
Rig: Topsail cutter
Homeport: Rarotonga, Cook Islands
Normal cruising waters: Hawaii to Cook Islands
Sparred length: 125'
LOA: 118'
LOD: 116'
LWL: 110'
Draft: 9' to 11'
Beam: 23'
Rig height: 70'
Freeboard: 2' to 4'
Sail area: 2,000 square feet
Tons: 179 GRT
Power: 365 HP Detroit diesel
Hull: steel

KWAI

Who sails: Trainees ages 18 to 80
Program type: Sail training and cargo
Season: Year-round
Built: 1950: Brmer Vulkan, Bremen, Germany
Crew: 6 **Trainees-passengers**: 2-4
Contact: Brad Ives, Senior Captain, KWAI,13-3988 Honua'ula St., Pahoa, Hawaii 96778 USA
Tel: 808-965-0221 **Fax:** 808-965-0224
E-mail: info@svkwai.com
Website: www.svkwai.com

Kwai is a traditional sailing cargo ship, trading between Hawaii, the Line Islands of Kiribati, and the Cook Islands on voyages lasting 5 to 10 weeks. She works today as a motor sailer carrying general cargo and will soon be rigged as a topsail ketch. The trainees sail as crew, standing watches, handling sail, working cargo, and maintain the ship with time ashore to share cultures on remote Pacific Islands. The ship is under a continuing refit into a full sailing vessel with additional accommodation for sail trainees and adventure travelers. Training in ironwork, ships carpentry and rigging are emphasized aboard and in our workshop ashore. *Kwai* is a working ship with an active relationship with our island clients. Trainees participate in all operations from sailing the ship across the trade winds to selling rice and t-shirts ashore islands like Puka-puka.

SPECIFICATIONS

Flag: France
Rig: Topsail schooner
Homeport: Brest, France
Sparred length: 124'
Draft: 12'
Beam: 24'
Hull: wood

LA BELLE POULE

Along with her sister ship *Etoile*, the schooner *La Belle Poule* serves the French Navy in the training of future officers. Designed with the hull shape and the rigging of fishing vessels from Breton, *La Belle Poule* and *Etoile* were built in 1932 in the fishing port of Fecamp in northern Normandy, France. During World War II, both vessels relocated to Portsmouth, England, where they served the Free France Forces. They are permitted to fly the French ensign with the imposed Cross of Lorraine in recognition of their service during the war.

Program type: Sail training vessel of the French Navy
Built: 1932: Fecamp, Normandy, France
Contact: Embassy of France, 4101 Resevoir Road, NW, Washington, DC 20007 USA
Tel: 202-944-6000
Fax: 202-944-6166

SPECIFICATIONS

Flag: USA
Rig: Pungy schooner
(gaff rigged), 2-masted
Homeport: Baltimore, Maryland
Normal cruising waters:
Chesapeake and Delaware Bays,
East Coast between Maryland
and Maine
Sparred length: 104'
LOD: 72'
LWL: 64' 3"
Draft: 7'
Beam: 22'
Rig height: 85'
Freeboard: 3'
Sail area: 2,994 square feet
Tons: 60 GRT
Power: twin 80 HP diesels

LADY MARYLAND

Who sails: Student and other organized groups, individuals, and families
Program type: Sail training with paying trainees; sea education in marine science, maritime history, and ecology for school groups from elementary school through college as well as adults
Season: March through November
Designer: Thomas Gilmer
Built: 1986: Baltimore, Maryland, G. Peter Boudreau
Coast Guard certification: Passenger Vessel (Subchapter T)
Crew: 6 day sails, 8 overnight **Trainees-passengers:** 32 daysails, 12-14 overnight
Contact: Living Classrooms Foundation, 802 South Caroline Street, Baltimore, MD 21231-3311 USA
Tel: 410-685-0295 **Fax:** 410-752-8433
Website: www.livingclassrooms.org

Lady Maryland is an authentic pungy schooner, an elegant boat designed to haul cargo, fish, dredge for oysters, and to carry luxury items quickly from port to port on Chesapeake Bay and along the Atlantic Coast. Instead of carrying watermelons and oysters, her mission today is to provide students with the opportunity to experience sailing a historic vessel while studying history, seamanship, marine science, and ecology on her traditional waters from Maryland to Maine. The Living Classrooms Foundation has developed a flexible educational program that can fit the needs of a variety of school and community groups. More than 50,000 students participate in LCF programs each year. The *Lady Maryland* operates educational day experiences for 32 trainees and extended live-aboard sail training and marine science programs for up to 14 people.

SPECIFICATIONS

Flag: USA
Rig: Brig
Homeport: Grays Harbor, Aberdeen, Washington
Normal cruising waters: Washington, West Coast of North America
Sparred length: 112'
LOA: 87'
LOD: 66' 9"
LWL: 58'
Draft: 11'
Beam: 24'
Rig height: 89'
Freeboard: 6'
Sail area: 4,400 square feet
Tons: 99 GRT
Power: diesel
Hull: wood

LADY WASHINGTON

As a privateer during the American Revolution, the original *Lady Washington* fought to help the colonies gain their independence from England. In 1788, she became the first American vessel to visit the West Coast of North America, opening trade between the colonies and the native peoples of the Northwest Coast. Built at Grays Harbor Historical Seaport in Aberdeen, Washington, and launched in 1989 as a Washington State Centennial project, the reproduction *Lady Washington* sails the waters of Washington State and the West Coast of North America as the tall ship ambassador for the state of Washington. With a busy year-round sailing schedule, *Lady Washington* regularly tours the West Coast, providing shipboard education programs for schools in 89 port communities in Washington, Oregon, California, British Columbia, and Alaska. More than 15,000 school children visit *Lady Washington* each year to learn about the rich and colorful maritime heritage of our nation. Crew are paid professionals and volunteer trainees.

Who sails: School groups from elementary school through college, individuals, and families
Program type: Sail training for crew, apprentices, and paying trainees; sea education in maritime history in cooperation with accredited institutions based on informal, in-house programming; passenger day sails, overnight passages, and family camps; dockside interpretation
Season: Year-round
Designer: Ray Wallace
Built: 1989: Aberdeen, Washington, Grays Harbor Historical Seaport Authority
Coast Guard certification: Passenger Vessel (Subchapter T)
Crew: 12 **Trainees-passengers:** 48 daysails, 8 overnight
Contact: Capt. Les Bolton, Executive Director, Grays Harbor Historical Seaport Authority, PO Box 2019, Aberdeen, WA 98520 USA
Tel: 800-200-5239 **Fax:** 360-533-9384
E-mail: les@historicalseaport.org
Website: www.historicalseaport.org

Flag: USA
Rig: Gaff topsail schooner, 2-masted
Homeport: New York, New York
Normal cruising waters: Northeast United States
Sparred length: 125'
LOD: 83'
LWL: 71'
Draft: 11'
Beam: 21'
Rig height: 91'
Freeboard: 4'
Sail area: 5,017 square feet
Tons: 54 GRT
Power: twin 85 HP diesels
Hull: wood

LETTIE G. HOWARD

Who sails: School groups, colleges and universities, corporate teambuilding programs, Elderhostel, individual adults, and families
Program type: Sea education and sail training programs focusing on nautical science, fishery and maritime history, natural and social sciences
Built: 1893: Essex, MA, A. D. Story (restored at South Street Seaport Museum in 1993)
Coast Guard certification: Sailing School Vessel (Subchapter R)
Crew: 7-9 **Trainees-passengers:** 33 daysails, 13 overnight
Contact: Lettie G. Howard, South Street Seaport Museum, 12 Fulton Street, New York, NY 10038 USA
Tel: 212-748-8684 (office) or 646-831-0494 (captain's cell)
Fax: 212-748-8610
E-mail: lettieghoward@southstseaport.org
Website: www.southstseaport.org
www.southstreetseaportmuseum.org

The *Lettie G. Howard* is the sole surviving example of a Georges Bank fishing schooner. A Fredonia model-fishing schooner built in Essex, Massachusetts, she exemplifies the type of craft used widely up and down the Eastern seaboard of the United States from Maine to the Gulf Coast. Operating out of Gloucester for her first eight years, the *Lettie* was similar to the schooners that carried their Long Island and New Jersey catches to New York City's Fulton Fish Market. In 1901, the *Lettie* was purchased by the E.E. Saunders company of Pensacola, Florida, for use off Mexico's Yucatan Peninsula. Completely rebuilt in 1923, she was fitted with her first auxiliary engine a year later. She remained in the Gulf of Mexico until 1968, when she was sold to the South Street Seaport Museum in New York City. The *Lettie G. Howard* was designated a National Historic Landmark in 1989. Between 1991 and 1993, the Museum completely restored her to her original 1893 appearance, while outfitting her to accommodate trainees on educational cruises.

SPECIFICATIONS

Flag: Argentina
Rig: Full-rigged ship
Homeport: Buenos Aires, Argentina
Sparred length: 356'
LOD: 317'
LWL: 263'
Draft: 21' 9"
Beam: 45' 3"
Rig height: 147' 6"
Freeboard: 15'
Sail area: 28,545 square feet
Power: two 1,200 HP diesel engines
Hull: steel

LIBERTAD

The frigate, A.R.A. *Libertad*, was initiated as a training ship in 1963 for the Argentine Navy. As a training ship, her mission is to enhance the maritime knowledge and cultural background of her midshipmen while integrating them to life at sea and instructing them on the fundamentals of the art of sailing. *Libertad* also serves as a floating ambassador representing the Argentine Republic establishing professional and friendly ties with navies around the world while preparing her cadets academically, physically and spiritually. In 1966, *Libertad* established the world record for speed crossing the North Atlantic sailing from Cape Race (Canada) to Dursey Island (Ireland) in six days and 21 hours. The International Sail Training Association (ISTA) officially recognized her record, and *Libertad* flies a pennant commemorating this achievement. Her figurehead was made by a Spanish sculptor and depicts Liberty, for which the ship is named. *Libertad* has sailed the seven seas and participates in regattas and port visits around the world.

Who sails: Cadets from the Military Naval School (20 – 23)
Program type: Naval training vessel
Season: May through December
Designer: Astilleros y Fabricas Navales del Estado (AFNE)
Built: 1960 (launched 1956): Rio Santiago (BA), Argentina, Astilleros y Fabricas Navales del Estado (AFNE)
Crew: 150 **Trainees-passengers:** 150
Contact: Argentine Naval Attache Office, Embassy of Argentina, 630 Indiana Avenue, NW, Washington, DC 20004 USA
Tel: 202-626-2164 **Fax:** 202-626-2180
Website: www.argnavattache-usa.org or www.ara.mil.ar

SPECIFICATIONS

Flag: USA
Rig: Gaff topsail schooner
Homeport: Boston, Massachusetts
Normal cruising waters: East Coast US
Sparred length: 125'
LOD: 86'
LWL: 76'
Draft: 8'(min.), 13'(max.)
Beam: 25'
Rig height: 78'
Freeboard: 5'
Sail area: 4,300 square feet
Tons: 99 GRT
Power: diesel
Hull: steel

LIBERTY CLIPPER

Who sails: School groups from elementary through high school, individuals, and families
Program type: Passenger day sails and overnight passages; corporate and private charters
Designer: Charles Wiftholz
Built: 1983: Warren, RI, Blount Marine Corporation
Coast Guard certification: Passenger Vessel (Subchapter T)
Crew: 5 daysails, 10 overnight **Trainees-passengers:** 115 daysails, 28 overnight
Contact: The Liberty Fleet of Tall Ships, 67 Long Wharf, Boston, MA 02210 USA
Tel: 617-742-0333 **Fax:** 617-742-1322
E-mail: info@libertyfleet.com
Website: www.libertyfleet.com

The *Liberty Clipper* is a replica of the mid-19th century Baltimore Clippers famous for their fast passages round Cape Horn on their way to California and other Pacific ports. The *Liberty Clipper* operates in Boston Harbor during the Summer, Baltimore, Maryland, in the fall and Nassau, the Bahamas, during the winter. In Boston, *Liberty Clipper* is available for charter on day and evening cruises for up to 115 passengers. Her spacious decks and on-board hospitality create an ambiance under sail that will meet the expectations of the most discriminating clients. In addition to a variety of high quality charter opportunities, during the summer months, she offers the Liberty Classroom program for Boston area youth groups, a sail training and harbor education program designed to give trainees an introduction to essential topics in seamanship, safety, and Boston's maritime history. For those interested in extended trips, *Liberty Clipper* offers three to six-day overnight cruises in the Chesapeake Bay and six-day island hopping cruises in the Bahamas where pricing includes a berth and excellent food prepared by the ship's chef.

SPECIFICATIONS

Flag: USA
Rig: Gaff topsail schooner
Homeport: Jersey City, New Jersey
Normal cruising waters: Jersey City, New Jersey (summer), Charleston, South Carolina (winter)
Sparred length: 80'
LOA: 78'
LOD: 63'
LWL: 61'
Draft: 7'
Beam: 17'
Rig height: 65'
Freeboard: 5'
Sail area: 1,744 square feet
Tons: 50 GRT
Power: 135 HP diesel
Hull: steel

LIBERTY SCHOONER

The *Liberty Schooner* provides a unique learning environment as a catalyst for a life transforming experience. Our leadership coaching and sail training programs realize positive life change for leaders and teams in such a way that they increase their effectiveness and influence in every area of their lives, in the office and at home.

Who sails: Individuals/groups of all ages
Program type: Passenger daysails and overnight passages; leadership coaching
Designer: Charles Witholtz
Built: 1993
Coast Guard certification: Passenger Vessel (Subchapter T)
Crew: 3 day sails, 4 overnight
Trainees-passengers: 49 daysails, 8 overnight
Contact: Philip du Plessis, 791 Rte. 10E Randolph, NJ 07869 USA
Tel: 973-309-1884 **Fax:** 973-252-8144
E-mail: libertyschooner@gmail.com
Website: www.libertyschooner.com

SPECIFICATIONS

Flag: United Kingdom
Rig: Barque, 3-masted
Homeport: Southampton,
United Kingdom
Normal cruising waters:
United Kingdom (summer),
Canary Islands/Mediterranean (winter)
Sparred length: 180'
LOA: 140' 5"
LOD: 133'
LWL: 121' 5"
Draft: 13' 6"
Beam: 29' 6"
Rig height: 108'
Freeboard: 6' 8"
Sail area: 11,030 square feet
Tons: 368 GRT
Power: twin 260 HP
Hull: steel

LORD NELSON

Who sails: Physically disabled and able-bodied people, aged 16 to 70+
Program type: Sail training for paying trainees; integration of physically disabled and able-bodied people through the challenge of tall ship sailing
Designer: Colin Mudie
Built: 1986: Wivenhoe, UK, James W. Cook & Co., Ltd.
Certification: Lloyds 10Oal A1
Crew: 10 **Trainees-passengers:** 40
Contact: Ms. Amanda Butcher, Jubilee Sailing Trust, Jubilee Yard, Hazel Road, Woolston, Southampton, Hampshire S019 7GB, United Kingdom
Tel: 44-23-8044-9108 **Fax:** 44-23-8044-9145
E-mail: jst@jst.org.uk
Website: www.jst.org.uk

The 180-foot, 3-masted barque *Lord Nelson* was built in 1986 for the Jubilee Sailing Trust to encourage integration between able-bodied and physically disabled people by offering them the opportunity to experience the excitement of tall ship sailing together. Voyages last from 4 to 11 days, departing from a wide variety of ports and sailing in the English Channel, and the North and Irish Seas. A winter season of voyages based in the Canary Islands is also available. Above deck, the ship's equipment enables physically disabled crew to work alongside their able-bodied crewmates. Features include power steering, wide decks to accommodate wheelchairs, a speaking compass, powered lifts between decks, and Braille marking. Down below are specially designed wheelchair-accessible cabins, showers, and heads. Voyages are open to anyone between the ages of 16 to 70+ with or without sailing experience. Twenty people with physical disabilities, including eight wheelchair users, sail alongside an equal number of able-bodied people. There is a permanent crew of ten including a medically trained person and a cook.

Flag: USA
Rig: Square topsail schooner
Homeport: Newport Beach, California
Sparred Length: 122'
LOA: 78'
LOD: 76'
LWL: 72'
Draft: 9'
Beam: 23'
Rig height: 94'
Freeboard: 5'
Sail Area: 4,669 square feet
Tons: 94 GRT
Power: Cat 3306B - 290 HP hundested variable pitch propeller
Hull: wood

LYNX

The square topsail schooner *Lynx* has been designed and built to interpret the general configuration and operation of a privateer schooner or naval schooner from the War of 1812, the original *Lynx* being a "letter of marque" Baltimore Clipper commissioned during the opening days of the war. Serving effectively as a blockade-runner and offensive weapon of war, she was among the first ships to defend American freedom. Dedicated to all those who cherish the blessings of America, *Lynx* sails as a living history museum, providing inspiration and resolve at this time in our nation's history. She is fitted with period ordnance and flies flags and pennants from the 1812 era. To complement her historic character, the *Lynx* crew members wear period uniforms and operate the ship in keeping with the maritime traditions of early 19th century America. *Lynx* also operates as a sail training vessel to serve as a classroom for the study of historical, environmental, and ecological issues. In addition, she undertakes "cruises of opportunity" to the Hawaiian Islands that lead to personal growth and awareness through the experience of life at sea aboard a traditional sailing vessel.

Who sails: Schools groups from elementary age thru college. Troops, individuals, families, and company charters
Program type: Sail training; maritime history; Life, Earth, and Physical Science; charters; team building; public sails, dockside programs
Season: Year-round
Designer: Melbourne Smith - International Historical Watercraft Society
Built: Rockport, ME, Rockport Marine; launched July 28, 2001 in Rockport, ME
Coast Guard certification: Passenger Vessel (Subchapter T)
Crew: 8 **Trainees-passengers:** 40 daysails, 6 overnight
Contact: Jeffrey Woods, Director of Operations, Lynx Educational Foundation, 509 29th Street, Newport Beach, CA. 92663 USA
Tel: 866-446-5969 **Fax:** 949-723-1958
E-mail: privateerlynx1812@verizon.net
Website: www.privateerlynx.org

SPECIFICATIONS

Flag: USA
Rig: Gaff topsail schooner, 2-masted
Homeport: Traverse City, Michigan
Normal cruising waters: Great Lakes
Sparred length: 92'
LOA: 55' 6"
LWL: 52'
Draft: 7' 7"
Beam: 16' 2"
Rig height: 71'
Freeboard: 2' 2"
Sail area: 2,270 square feet
Tons: 42 GRT

MADELINE

Who sails: Trained crew members and guests of the Maritime Heritage Alliance
Program type: Adult sail training and maritime history
Designer: Kenneth (Bob) Core
Built: 1990: Traverse City, MI, Maritime Heritage Alliance
Coast Guard certification: Uninspected Vessel
Crew: 9
Contact: Mark Thompson, Executive Director, Maritime Heritage Alliance, 322 Sixth Street, Traverse City, MI 49684 USA
Tel: 231-946-2647 **Fax:** 231-946-6750
E-mail: mark@maritimeheritagealliance.org
Website: www.maritimeheritagealliance.org

Madeline is a reconstruction of a mid-19th-century schooner, typical of the trading schooners that once sailed the Great Lakes. The original *Madeline* was the first Euro-American School in the Grand Traverse region and for a short time served as a lightship in the Straits of Mackinac. Launched in 1990, the modern *Madeline* was built over a period of five years by volunteers of the Maritime Heritage Alliance (MHA), using traditional methods and materials. From her homeport in Traverse City, Michigan, she has sailed with her volunteer crew on all five Great Lakes, visiting over 60 ports with dockside tours and historical interpretation. *Madeline* is designated as the City of Traverse City's goodwill ambassador. Crewmembers, trained as historical interpreters, share their knowledge of history, marlinespike skills, and wooden boat building. School programs with special hands-on activities are also available. The Maritime Heritage Alliance, a nonprofit organization, is dedicated to preserving, interpreting, and sharing the maritime heritage of the Great Lakes.

SPECIFICATIONS

Flag: USA
Rig: Staysail schooner, 3-masted
Homeport: Kaneohe Bay, Hawaii
Normal cruising waters:
Hawaiian Islands
Sparred length: 96'
LOA: 85'
LOD: 75'
LWL: 63'
Draft: 8'
Beam: 20'
Rig height: 65'
Freeboard: 5'
Sail area: 2,000 square feet
Tons: 68 GRT
Power: 210 HP
Hull: steel

MAKANI OLU (GRACIOUS WIND)

The *Makani Olu* (Gracious Wind) is owned and operated by Marimed Foundation, a non-profit organization involved with sail training since 1988. The 96-foot, 3-masted staysail schooner, retrofitted for sail training in Hawaiian waters, is the central component of a model experiential education and treatment program for at-risk adolescents built around ocean voyaging. Voyaging challenges and experiences are designed to be powerful and transformational. From *Makani Olu's* home port in Kaneohe Bay on Oahu, cadets make a series of six-day voyages throughout the Hawaiian Island chain. While learning to operate the sailing ship, the cadets learn marine, navigation and team-building skills. Elderhostel International provides sail training experiences aboard *Makani Olu* as well. These programs feature a six-day voyage that includes hands-on opportunities to sail and operate the ship and additional learning opportunities at ports-of-call. The *Makani Olu* is also available to youth, families and community organizations for sail training and team building trips.

Who sails: Groups and individuals of all ages
Program type: Sail training for paying trainees; fully accredited sea education in marine science, maritime history, and ecology, as well as service learning, in cooperation with accredited institutions and other organized groups, and as informal in-house programming
Season: Year-round
Designer: Thomas Kolvin
Built: 1998: St. Augustine, FL, Schrieber
Coast Guard certification: Sailing School Vessel (Subchapter R)
Crew: 5 **Trainees-passengers:** 30 daysails, 20 overnight
Contact: Matthew Claybaugh, Ph.D., President and CEO, Marimed Foundation, 45-021 Likeke Place, Kaneohe, HI 96744 USA
Tel: 808 235-1377 **Fax:** 808-235-1074
E-mail: info@marimed.org
Website: www.marimed.org

SPECIFICATIONS

Flag: USA
Rig: Staysail schooner
Homeport: Seattle, Washington
Normal Cruising Waters: Pacific Northwest, Canada and Alaska
Sparred Length: 65'
LOA: 60'
LOD: 60'
LWL: 50'
Draft: 5' (min) 8' (max)
Beam: 16'
Rig height: 65'
Freeboard: 5'
Sail Area: 1,545 square feet
Tons: 38 GRT
Power: diesel
Hull: composite

MALLORY TODD

Who sails: All ages for volunteers, paying trainees, and apprentices
Program type: Sail training for crew, volunteers, trainees, and apprentices; sea education based on programmed and day to day events; passenger day sails for corporate team building or recreational events
Season: All year, but primarily May through September. MT is sometimes gone April and May on charters to Alaska
Designer: Perry & Todd
Built: 1981: Seattle, WA
Coast Guard certification: Passenger Vessel (Subchapter T)
Crew: 2 **Trainees-passengers:** 25 daysails, 6 overnight
Contact: Captain George Todd, Sailing Heritage Society, 10042 NE 13th Street Bellevue, WA 98004 USA
Tel: 206-381-6919 **Fax:** 206-381-9556
E-mail: info@sailingheritage.org
Website: www.sailingheritage.org

Named for Captain Mallory Todd, who served as master on American vessels during the Revolutionary War, the *Mallory Todd* is a modern 65-foot schooner built in the classic style with fireplaces and exceptionally intricate woodwork. Designed for long distance voyages, she has sailed the West Coast from Mexico to Alaska for 18 years. Sail training trips to the San Juan Islands, Canada, and Alaska via the Inside Passage, are blessed with the full bounty of nature. These trips are open to anyone between 18 and 80 with or without sailing experience. When at homeport in Seattle, she relieves the tedium of long-term cancer treatment with recreational outings for hospital patients and their caregivers under the auspices of the nonprofit Sailing Heritage Society. Together, part time volunteers, trainees, and professionals get the job done. Hands on tending the sails, steering, scrubbing, navigating, fishing, or clamming, each contributes where a need fits their abilities. Schooner *Mallory Todd* also offers corporate and private charters that provide a unique and delightful venue for business or recreational activities.

SPECIFICATIONS

Flag: USA
Rig: Gaff topsail schooner
Homeport: Traverse City, Michigan
Normal cruising waters: Great Lakes
Sparred length: 114'
LOD: 77'
LWL: 65'
Draft: 7' (min.) 11' (max.)
Beam: 21'
Rig height: 77'
Freeboard: 6'
Sail area: 3,000 square feet
Tons: 82 GRT
Power: 150 HP diesel
Hull: steel

MANITOU

Owned and operated by Traverse Tall Ship Co., LLC, the schooner *Manitou* is one of the largest sailing vessels on the Great Lakes. This replica of a 19th century "coaster" can accommodate 24 overnight guests and 62 passengers for day excursions. *Manitou* is fully certified by the US Coast Guard and offers day sails on Grand Traverse Bay, Lake Michigan. In addition, join us for an adventurous overnight as part of our "Floating Bed & Breakfast." Wake up in the morning to hot coffee and fresh baked muffins from the galley before sitting down to a full breakfast prepared from scratch on the wood stove. For a more in-depth experience, *Manitou* offers three and four day sailing adventures to the islands, bays and coastal villages of northern Lake Michigan. In conjunction with Inland Seas Education Association, *Manitou* operates the Schoolship Program, which provides an environmental, historical, and sail training education for students during the spring. The schooner offers partial as well as private charter service to family, company, and motor coach groups.

Who sails: School groups; individual, family, and corporate groups for day sails and bed & breakfast
Program type: Sail training for crew; sea education in marine science, maritime history and ecology; individual and group day sails; "Floating Bed & Breakfast"
Season: May to October
Designer: Woodin & Marean
Built: 1982: Portsmouth, NH, Roger Gagnon Steel Ship Company
Coast Guard certification: Passenger Vessel (Subchapter T)
Crew: 5 **Trainees-passengers:** 62 daysails, 24 overnight
Contact: Captain Dave McGinnis, Traverse Tall Ship Co., LLC, 13390 SW Bay Shore Drive, Traverse City, MI 49684 USA
Tel: 231-941-2000 **Fax:** 231-941-0520
E-mail: info@tallshipsailing.com
Website: www.talishipsailing.com

SPECIFICATIONS

Flag: USA
Rig: Gaff-rigged schooner
Homeport: Essex, Connecticut
Normal cruising waters:
Connecticut River to New York City
Sparred Length: 73'
LOA: 53'
LOD: 50'
LWL: 46'
Draft: 6'
Beam: 14'
Rig height: 50'
Freeboard: 2'
Sail area: 1,500 square feet
Tons: 14 GRT
Power: GM 471 diesel
Hull: Oak

MARY E

Who sails: Students and adult passengers of all ages
Program type: Educational sails, private sailing excursions and day sails
Season: May until October
Designer: William Donnell
Built: 1906:Thomas Hagan, Bath, Maine
Coast Guard certification: Passenger Vessel (Subchapter T)
Crew: 3 **Trainees-passengers:** 25 daysails, 6 overnight
Contact: Matt Culen or Eric Van Dormolen, Operations Manager, Halyard Enterprises LLC, 210 Bellerose Ave., East Northport, NY 11731 USA
Tel: 631-332-0699
E-mail: captericvandy@aol.com
Website: www.schoonermarye.com

The *Mary E* is the last Clipper Bow Schooner of 4,000 built in Bath, ME still afloat. She was a sword fishing, cargo, passenger, mail carrier, and rum running schooner that sailed out of Providence, Rhode Island. Captain Dunn sailed her to Block Island delivering goods. In 1938, her sail rig was cut down and she was converted to a motorized fishing dragger. In November of 1963 a hurricane washed her ashore. Captain Donnell, the original designer's great great-grandson, salvaged and restored her from 1965-1970 and made her a magnificent schooner once again. Since 1969, she has sailed in Camden, Rockport, Boothbay, New York City, City Island, Greenport, and the *Mary E* has found her new home at the Connecticut River Museum in Essex, Connecticut. The *Mary E's* primary goal is to educate the public about the Connecticut River as well as offer a sight seeing sails for adults with the occasional pirate or shanty sing along. The *Mary E* will sail to any port in the New York and Connecticut area for special events.

SPECIFICATIONS

Flag: USA
Rig: Gaff schooner
Homeport: Camden, Maine
Normal cruising waters:
Penobscot Bay – off the coast of
mid-coast Maine
Sparred length: 115'
LOD: 80'
LWL: 72'
Draft: 6' board up 16' board down
Beam: 22'
Rig height: 62'
Freeboard: 4'
Sail area: 3,800 square feet
Tons: 47 GRT
Power: 14' yawl boat w/diesel motor
Hull: wood

Photo by Barbara Hatch

MERCANTILE

The *Mercantile* was launched in 1916. In the early 40s, sailing out of Camden, Maine, with her first passengers under the ownership of Capt. Frank Swift, she became part of the original Maine Windjammer Cruises® fleet. The Schooner *Mercantile* was totally restored in 1989, by present owners Capt. Ray and Ann Williamson, and designated a National Historic Landmark. The *Mercantile* carries 29 passengers and does three- and four-day cruises off the coast of Maine and is one of five surviving two-masted coasting schooners in the USA. She is a pure sailing vessel with cotton sails and all natural fiber running rigging. Her traditional yawl boat provides motor assist. The full time crew of four includes Captain, Cook, First Mate and Deckhand. The fifth crew position is an Apprentice, which rotates every month.

Who sails: 16 and up (any age with full boat charter)
Program type: Cruising
Season: End of May thru early October
Designer: Billings
Built: 1916: Billings Family, Little Deer Isle, Maine
Coast Guard certification: Passenger Vessel (Subchapter T)
Crew: 5 **Trainees-passengers:** 49 daysails 29 overnight
Contact: Captain Ray and Ann Williamson, owners, Maine Windjammer Cruises®, PO Box 617, Camden, Maine 04843 USA
Tel: 207-236-2938 Reservations 800-736-7981
E-mail: sail@MaineWindjammerCruises.com
Website: www.MaineWindjammerCruises.com

SPECIFICATIONS

Flag: USA
Rig: Gaff topsail schooner, 2-masted
Homeport: Biloxi, Mississippi
Normal cruising waters: Coastwise Gulf of Mexico
Sparred length: 78'
LOA: 78'
LOD: 50'
LWL: 43'
Draft: 5' 10"
Beam: 17'
Sail area: 2,499 square feet
Tons: 24 GRT
Power: 4-71 Detroit diesel
Hull: wood

MIKE SEKUL

Who sails: Elementary students through college age, adults, and families
Program type: Sail training for paying and volunteer trainees; sea education in marine science, maritime history, and ecology in cooperation with accredited institutions and organized groups and as informal, in-house programming
Season: Year-round
Designer: Neil Covacevich
Built: 1994: Biloxi, Mississippi, Neil Covacevich
Coast Guard certification: Passenger Vessel (Subchapter T)
Crew: 3 **Trainees-passengers:** 45 daysails
Contact: Robin Krohn, Executive Director, Maritime and Seafood Industry Museum of Biloxi, PO Box 1907, Biloxi, MS 39533 USA
Tel: 228-435-6320 **Fax:** 228-435-6309
E-mail: schooner@maritimemuseum.org
Website: www.maritimemuseum.org

The *Mike Sekul* is one of the two Biloxi oyster schooner replicas built as part of the Biloxi Schooner Project under the auspices of the Maritime and Seafood Industry Museum. She was launched in April 1994 as part of the effort to preserve the maritime and seafood industry of the Mississippi Gulf Coast. Money for construction and fitting out of the *Mike Sekul* and her sister ship, *Glenn L. Swetman*, has come from donations and fundraising events. The *Mike Sekul* is available for charter for two and a half hour, half-day, and full-day trips in the Mississippi Sound and to the barrier islands, Cat Island, Horn Island, and Ship Island. Walkup day sailing trips are made when she is not under charter. Groups of up to 45 passengers learn about the maritime and seafood heritage of the Gulf Coast and about the vessels working in Biloxi's seafood industry. Sailing classes are offered through local colleges and the museum's Sea and Sail Adventure summer camp. Wedding parties, Elderhostel, and school groups are also accommodated.

SPECIFICATIONS

Flag: USA
Rig: Sloop
Homeport: Baltimore, Maryland
Normal cruising waters:
Baltimore Harbor
Sparred length: 69'
LOD: 45' 3"
Draft: 3'
Beam: 15' 7"
Rig height: 58'
Freeboard: 2'
Sail area: 1,450 square feet
Tons: 10 GRT
Hull: wood

MINNIE V

The skipjack *Minnie V*, built in Wenona, Maryland, was used to dredge oysters on the Chesapeake Bay for many years. The vessel was rebuilt by the City of Baltimore in 1981 and is now owned and operated by the Living Classrooms Foundation. The Foundation uses the vessel for educational programs and as a tourist attraction offering interpretive tours of the historic port of Baltimore. While on board the *Minnie V*, students learn about the oyster trade, its importance to the economy of Maryland, and the hard life of a waterman as they relive history by raising the sails on one the Chesapeake's few remaining skipjacks.

Who sails: School groups from middle school through college; individuals and families
Program type: Sea education in marine science, maritime history, and ecology in cooperation with accredited schools, colleges, and other organized groups; passenger day sails; dockside interpretation
Season: April through October
Built: 1906: Wenona, MD, Vetra
Coast Guard certification: Passenger Vessel (Subchapter T)
Crew: 2   **Trainees-passengers:** 24
Contact: Christine Truett, Director of Education, Living Classrooms Foundation, 802 South Caroline Street, Baltimore, MD 21231-3311 USA
Tel: 410-685-0295 **Fax:** 410-752-8433
Website: www.livingclassrooms.org

SPECIFICATIONS

Flag: Russia
Rig: Full-rigged ship
Homeport: St. Petersburg, Russia
Normal cruising waters:
West and southwest European
Sparred length: 345' 9"
LOA: 328'
LOD: 300' 9"
LWL: 254'
Draft: 18'
Beam: 44' 9"
Rig height: 149'
Freeboard: 34' 6"
Sail area: 29,997 square feet
Tons: 2,856 GRT
Power: Twin 570 HP diesels
Hull: steel

MIR

Who sails: Students and individuals of all ages.
Affiliated with Tall Ship Friends clubs in France,
UK, Switzerland, Austria, Ireland, and Italy
Program type: Sail training for paying trainees;
fully accredited sea education in traditional
seamanship; dockside interpretation during port
visits
Designer: Z. Choren
Built: 1987: Gdansk, Poland, Stocznia Gdanska
Certification: Russian registered Sailing School
Vessel
Crew: 45-70 **Trainees-passengers:** up to 250
daysails, 60 overnight
Contact: Wulf Marquard, Managing Director,
Tall Ship Friends Germany, Schweriner Str. 17,
Hamburg, D22 143 Germany
Tel: 49-40-675 635 97 **Fax:** 49-40-675 635 99
E-mail: tallshipl@aol.com
Website: www.tallship-friends.de

Mir is regarded by many as the fastest Class A sail training
ship in the world. She was the overall winner of the 1992
Columbus Race and the winner of the Cutty Sark Tall Ship
Races in 1996, 1997, and 1998 under the command of
Captain Victor Antonov. *Mir* was launched in 1989 at the
Lenin Shipyard in Gdansk, Poland, the builders of five
more of the M 108 type ships: *Dar Mlodziezy, Pallada,
Khersones, Druzhba,* and *Nadezhda. Mir* is the school
ship of the Makaroz Maritime Academy in St. Petersburg,
Russia, training future navigators and engineers for the
Russian merchant fleet. Since 1990, up to 60 trainees
of all ages are welcomed on board to sail along with
the Russian students, learning the ropes, manning the
helm, or climbing the rigging to set the sails. No previous
experience is necessary. *Mir* is supported by Tall Ship
Friends, a nonprofit organization in Hamburg, Germany.
The goals of Tall Ship Friends are to promote sail training
on square-riggers, to contribute to the further existence
of these beautiful ships, and to provide an unforgettable
experience for the participants.

SPECIFICATIONS

Flag: Romania
Rig: Barque
Homeport: Constanta, Romania
Sparred length: 328'
LOA: 266'
LOD: 241' 6
LWL: 203'
Draft: 18'
Beam: 39' 6"
Rig height: 144'
Freeboard: 8'
Sail area: 18,837 square feet
Tons: 1320 GRT
Power: 1,100 hp Diesel
Hull: steel

MIRCEA

Mircea is the flagship and the training vessel of the Romanian Naval Forces. The last of a quartet of sailing school ships built in Blohm & Voss Shipyard, Hamburg, Germany, in the 1930s, *Mircea* and her sister ships became the models for sailing vessels built during the last three decades. During overhaul concluded in 2002, *Mircea* has been equipped with modern navigation and communication devices that made her up-to-date despite the 65 years of age.

Who sails: Students and cadets of the Romanian Naval Academy and Romanian Petty Officer School
Program type: Schoolship for the Romanian Naval Forces' cadets
Built: 1938: Hamburg, Germany, Blohm & Voss Shipyard
Crew: 65 **Trainees-passengers:** 120
Contact: Public Affairs Officer, Romanian Naval Academy, Fulgerului Street, Constanta, Romania 900218
Tel: +40 241 643040
Fax: +40 241 643096
E-mail: relpub@navedo.anmb.ro
Website: www.anmb.ro

SPECIFICATIONS

Flag: USA
Rig: Gaff schooner
Homeport: Camden, Maine
Normal cruising waters:
Penobscot Bay – off the coast of
mid-coast Maine
Sparred length: 60'
LOD: 46'
LWL: 40'
Draft: 6'
Beam: 13'
Rig height: 45'
Freeboard: 4'
Sail area: 1,200 square feet
Tons: 13 GRT
Power: Propulsion engine: 60 HP
diesel
Hull: wood

Photo by Robert C. Jenks

MISTRESS

Who sails: 16 and up (any age with full boat charter)
Program type: Cruising
Season: End of May thru early October
Built: 1967: Deer Isle, Maine
Crew: 2
Contact: Captain Ray and Ann Williamson, owners, Maine Windjammer Cruises®, PO Box 617, Camden, Maine 04843 USA
Tel: 207-236-2938 – Reservations 800-736-7981
E-mail: sail@MaineWindjammerCruises.com
Website: www.MaineWindjammerCruises.com

The *Mistress* was built in 1967, Deer Island, Maine for private use. Before she ever hit the water, Capt. Jim Nesbit, owner of Maine Windjammer Cruises® at the time, admired and purchased her to add to his fleet as a more private six-passenger windjammer. She was fitted out with three private cabins, each with its own head and sink. This vessel has filled a nitch in the industry for people who want to go windjamming but require more privacy than the larger boats offer. She is rigged in the traditional manner, block and tackle, deadeyes and lanyard, etc. In 1992, this vessel was significantly rebuilt. At that time seven feet was added to her length, the beam was increased and a lead keel was fixed externally. She also had new masts, riggings, and sails during this refit. Owned by Capt. Ray & Ann Williamson, Camden, Maine, she does weekend, three-day, four-day and five-day cruises.

SPECIFICATIONS

Flag: USA
Rig: Gaff-rigged schooner
Homeport: New London, Connecticut
Normal cruising waters:
Hudson River in Spring, Southeast
New England in Summer, Chesapeake
Bay in Fall
Sparred length: 110'
LOA: 83'
LOD: 83'
LWL: 78'
Draft: 7' 6" (min.) 13' (max.)
Beam: 25'
Rig height: 90'
Freeboard: 7'
Sail Area: 3,000 square feet
Tons: 100 GRT
Power: 175 HP diesel
Hull: steel

MYSTIC WHALER

Built in 1967 and rebuilt in 1993, the *Mystic Whaler* carries passengers and trainees on a variety of cruises, ranging from three hours to five days. In April, May and early June, the schooner joins *Clearwater* on the Hudson River, for environmental education programs. Sailing from New London, CT throughout the summer months, the *Mystic Whaler* offers great sailing opportunities for both novice and experienced passengers. Three-hour Lobster Dinner Cruises are popular, as are the five-hour day sails, or try an overnight of two, three or five days. In September and October, the *Mystic Whaler* travels to Baltimore, Maryland for three weeks of three-day overnight sails and to participate in the Great Chesapeake Bay Schooner Race. Some of the overnight cruises have special interest extras such as lighthouse tours, sea music and full moon cruises. Two-week apprenticeship programs run throughout the season (June-September).

Who sails: School groups from elementary school through college, as well as individuals and families ages 5 and up
Program type: Sail training for crew and apprentices; sea education in maritime history and ecology based on informal programming with organized groups such as Scouts; passenger day sails and overnight passages
Season: March through November
Designer: "Chub" Crockett
Built: 1967: Tarpon Springs, Florida, George Sutton
Coast Guard certification: Passenger Vessel (Subchapter T)
Crew: 5 **Trainees-passengers:** 65 daysails, 34 overnight
Contact: Captain John Eginton, Mystic Whaler Cruises Inc., PO Box 189, Mystic, CT 06355-0189 USA
Tel: 800-697-8420 **Fax:** 860-447-1268
E-mail: info@mysticwhaler.com
Website: www.mysticwhaler.com

SPECIFICATIONS

Flag: Russia
Rig: Ship
Homeport: Vladivostok, Russia
LOA: 359'
Draft: 21' 5"
Hull: steel

Photo by Thad Koza

NADEZHDA

Contact: FESMA (Far Eastern State Maritime Academy), 50a Verkhneportovaya St., Vladivostok, 690059 Russia
E-mail: fesma@ints.vtc.ru

Nadezhda, the Russian word for "hope", is the last of six "DAR–class" full-rigged ships that were built in the Gdansk Shipyard in the 1980s. *Nadezhda* was completed in 1990, and delivered and commissioned to the Far Eastern State Maritime Academy in Vladivostok, Russia in 1991.

SPECIFICATIONS

Flag: USA
Rig: Marconi cutter
Homeport: Mystic, Connecticut
Sparred Length: 53'
LOD: 53'
LWL: 40'
Draft: 8'
Beam: 10' 6"
Rig height: 76'
Power: 50 HP Yanmar diesel
Hull: wood

NEITH

Neith is a 1907 Herreshoff cutter with a long and colorful history. She cruises and participates in classic regattas in New England waters during spring/summer/fall seasons. She wet stores winters in Mystic, CT, her home base.

Who sails: Adults and families
Program type: Daysails and overnight passages
Designer: Herreshoff
Built: 1907
Crew: 2 **Trainees/passengers:** 11 daysails, 6 overnight
Contact: Ms. Laurie Belisle, PO Box 13, West Mystic, CT 06388 USA
Tel: 860-460-5620
E-mail: lauriebelisle@sbcglobal.net

SPECIFICATIONS

Flag: USA
Rig: Brig
Homeport: Erie, Pennsylvania
Normal cruising waters: Great
Lakes and connecting waters
Sparred length: 198'
LOA: 123'
LOD: 116'
LWL: 110'
Draft: 11'
Beam: 32' 6"
Rig height: 120'
Sail area: 11,600 square feet
Tons: 162 GRT
Power: twin 200 HP diesels
Hull: wood

NIAGARA

Who sails: Trainees must be at least 16 years-old, ambulatory, and of average physical fitness. No previous experience is required.
Program type: Experiential-education with focus on seamanship skills, technology of a sailing warship, and War of 1812 history.
Designer: Melbourne Smith **Built:** 1988: Erie, PA
Coast Guard certification: Sailing School Vessel (Subchapter R) and Attraction Vessel
Crew: 18 professionals **Trainees/passengers:** 22 trainees (3-week, live-aboard) and up to 50 daysail students
Contact: Captain Wesley W. Heerssen, Jr., Pennsylvania Historical and Museum Commission, Erie Maritime Museum, 150 East Front Street, Suite 100, Erie, PA 16507 USA
Tel: 814-452-2744 **Fax:** 814-455-6760
E-mail: sail@brigniagara.org
Website: www.brigniagara.org

The US Brig *Niagara* was built in 1988 as a reconstruction of the warship aboard which Oliver Hazard Perry won the Battle of Lake Erie in 1813 during the War of 1812. Her mission is to interpret War of 1812 history, promote the Commonwealth of Pennsylvania and the Erie Region, and to preserve the skills of square-rig seafaring. Each summer, U.S. Brig *Niagara* sails out of Erie, PA and makes passages to other ports throughout the Great Lakes. On summer day sails, overnight training sails, and longer voyages, the 18 professional crewmembers teach up to 20 live-aboard trainees the way of a ship at sea, square-rig seafaring skills, and how to assist in conducting public tours at port festival events. All hands on board experience a one-of-a-kind adventure within the confines of a large wooden square-rigger. Deckhands and trainees sleep in hammocks on a single berth deck, which is converted three times a day into a mess hall for meals. They are divided into watches and divisions and taught to climb aloft, stand watch, handle sails, and many other skills of the seaman. Together, the crew and trainees learn the value of maintaining effective communication, camaraderie, discipline, and respect for one another while serving the broader needs of the ship.

SPECIFICATIONS

Flag: USA
Rig: 15th century caravel redondo
Homeport: Wilmington, Deleware
Sparred length: 92'
LOA: 68'
LOD: 65'
LWL: 58'
Draft: 7'
Beam: 18'
Rig height: 54'
Freeboard: 5'
Sail area: 1,919 square feet
Tons: 37 GRT
Power: 128 HP diesel
Hull: wood

NINA

The *Nina* is a historically accurate replica of a 15th century caravel. John Sarsfield, the leading authority on caravels, was designer and builder until his death halfway through the project. Jonathan Nance, a noted British designer and archaeologist, finished the vessel and designed the sail plan and rig. She was built in Valenca, Bahia, Brazil, using only traditional tools and techniques of the 15th century. Her mission today is to educate the public on the "space shuttle" of the 15th century, and over one million students and teachers have visited the *Nina* since her completion in 1992. The ship is available for filming and charters.

Program type: Attraction vessel
Designer: John Sarsfield/Jonathon Nance
Built: 1988-1991: Valenca, Brazil, John Sarsfield/Jonathan Nance/Ralph Eric Nicholson
Coast Guard certification: Attraction Vessel
Crew: 6
Contact: Morgan P. Sanger, Captain/Director, Columbus Foundation, Box 305179, St. Thomas, VI 00803
Tel: 284-495-4618 **Fax:** 284-495-4616
E-mail: columfnd@surfbvi.com
Website: www.thenina.com

SPECIFICATIONS

Flag: USA
Rig: Viking longship (single square sail)
Homeport: Wilmington, Delaware
Normal cruising waters: Chesapeake Bay, Delaware River, Jersey Shore, New York Bay, Hudson River, and Long Island Sound
Sparred length: 40'
LOD: 32'
LWL: 30'
Draft: 3'
Beam: 9'
Rig height: 30'
Freeboard: 3'
Sail area: 297 square feet
Tons: 2 GRT
Power: 19 HP Volvo Penta diesel, or 10 oarsmen
Hull: Fiberglass

NORSEMAN

Who sails: Students and individuals of all ages
Program type: Sail training for volunteer crew and apprentices; sea education in maritime history relevant to Viking period; dockside interpretation during port visits
Designer: Applecraft, Inc. **Built:** 1992: Isle of Man, UK, Applecraft, Inc.
Crew: 7-12 **Trainees:** 7-12
Contact: President & Captain Dave Segermark, Leif Ericson Viking Ship, Inc., P.O. Box 393 Swarthmore, PA 19081-0393 USA
Tel/Fax: 410-275-8516
E-mail: info@vikingship.org
Website: www.vikingship.org

Built in 1992, the *Norseman* offers people a glimpse of Viking culture and reminds everyone of the first discovery of North America by Europeans Leif Ericson and his fellow Vikings, who sailed from Greenland around the year 1000 to explore the new lands to the west. Crewmembers appear in full Viking costume, share their interests in Viking culture and their Scandinavian heritage, and practice their sailing and rowing skills. Over the years, the *Norseman* has appeared in sailing events concentrating on the Mid-Atlantic region of the US, but traveling where invited. The organization has also traveled to Stockholm, Sweden, St. Petersburg, Russia, and Newfoundland, Canada. The *Norseman's* sailing season runs from April to November with the majority of events held in the summer. The crewmembers, however, bring Viking history to local schools and associations throughout the year. The off-season is devoted to cleanup and training. Leif Ericson Day is the organization's "main event" and is held in Philadelphia, Pennsylvania area on or near October 9.

SPECIFICATIONS

Flag: United Kingdom
Rig: Schooner, 2-masted
Homeport: Road Town, Tortola, British Virgin Islands
Normal cruising waters: Eastern Caribbean
Sparred length: 88'
LOA: 77'
LOD: 71'
LWL: 66'
Draft: 9'
Beam: 18'
Rig height: 92'
Freeboard: 5'
Sail area: 3,100 square feet
Tons: 74 GRT
Power: 210 HP diesel
Hull: steel

OCEAN STAR

Launched in 1991 as the school ship for Ocean Navigator Magazine, *Ocean Star* has now sailed under the banner of Sea|mester, since 1998 hosting college level semester voyages aboard. Sea|mester offers 20, 40, and 80-day semesters that are based on the principles of experiential and adventure education. Learning through interaction and practical activities, the primary academic foci of oceanography, marine science, communication and leadership skills development are brought from the textbook into real-life application. Under the guidance of professional staff, our students earn college credits for both academic and vocational activities, while piloting *Ocean Star* throughout the islands of the Lesser Antilles. Along the way the crew visit up to 20 individual Caribbean islands, undertaking research and service projects with local government and private organizations. They also earn certifications in sailing and scuba diving. No experience is necessary. Programs are available to high school seniors, high school graduates and college students.

Who sails: High school graduates and college students (fall, spring, and summer)
Program type: Experiential education semesters for high school graduates and college students; accredited academics with sail and scuba training and service projects and adventure travel
Season: Year-round
Designer: Bill Peterson
Built: 1991: Norfolk, VA, Marine Metals
Crew: 4 **Trainees-passengers:** 16
Certification: MCA (UK) inspected Small Commercial Vessel up to 24 meters LWL, Catergory 1 service
Contact: Sea|mester, P.O. Box 5477, Sarasota, FL 34277 USA
Tel: 941-924-6789 or 800-317-6789
Fax: 941-924-6075
E-mail: info@seamester.com
Website: www.seamester.com

SPECIFICATIONS

Flag: USA
Rig: Full-rigged ship
Homeport: Newport, Rhode Island
Normal cruising waters:
East Coast US and Caribbean
Sparred length: 207'
LOA: 132'
LWL: 110'
Draft: 13'
Beam: 30' 6"
Rig height: 128'
Sail area: 14,000 square feet
Tons: 74 GRT
Power: twin diesels
Hull: steel

OLIVER HAZARD PERRY

Who sails: Individuals and students ages 16 and over
Program type:
Season: Year-round
Crew: 14   **Trainees-passengers:** 86 daysails, 35 overnight
Contact: Mr. Perry Lewis, Tall Ships® Rhode Island, 49B Bowen's Wharf, Newport, RI 02840 USA
Tel: 401-841-0080 **Fax:** 401-841-0149
E-mail: TSRI07@verizon.net
Website: www.tallshipsrhodeisland.org

In October 2008, Newport welcomed a 132-foot steel hull which will soon become the flag ship of the state of Rhode Island. The hull will be transformed into a 207-foot, 3-masted, square-rigged ship. The process of transforming the hull into a traditional sailing ship, to be used in a comprehensive sail training program, is being undertaken by the nonprofit organization Tall Ships® Rhode Island. Anticipated to set sail in 2011, the vessel will be based in Newport. While it will ply New England waters, traveling to Canada and the Great Lakes during the summer and venturing to the Caribbean in winter, hopes are that it will play a significant role in the planned Bicentennial Celebration of the War of 1812. Rhode Island's rich maritime heritage will be embodied in the *Oliver Hazard Perry* which will act as a floating ambassador, promoting tourism for the city and state in every port she visits, while building respect and a love for the sea in the young people who sail on her.

SPECIFICATIONS

Flag: Canada
Rig: Marconi rigged ketch
Homeport: Esquimalt, British Columbia, Canada
LOA: 102'
LOD: 91'
LWL: 19'
Draft: 10'
Beam: 19'
Rig height: 67' 8"
Freeboard: 6' 8" (forward) 4' 9" (aft)
Sail area: 15,700 square feet
Power: 261 HP Detroit Diesel

HCMS ORIOLE

The oldest commissioned ship in the Canadian Navy has a pedigree that goes back to 1880 when George Gooderham sailed the first *Oriole* as the flagship of the Royal Canadian Yacht Club of Toronto, Ontario. Gooderham, who was for several years Commodore of the Toronto club, built *Oriole II* in 1886 and *Oriole III* in 1909. In 1921, the last of the *Orioles* - then called *Oriole IV*, was thought to be the most majestic of all R.C.Y.C. flagships. She was started by the Toronto Dominon Shipbuilding company but due to labor problems, was completed by George Lawley & Sons, a Boston shipyard. She was launched at Neponset, Massachusetts, June 4, 1921, commissioned *HMCS Oriole* June 19, 1952, and two years later the navy moved her to the West Coast to become a training vessel to VENTURE, the Naval Officer Training Center. She was purchased by the Royal Canadian Navy in 1957. HMCS *Oriole* is both the oldest vessel and the longest serving commissioned ship in the Canadian Navy. Her distinctive red, white, and blue spinnaker displays an orange oriole.

Program type: Training vessel of the Canadian Navy
Built: 1921
Crew: 5 **Trainees-passengers:** 16
Contact: Embassy of Canada, 501 Pennsylvania Avenue, NW, Washington, DC 20001 USA
Tel: 202-682-1740 **Fax:** 202-682-7726

SPECIFICATIONS

Flag: Canada
Rig: Gaff topsail schooner
Homeport: Victoria, British Columbia, Canada
Normal cruising waters: Coastal waters of British Columbia
Sparred length: 138' 7"
LOA: 115'
LOD: 108' 7"
LWL: 89' 6"
Draft: 11' 6"
Beam: 22' 2"
Rig height: 115'
Freeboard: 3' 7"
Sail area: 7,564 square feet
Tons: 175 GRT
Power: twin diesels
Hull: wood

PACIFIC GRACE

Who sails: Students and young adults ages 13 – 25
Program type: Sail training for paying trainees
Season: March through October
Built: 1999: Victoria, British Columbia, Canada, SALTS
Certification: Passenger Vessel, Sailing School Vessel
Crew: 5 **Trainees-passengers:** 40 daysails, 30 overnight
Contact: Sail and Life Training Society (SALTS), PO Box 5014, Station B, Victoria, British Columbia V8R 6N3 Canada
Tel: 250-383-6811 **Fax:** 250-383-7781
E-mail: info@salts.ca
Website: www.salts.ca

Pacific Grace was launched at her homeport of Victoria, British Columbia in 1999. She replaces the *Robertson II*, one of Canada's last original Grand Banks fishing schooners, and is built along the lines of the old ship using traditional methods. *Pacific Grace* embarked on a nine-month offshore voyage in 2003 to the South Pacific. In 2007-08 she visited 15 countries in the South Pacific and Asia, traveling 18,000 nautical miles over 12 months. Most years, she sails coastally in southern British Columbia, Canada. During the summer months of July and August 10-day trips are available to anyone aged 13 - 25. In the spring and fall, five-day school programs are offered. Each year, over one thousand young people board *Pacific Grace* for an experience which combines all aspects of shipboard life from galley chores to helmsmanship, with formal instruction in navigation, pilotage, seamanship and small boat handling. S.A.L.T.S. is a registered charity that seeks to develop the spiritual, relational and physical potential of young people through shipboard life in a Christian environment.

SPECIFICATIONS

Flag: Canada
Rig: Square topsail schooner, 2-masted
Homeport: Victoria, British Columbia, Canada
Normal cruising waters: Coastal waters of British Columbia
Sparred length: 111'
LOA: 81'
LOD: 77' 3"
LWL: 73'
Draft: 10' 8"
Beam: 20' 6"
Rig height: 88'
Freeboard: 3' 6"
Sail area: 5,205 square feet
Tons: 98 GRT
Power: 220 HP diesel
Hull: wood

PACIFIC SWIFT

Built as a working exhibit at Expo '86 in Vancouver, British Columbia, the *Pacific Swift* has sailed over 100,000 deep-sea miles on training voyages for young crewmembers. Her offshore travels have taken her to Australia and Europe, to remote communities on Easter and Pitcairn Islands, and to many other unusual and far-flung ports of call. When not offshore, the *Swift* provides coastal sail training programs among the cruising grounds of the Pacific Northwest, which include shorter school programs in the spring and fall, and 10-day summer trips open to anyone aged 13 to 25. Each year, over one thousand young people participate in an experience, which combines all aspects of shipboard life, from galley chores to helmsmanship, with formal instruction in navigation, pilotage, seamanship, and small boat handling. Rooted in Christian values, SALTS believes that training under sail provides the human spirit a real chance to develop and mature. SALTS received the 1998 Sail Training Program of the Year Award from the American Sail Training Association.

Who sails: Individuals and groups
Program type: Offshore and coastal sail training
Season: March through October
Built: 1986: Vancouver, British Columbia, Canada, SALTS
Certification: Passenger vessel, Sailing School Vessel
Crew: 5   **Trainees-passengers:** 35 Age: 13–25
Contact: Sail and Life Training Society (SALTS), PO Box 5014, Station B, Victoria, British Columbia V8R 6N3 Canada
Tel: 250-383-6811 **Fax:** 250-383-7781
E-mail: info@salts.ca
Website: www.salts.ca

SPECIFICATIONS

Flag: Italy
Rig: Barquentine
Homeport: La Maddalena, Sardinia, Italy
Normal cruising waters:
Mediterranean
Sparred length: 226'
Draft: 16'
Beam: 33'
Hull: steel

Photo by Thad Koza

PALINURO

Who sails: Cadets of the Italian Navy
Program type: Sail training
Season: Year-round
Built: 1934
Contact: Embassy of Italy, 3000 Whitehaven Street, NW, Washington DC 20008 USA
Tel: 202-612-4400 **Fax:** 202-518-2151
Website: www.ambwashingtondc.esteri.it/ambasciata_washington

In her first incarnation, *Palinuro* enjoyed a long career fishing for cod on the Grand Banks. Built in Nantes, France in 1933, she was known originally as *Commandant Louis Richard*, and later as *Jean Marc Aline*. Purchased in 1950 by the Italian Navy, she was renamed after the helmsman in the Greek legend of Aeneas, a prince of Troy and son of Venus. Aeneas fled Troy after its destruction and sailed on a course toward Italy in search of a new homeland. Venus interceded with Neptune to allow Aeneas to reach his goal safely. Neptune agreed but exacted a life as ransom. Palinurus, the victim in this bargain, was drugged at Neptune's behest by Somnus, who then pushed the unlucky Palinurus overboard. True to his promise however, Neptune insured the safe arrival in Italy of Aeneas and his ship. After an extensive refitting in 1955, *Palinuro* began her new role as a sail training ship for future naval petty officers. Recently overhauled, *Palinuro's* white-striped color scheme echoes the style of *Amerigo Vespucci*, the other Italian naval sail training vessel. *Palinuro* sails mainly in the Mediterranean.

SPECIFICATIONS

Flag: Russia
Rig: Full-rigged ship
Homeport:
Vladivostok, Russia
Normal cruising waters:
Worldwide
Sparred length: 356' 4"
Draft: 22' 4"
Beam: 45' 9"
Hull: steel

Photo by Thad Koza

PALLADA

Pallada is the fifth ship of the *Dar Mlodziezy*-class built in Poland during the 1980s. Unlike her white-hulled sisters, *Pallada* has a black hull with false gunports and resembles the great Russian Barque *Kruzenshtern*. She is named for the Greek goddess Pallas Athena. She is owned by Dalryba, a conglomerate of fishing companies, and offers sail training to foreign marine-college cadets. Though her homeport is in Vladivostok, which is on the far eastern coast of Russia, *Pallada* voyages widely. She visited the West Coast of the United States in 1989 and Europe in 1991; participated in the European Columbus Regatta in 1992; completed a circumnavigation to celebrate the 500th anniversary of the Russian navy in 1996; and sailed in the 1997 Hong Kong to Osaka race. *Pallada* sails with a compliment of 143 cadets and a permanent crew of 56 officers, teachers, and professionals. With 26 sails and masts soaring 162 feet above the deck, *Pallada* combines traditional sail training with a modern maritime college curriculum.

Who sails: Marine-college cadets
Program type: Sail training and sea education for marine-college cadets
Season: Year-round
Designer: Zygmunt Choren
Built: 1989: Gdansk, Poland
Crew: Crew: 56   **Trainees-passengers:** 143
Contact: Evgeny N. Malyavin, Far Eastern State Technical Fisheries University, 52-B, Lugovaya Street, Vladivostok 690950 Russia
Tel: +0117 42 32 44-03-06
Fax: +011 7 42 32 44-24-32

SPECIFICATIONS

Flag: Canada
Rig: Brigantine
Homeport: Toronto, Ontario, Canada
Normal cruising waters:
Great Lakes
Sparred length: 72'
LOA: 60'
LOD: 58'
LWL: 45'
Draft: 8'
Beam: 15' 3"
Rig height: 54'
Freeboard: 4'
Sail area: 2,600 square feet
Tons: 31.63 GRT
Power: 150 HP diesel
Hull: steel

PATHFINDER

Who sails: In July and August, youth programs for ages 13-18; in May, June, and September, school groups from middle school through college, and interested adult groups
Program type: Sail training for paying trainees, including seamanship and leadership training based on informal, in-house programming; shoreside winter program; dockside interpretation. Affiliated institutions include the Canadian Sail Training Association and the Ontario Camping Association. A bursary fund is available for qualified applicants
Designer: Francis A. Maclachian
Built: 1963: Kingston, Ontario, Canada, Kingston Shipyards
Crew: 10 **Trainees:** 25 daysails, 18 overnight
Contact: Toronto Brigantine, Inc., 215 Spadina Avenue, Suite 405, Toronto, Ontario M5T 2C7 Canada
Tel: 416-596-7117 **Fax:** 416-596-7117
E-mail: mail@tallshipadventures.on.ca
Website: www.tallshipadventures.on.ca

Tall Ship Adventures conducts sail training on board *Pathfinder*, a square-rigged ship designed specifically for youth sail training on the Great Lakes. Since 1964 over 15,000 young people have lived and worked aboard *Pathfinder* and her sister ship, *Playfair*. Youth between the ages of 13 and 18 become the working crew on one or two week adventures, making 24-hour passages from ports all over the Great Lakes. The program is delivered by youth officers between the ages of 15 and 18, trained and qualified during Tall Ship Adventures' Winter Training Programs. The captain is the only adult on board. Every year, each ship sails over 4,000 miles, spends over 40 nights at sea, and introduces 300 trainees to the tall ship experience. *Pathfinder* is inspected by Transport Canada under guidelines established for Sail Training Vessels and the Captain and Executive Officer hold appropriate Transport Canada qualifications. *Pathfinder* is owned and operated by Toronto Brigantine, Inc., a registered charity.

SPECIFICATIONS

Flag: USA
Rig: Barquentine
Normal cruising waters: Atlantic Ocean
Sparred length: 150'
LOA: 128'
LOD: 124'
LWL: 108'
Draft: 14'
Beam: 33'
Rig height: 123'
Sail area: 10,000 square feet
Power: 2 400Hp diesel
Hull: wood

PEACEMAKER

Peacemaker was built on a riverbank in southern Brazil using traditional methods and the finest tropical hardwoods. First launched as the *Avany* in 1989, the owner and his family motored in the southern Atlantic before bringing the ship up through the Caribbean to Savannah, Georgia. In the summer of 2000, she was purchased by the Twelve Tribes, a religious group with about 50 communities in North and South America, Europe, and Australia. They spent the next seven years replacing all of the ship's mechanical and electrical systems and rigging it as a barquentine. The vessel set sail for the first time in the spring of 2007 under the name *Peacemaker*, which expresses in a word their vocation as a people: bringing people into peace with their Creator and with one another. *Peacemaker* travels between the communities of the Twelve Tribes providing an apprenticeship program for youth in sailing, seamanship, and navigation, as well as maintaining all of the ship's mechanical and structural systems. This handsome ship is available for festivals, dockside tours and hospitality events.

Who sails: Members, friends and volunteers
Program type: Attraction vessel
Season: Year-round
Designer: Frank Walker
Built: 1989: Brazil
Coast Guard certification: Moored Attraction Vessel
Crew: 20
Contact: Lee Philips, Peacemakers, 927 Union St, Brunswick, GA 31520 USA
Tel: 912-399-6946
E-mail: lee@peacemakermarine.com
Website: www.peacemakermarine.com

SPECIFICATIONS

Flag: USA
Rig: Barque, 4-masted
Homeport: New York, New York
Sparred length: 377' 6"
LOD: 320'
Draft: 16'
Beam: 45' 8"
Rig height: 170' 5"
Freeboard: 3' 6"
Sail area: 44,132 square feet
Tons: 3,100 GRT
Hull: steel

PEKING

Program type: Sea education in marine science, maritime history, and ecology based on informal, in-house programming
Built: 1911: Hamburg, Germany, Blohm & Voss
Contact: South Street Seaport Museum, 12 Fulton Street, New York, NY 10038 USA
Tel: 212-748-8594 **Fax:** 212-748-8610
Website: www.southstseaport.org

Peking was launched in 1911 at Hamburg, Germany by the Blohm & Voss shipyard. She was owned by the F. Laeisz Company of that port, who used her to carry fuel and manufactured goods to the West Coast of South America, around Cape Horn, and return to European ports with nitrate mined in northern Chile. With her 4-masted barque rig, steel hull and masts, and mid-ship bridge deck, *Peking* represents the final generation of sailing ships built for world trade. Though a product of the 20th century, she still sailed in the traditional way, with few labor saving devices or safety features. Her crew followed the standard sailing vessel routine of four hours on duty and four hours off duty, around the clock, seven days a week. *Peking* was retired in 1933, when steamers using the Panama Canal took over what was left of the nitrate trade. She served as a nautical school for boys, moored on a British River, until she was acquired by the South Street Seaport Museum in 1974. She now serves as a floating dockside exhibit. Educational programs for children and young adults take place on board.

SPECIFICATIONS

Flag: Cook Islands
Rig: Barque, 3-masted
Homeport: Avatiu, Rarotonga, Cook Islands
Normal cruising waters: Worldwide service with refits in Lunenburg, Nova Scotia, Canada
Sparred length: 179'
LOA: 148'
LOD: 135'
LWL: 130'
Draft: 14' 6"
Beam: 24'
Rig height: 100'
Freeboard: 6'
Sail area: 12,450 square feet
Tons: 284 GRT
Power: 690 HP diesel
Hull: steel

PICTON CASTLE

The 284-ton Barque *Picton Castle* is a traditionally rigged and operated sail training ship based in Lunenburg, Nova Scotia, Canada but best known for her voyages around the world. Over the past decade, the ship has made four complete circumnavigations of the globe, as well as a year-long voyage around the Atlantic Basin, two trips to the Great Lakes and numerous jaunts up and down the east coast of the United States and Canada. Along the way, we've introduced more than 1,000 people to the challenges and rewards of square-rig sailing. In 2006, ASTA named us its Sail Training Program of the Year. In 2010, the *Picton Castle* will cast off on her fifth world voyage. Applications are now being accepted. Join Capt. Daniel Moreland and his crew as they set off on this 30,000-mile voyage and visit more than 20 ports of call. As a training ship, all on board work, stand watch, and learn the ways of a square-rigged sailing ship. Onboard workshops are conducted in wire and rope rigging, sail making, boat handling, navigation and practical seamanship. The ship is outfitted to the highest standard with safety gear and equipment. She is a strong, seaworthy home afloat for adventurers devoted to learning the art of deep-water seafaring.

Who sails: Men and women ages 18 and older (16 years and up on shorter training cruises)
Program type: Deep water sail training; maritime education in cooperation with various institutes and organized groups; comprehensive instruction in the arts of seafaring under sail; dockside school visits and receptions; charitable educational/medical supply to isolated islands
Season: Year-round
Designer: Masting and rigging, decks and layout: Daniel Moreland, MM - Stability, calculations and ballasting: Daniel Blachley, NA/ME Webb Institute
Certification: Registered and certified as a Sail Training Vessel for worldwide service by the Cook Islands Ministry of Transportation
Crew: 12 **Trainees:** 38 coed
Contact: Barque Picton Castle, PO Box 1076, Lunenburg, Nova Scotia B0J 2C0 Canada
Tel: 902-634-9984 **Fax:** 902-634-9985
E-mail: info@picton-castle.com
Website: www.picton-castle.com

SPECIFICATIONS

Flag: USA
Rig: Snow brig
Homeport: Dana Point, California
Normal cruising waters: Point Conception to Ensenada, Mexico
Sparred length: 130'
LOD: 98'
Draft: 9'
Beam: 24' 6"
Rig height: 104'
Freeboard: 8'
Sail area: 7,600 square feet
Tons: 99 GRT
Power: diesel
Hull: wood

PILGRIM

Who sails: Student groups and individual volunteers
Program type: Maritime living history and volunteer sail training
Season: Year-round
Designer: Ray Wallace
Built: 1945: Holbaek, Denmark, A. Nielsen
Coast Guard certification: Uninspected Vessel
Crew: 35 **Dockside visitors:** 50
Contact: Karin Wyman, Maritime Director, Ocean Institute, 24200 Dana Point Harbor Drive, CA 92629 USA
Tel: 949-496-2274 **Fax:** 949-496-4715
E-mail: kwyman@ocean-institute.org
Website: www.ocean-institute.org

The Pilgrim is a full-scale replica of the ship immortalized by Richard Henry Dana in his classic book Two Years Before the Mast. Owned and operated by the Ocean Institute, Pilgrim is dedicated to multidisciplinary education. During the school year, the Ocean Institute has an 18-hour, award-winning living history program that offers a hands-on exploration of literature, California history, and group problem solving in which crewmembers recreate the challenge of shipboard life. Students live like sailors of the 1830s as they hoist barrels, row in the harbor, stand night watches, swab the decks, and learn to cope with a stern captain. On summer evenings, audiences are treated to the sights and sounds of the sea as the Pilgrim's decks come alive with theatrical and musical performances. In late summer, the Pilgrim sails on her annual cruise with an all volunteer crew to ports along the California coast as a goodwill ambassador for the City of Dana Point. She returns in September to lead the annual tall ship parade and festival.

SPECIFICATIONS

Flag: USA
Rig: 15th century caravel rodonda
Homeport: Wilmington, Delaware
Sparred length: 115'
LOA: 95'
LOD: 85'
LWL: 78'
Draft: 8'
Beam: 23'
Rig height: 64'
Freeboard: 6'
Sail area: 3,850 square feet
Tons: 101 GRT
Power: 260 HP
Hull: wood

PINTA

The *Pinta* was built in Valenca, Bahia, Brazil at the same shipyard as our foundation's *Nina*. Construction started in January 2002 and was completed in April 2005. For three years she toured 20 Islands in the Caribbean and in April of 2009 started touring with the *Nina* in her Tall Ship Tour. Together the vessels are a spectacular venue for dockside charters as well as their regular daytime tours.

Program type: Attraction vessel
Designer: Jonathan Nance, Morgan Sanger
Built: Nicholson Shipyard, Valenca, Brazil
Crew: 6
Contact: Morgan P. Sanger, Captain/Director, Columbus Foundation, Box 305179, St. Thomas, VI 00803
Tel: 284-495-4618 **Fax:** 284-495-4616
E-mail: columfnd@surfbvi.com
Website: www.thenina.com

SPECIFICATIONS

Flag: USA
Rig: Gaff topsail schooner, 2-masted
Homeport: New York, New York
Normal cruising waters: New York Harbor, Hudson River, and Atlantic Coast
Sparred length: 102'
LOA: 65'
LOD: 65'
LWL: 58' 11"
Draft: 4' 8" (min.) 12' (max.)
Beam: 21' 6"
Rig height: 79'
Sail area: 2,700 square feet
Tons: 43 GRT
Power: diesel
Hull: steel

PiONEER

Who sails: School groups from elementary school through college, charter groups, museum members, and the general public
Program type: Sail training for crew and volunteers; hands-on education sails designed to augment school curriculums in history, ecology, marine science, physics, and math; corporate and private charters, Elderhostel programs, and public sails
Season: April through October
Built: 1885: Marcus Hook, PA, Pioneer Iron Works (rebuilt 1968; Somerset, MA)
Coast Guard certification: Passenger Vessel (Subchapter T)
Crew: 4
Contact: South Street Seaport Museum, 12 Fulton Street New York, NY 10038 USA
Tel: 212-748-8596 **Fax:** 212-748-8610
Website: www.southstseaport.org

The first iron sloop built in the United States, *Pioneer* is the only surviving American iron-hulled sailing vessel. Built in 1885 by the *Pioneer* Iron Foundary in Chester, Pennsylvania, she sailed the Delaware River, hauling sand for use in the iron molding process. Ten years later *Pioneer* was converted to a schooner rig for ease of sail handling. In 1966, the then abandoned vessel was acquired and rebuilt by Russell Grinnell, Jr. of Gloucester, Massachusetts. In 1970, the fully restored schooner was donated to the South Street Seaport Museum. Today historic *Pioneer* serves as a vital education platform. Students of all ages can come on history and other curricular subjects during the hands-on program. *Pioneer* also offers corporate and private charters, Elderhostel day programs, and public sails.

SPECIFICATIONS

Flag: Canada
Rig: Brigantine
Homeport: Toronto, Ontario, Canada
Normal cruising waters: Great Lakes
Sparred length: 72'
LOA: 60'
LOD: 58'
LWL: 45'
Draft: 7' 6"
Beam: 16'
Rig height: 54'
Freeboard: 4'
Sail area: 2,600 square feet
Tons: 33 GRT
Power: 110 HP diesel
Hull: steel

PLAYFAIR

Tall Ship Adventures conducts sail training on board *Playfair*, a square-rigged ship designed specifically for youth sail training on the Great Lakes. Since 1964, over 15,000 young people have lived and worked aboard *Playfair* and her sister ship, *Pathfinder*. Youth between the ages of 13 and 18 become the working crew on one or two week adventures, making 24-hour passages from ports all over the Great Lakes. The program is delivered by youth officers between the ages of 15 and 18. Our youth officers are trained and qualified during Tall Ship Adventures' Winter Training Programs. The captain is the only adult on board. Every year, each ship sails over 4,000 miles, spends over 40 nights at sea, and introduces 300 trainees to the tall ship experience. *Playfair* is inspected by Transport Canada under guidelines established for Sail Training Vessels and the Captain and Executive Officer hold appropriate Transport Canada qualifications. *Playfair* is owned and operated by Toronto Brigantine, Inc., a registered charity.

Who sails: In July and August, youth programs for ages 13-18; in May, June, and September, school groups from middle school through college, and interested adult groups
Program type: Sail training for paying trainees, including seamanship and leadership training based on in-house programming; shoreside winter program; dockside interpretation. Affiliated institutions include the Canadian Sail Training Association and the Ontario Camping Association. A bursary fund is available for qualified applicants.
Designer: Francis A. Maclachian
Built: 1973: Kingston, Ontario, Canada, Canada Dredge and Dock Co.
Crew: 10 **Trainees:** 25 daysails, 18 overnight
Contact: Toronto Brigantine, Inc., 215 Spadina Avenue, Suite 405, Toronto, Ontario M5T 2C7 Canada
Tel: 416-596-7117 **Fax:** 416-596-7117
E-mail: mail@tallshipadventures.on.ca
Website: www.tallshipadventures.on.ca

SPECIFICATIONS

Flag: Poland
Rig: Barkentine
Homeport: Gdynia, Poland
Sparred Length: 154'
Draft: 11' 6"
Beam: 26'
Hull: steel

POGORIA

Who sails: Youth ages 15 - 25
Program type: Sail training
Crew: 8 **Trainees-passengers:** 40
Contact: Sail Training Association Poland, PO Box 113, 81-964 Gdynia 1, Poland
Tel: +48 58 614770 **Fax:** +48 58 206225
Website: www.pogoria.pl

Pogoria holds the distinction of being the first completed square-rigger by Polish naval architect Zygmunt Choren. Built for the Steel Workers Union in 1980, *Pogoria* has served as the background for a movie and as a floating classroom for West Island College of Quebec, Canada. She is now the flagship of the Polish Sail Training Association in Gdansk. Pogoria's hull design served as the model for three other vessels: *Iskra* for the Polish navy, *Kaliakra* for the Bulgarian navy, and *Oceania,* a specially rigged oceanographic vessel from Gdynia, Poland. Trainees live in the four, eight, ten and twelve person cabins, and each of them has his/her own bunk. They are divided into four watches of eight to ten each. Three of those do four hours on watch and eight off while the fourth one is the galley watch, helping the cook and keeping the ship tidy. Most of the watch time is spent on look-out, taking the helm, keeping the log and trimming sails. One doesn't have to go aloft, but most trainees do for the experience and thrill of handling square sails. The usual trainee age is between 15 and 25.

SPECIFICATIONS

Flag: USA
Rig: Topsail schooner
Homeport: Baltimore, Maryland
Normal cruising waters: East and Gulf Coasts, Canada, Great Lakes and Europe
Sparred length: 157'
LOA: 105'
LOD: 100'
LWL: 91'
Draft: 12' 6"
Beam: 26' 4"
Rig height: 107'
Freeboard: 4' 4"
Sail area: 9,018 square feet
Tons: 97 GRT
Power: 2-165 HP Caterpillar diesel
Hull: wood

PRIDE OF BALTIMORE II

Pride of Baltimore II is a topsail schooner built to the lines of an 1812-era Baltimore Clipper. Operated by Pride of Baltimore, Inc., a 501(c)(3) non profit, her mission is threefold: To promote historical education regarding Baltimore Clippers, naval innovation, the War of 1812, and the penning of "the Star-Spangled Banner"; To serve as a unique learning platform to build math, science and social studies programs; and to serve as a visual representative of American History and entrepreneurship for Maryland and the Port of Baltimore in every port she visits. *Pride of Baltimore II* is available for chartered onboard dockside (107) and sailing receptions (35) in each of her destinations as well as public daysails. She accommodates up to six paying guest crew/trainees between ports of call. *Pride of Baltimore II* maintains an international sailing schedule. She sails with two rotating professional captains and a crew of eleven. Crew positions are open to qualified male and female sailors.

Who sails: Minimum professional crew member age is 18; overnight guest crew/trainee minimum age is 16. Day sail minors must be accompanied by an adult and supervised one-on-one. There is no maximum age limit.
Program type: U.S. historical education; charters; daysails; team building; and overnight guest crew/trainees.
Season: Spring, summer, fall
Designer: Thomas C. Gillmer **Built:** 1987-88: Baltimore, MD, G. Peter Boudreau
Coast Guard certification: Passenger Vessel (Subchapter T)
Crew: 12 **Professionals:** 6 paying guest crew/trainees for overnight sails; 35 paying day sail guests
Contact: Linda E. Christenson, Esq., Executive Director, Pride of Baltimore, Inc., 1801 South Clinton St., Suite 250, Baltimore, MD 21224 USA
Tel: 410-539-1151; toll-free 888-55-PRIDE
Fax: 410-539-1190
E-mail: pride2@pride2.org
Website: www.pride2.org

SPECIFICATIONS

Flag: USA
Rig: Gaff schooner, 2-masted
Homeport: New Haven, Connecticut
Normal cruising waters: Long Island Sound
Sparred length: 91'
LOA: 65'
LOD: 62'
LWL: 58'
Draft: 4' 5" - 11'
Beam: 20'
Rig height: 77'
Freeboard: 5' 2"
Sail area: 2,400 square feet
Tons: 41 GRT
Power: 135 HP diesel
Hull: wood

QUINNIPIACK

Who sails: School groups from middle school through college, individuals and families
Program type: Sail training; marine science, maritime history, and ecology in cooperation with primary and secondary schools, colleges, community groups and as informal, in-house programming; dockside interpretation during port visits; passenger day sails
Season: April – November
Designer: Philip Shelton
Built: 1984: Milbridge, ME, Philip Shelton
Coast Guard certification: Passenger Vessel (subchapter T)
Crew: 5 **Trainees-passengers:** 40 daysails, 4-6 overnight
Contact: Schooner Inc., 60 South Water Street, New Haven, CT 06519 USA
Tel: 203-865-1737 **Fax:** 203-624-8816
E-mail: director@schoonerinc.org or captain@schoonerinc.org
Website: www.schoonerinc.org

Built in 1984 for the passenger service, *Quinnipiack* now serves as the primary vessel for Schooner Inc., an organization dedicated to teaching environmental education programs focused on Long Island Sound. Since 1975, Schooner Inc. has taught programs in classrooms, on the shore, and aboard the *Quinnipiack* and a fleet of smaller sailing vessels. Participants of all ages learn about the importance of protecting Long Island Sound. Sail training programs teach students life skills including teamwork, communication, self-reliance, responsibility and interdependence. Hands on learning activities include collection and identification of marine life, water chemistry, plankton and benthic studies, sail training and seamanship. Expedition is an overnight program for high school and college students that combines marine science, sail training and teambuilding in an intensive three-day or five-day program. During the summer Schooner Inc. offers weeklong programs for grades K-12 and public sails and charters. The *Quinnipiack* also participates in tall ship festivals and other events outside of New Haven.

SPECIFICATIONS

Flag: USA
Rig: Full rigged ship
Homeport: Culver, Indiana
Normal cruising waters: Lake Maxinkuckee in Culver, Indiana
Sparred length: 65'
LOA: 54'
LOD: 50'
Draft: 5'
Beam: 13'
Rig height: 49'
Freeboard: 5'
Tons: 25 GRT
Power: diesel

R. H. LEDBETTER

The *R.H. Ledbetter* is the flagship of the Culver Summer Naval School, located on Lake Maxinkuckee in Culver, Indiana. The 3-masted square-rigger, named in honor of Georgia philanthropist and Culver alumnus Robert H. Ledbetter, was built in 1983-84 by the T. D. Vinette Co. of Escanaba, Michigan. Culver Summer Camps offer two simultaneous coed six-week camps from mid-June to early August (Woodcraft for ages 9-13, and Upper Camp for 13-17) and 10 two-week specialty camps from early June to mid-August. Administered by The Culver Educational Foundation, which also operates the Culver Academy, the camps use the facilities of the 1,800-acre wooded campus along the north shore of Indiana's second-largest lake.

Who sails: Students and Alumni of Culver Academy
Program type: Sail training for students of Culver Academy; sea education in cooperation with organized groups such as the American Camping Association; dockside interpretation while in home port
Designer: Marine Power
Built: 1984: Escanoba, MI, T. D. Vinette
Contact: Anthony Mayfield, Director, Culver Summer Camps, 1300 Academy Road, RD# 138, Culver, IN 46511 USA
Tel: 800-221-2020 **Fax:** 574-842-8462
E-mail: mayfiea@culver.org
Website: www.cuiver.org

SPECIFICATIONS

Flag: USA
Rig: Gaff schooner
Homeport: Chicago, Illinois
Normal cruising waters:
Great Lakes
Sparred length: 77'
LOA: 57'
LOD: 54'
LWL: 49'
Draft: 6' 6"
Beam: 17' 6"
Rig height: 73'
Freeboard: 4' 6"
Sail area: 2,100 square feet
Tons: 41 GRT
Power: 125 HP diesel
Hull: wood

RED WITCH

Who sails: School groups from elementary school through college; individuals and families, professional groups

Program type: Sail training for volunteer or paying trainees; sea education in marine science and maritime history in cooperation with accredited institutions and organized groups; passenger day sails, evening sails, and private parties

Season: May through October

Designer: John Alden **Built:** 1986: Bayou La Batre, Alabama, Nathaniel Zirlott

Coast Guard certification: Passenger Vessel (Subchapter T)

Crew: 4 **Trainees-passengers:** 49

Contact: Captain Bruce L. Randall, Lakeshore Maritime Collective, Tall Ship Adventures Of Chicago, 401 E. Illinois Street, Suite 332 Chicago IL 60611 USA

Tel: 312-404-5800 **Fax:** 312-222-9048

E-mail: info@redwitch.com

Website: www.redwitch.com

Red Witch is typical of the schooners that once plied Lake Erie and the Great Lakes. She was built in the tradition of the schooners which were the workhorses of America's 19th century transportation system. Designed by John G. Alden, the *Red Witch* has a hull of cyprus on oak, wooden blocks, and a gaff rig. Although traditional in appearance, the schooner was purpose-built for charter and day cruise service. She has full amenities for up to 49 passengers. Since 2004, *Red Witch's* home port has been Chicago. She has sailed as far as Hawaii and worked in San Diego before coming to the Great Lakes. As Ohio's Bicentennial flagship, she represented the state on goodwill cruises to Michigan, Indiana, Wisconsin, and Illinois as well as Ontario, Canada during 2003. In 2006, she represented the city of Chicago in their Tall Ships® Festival. In addition to private charters and daysails, *Red Witch* offers sea chanty concert cruises, Chicago Special Event cruises, and freshwater whale watching (none seen yet, but still trying!) Sail training programs for school groups, as well as disadvantaged and at-risk youth, are conducted.

SPECIFICATIONS

Flag: USA
Rig: Yawl
Homeport: Olympia, Washington
Normal cruising waters:
Puget Sound, Canada Inland
Sparred length: 44'
LWL: 30'
Draft: 6'
Beam: 11'
Rig height: 57' 6"
Freeboard: 3'
Sail area: 1,120 square feet
Tons: 15 GRT
Power: Perkins 40
Hull: Mahogany

RESOLUTE

Resolute was the third of twelve identical wooden yawls built for the U.S. Naval Academy at Annapolis, Maryland. Over the course of 25 years, some 70,000 American midshipmen trained aboard these vessels. Now the Resolute Sailing Foundation, a 501(c)(3) organization, continues that rich heritage, operating *Resolute* to teach traditional nautical skills, maritime history and an appreciation of the marine environment to youth groups, youths at risk, and students at educational institutions. Young people who sail on her learn to overcome their fears, acquire traditional sailing skills and develop self-confidence and personal responsibility. *Resolute* provides that special challenge of sea and sail which encourages teamwork and develops leadership qualities in these youngsters just as she trained great leaders of the past for so many years at Annapolis. Resolute participated in the TALL SHIPS CHALLENGE® Race Series in 2005 in Victoria, B.C., and 2005 and 2008 in Tacoma, WA. *Resolute* is available year round for day and overnight charters out of Olympia, Washington, her hailing port.

Who sails: High school and college age students, adults and families
Program type: Sail training for volunteer crew and paying trainees; sea education in cooperation with accredited institutions
Season: Year round
Designer: Bill Luders
Built: 1939: Stamford, CT, Luders Shipyard
Crew: 2 **Trainees-passengers:** 10 daysails, 5 overnight
Contact: Resolute Sailing Foundation, PO Box 88834, Steilacoom, WA 98388 USA
Tel: 253-588 3066
E-mail: CaptainJohn@resolutesailing.org
Website: www.resolutesailing.org

SPECIFICATIONS

Flag: Germany
Rig: Brig
Homeport: Eckernförde, Germany
Normal cruising waters: Baltic Sea, North Sea, Eastern North Atlantic, Mediterranean
Sparred length: 165'
LOD: 130'
LWL: 125'
Draft: 14'
Beam: 24'
Rig height: 105'
Freeboard: 6'
Sail area: 9,150 square feet
Tons: 284 GRT
Power: 300 HP diesel
Hull: steel

ROALD AMUNDSEN

Who sails: Individuals ages 14 and older
Program type: Sail training
Season: Year-round
Designer: Detlev Loell
Built: 1952/1992: Rosslau / Wolgast
Certification: Registered and certified as a Sail Training Vessel for worldwide service by the German Maritime Authority
Crew: 17 **Trainees-passengers:** 60 daysails, 31 overnight
Contact: Ship's Office Roald Amundsen LLaS e.V., Jungfernstieg 104, Eckernförde Germany
Tel: +49 [0] 43 51-72 6074
Fax: +49 [0] 43 51-72 6075
E-mail: office@sailtraining.de
Website: www.sailtraining.de

Initially designed as a deep-sea fish lugger, the hull was built in 1952 and equipped to service the military fleet of former East Germany. When the Berlin Wall came down, history rendered her obsolete. Discovered by a handful of enthusiasts in Wolgast in 1992, she was converted and rigged as a traditional brig - a tall ship intended for sail training. *Roald Amundsen* has since been run by the LLaS e.V., a German not-for-profit organization. Offering sail training experiences for beginners as well as young and old salts, *Roald Amundsen* operates all-year round with voyages lasting between one and three weeks, sailing the waters of the North Sea, and Baltic Sea and Channel in the summer - often joining Tall Ship Races - and travels south to the Canary Islands in the winter through some of Europe's most famous seas, such as the Bay of Biscay and the Mediterranean. Planning to join the Great Lakes CHALLENGE in 2010, the brig will again visit the other side of the Atlantic. She is crewed and maintained by a large group of enthusiastic regular crew members, many of whom first joined as trainees. Training and qualifying the regular crew is part of her permanent program.

ROBERT C. SEAMANS

Along with the SSV *Corwith Cramer*, the SSV *Robert C. Seamans* is owned and operated by the Sea Education Association (SEA) of Woods Hole, Massachusetts. Built in 2001 and named for a former SEA trustee and chairman of the board, the 134-ft steel brigantine is a highly sophisticated oceanographic research/sailing vessel built in the US. She is outfitted with an oceanographic wet/dry laboratory, classroom, library, and computer laboratory. SEA students investigate and study the ocean from multiple perspectives ashore in Woods Hole and then at sea during open ocean passages. Our 12-week SEA Semesters are tailored to meet a wide variety of undergraduate majors and interests and offer 17 academic credits. SEA's traditional semester "Ocean Exploration" is open to students from all majors and takes an interdisciplinary approach to understanding the sea. SEA also offers a semester for advanced science students focused on "Oceans and Climate" as well as semesters focused on humanities and social sciences, "Documenting Change in the Caribbean" and "Sustainability in Polynesian Island Cultures and Ecosystems."

Who sails: College students admitted by competitive selection from over 150 colleges and universities worldwide. Also high school students participating in summer seminar programs.
Program type: SEA programs combine 6 weeks of academic study on campus in Woods Hole, MA with 6 weeks of oceanographic research at sea aboard *Robert C. Seamans* or *Corwith Cramer*. Courses on shore include oceanography, nautical science, and maritime studies. Program offerings include SEA Semester (college level, 12 weeks long, 17 credits), SEA Summer Session (college level, 8 weeks long, 12 credits), and SEA seminars for high school students.
Designer: Laurent Giles, Ltd., Hampshire, England
Built: 2001
Coast Guard certification: Sailing School Vessel (Subchapter R) for Ocean service
Crew: 7 professional mariners and 4 scientists
Trainees-passengers: Up to 25 in all programs
Contact: Sea Education Association (SEA), PO Box 6, Woods Hole, MA 02543 USA
Tel: 508-540-3954/800-552-3633
Fax: 508-540-0558 **E-mail:** admissions@sea.edu
Website: www.sea.edu

SPECIFICATIONS

Flag: USA
Rig: Schooner
Homeport: St. Croix, US Virgin Islands
Normal cruising waters:
New England (summer); Caribbean
(winter)
Sparred length: 137'
LOD: 112'
LWL: 89'
Draft: 12' 5"
Beam: 25'
Rig height: 103'
Freeboard: 4'
Sail area: 5,600 square feet
Tons: 260 GRT
Power: 400 HP diesel
Hull: wood

Photo by Kate Wood

ROSEWAY

Who sails: Middle school through college
students; individuals of all ages
Program type: Sea education in community
and leadership, cross-cultural partnerships, and
environmental stewardship through sail training;
dockside interpretations, port appearances, day
sails, and private charters.
Season: Year-round
Designer: John F. James & Sons
Built: 1925: Essex, MA, John F. James & Sons
Coast Guard certification: Passenger Vessel
(subchapter T)
Crew: 10
Contact: Abby Kidder, Executive Director,
World Ocean School, PO Box 701, Camden,
ME 04843 USA
Tel: 207-236-7482 **Fax:** 207-236-7482
E-mail: wos@worldoceanschool.org
Website: www.worldoceanschool.org

The World Ocean School on *Roseway*, creates and
provides a method of experiential education at sea that
affords teenage students a practical application for their
studies as well as cultivating teamwork, community service,
environmental responsibility, and cross-cultural friendships
so that they gain insight into becoming empowered,
motivated and engaged citizens. The 137-foot *Roseway*
was built in 1925 in Essex, Massachusetts as a private
fishing yacht. She was purchased by the Boston Pilots
Association in 1941. The *Roseway* was the last pilot
schooner in the United States when she was retired in
1973. In September 2002, she was donated to the World
Ocean School. Today, after 78 years of service, she is one
of the last Grand Banks schooners built in Essex, and a
registered U.S. National Historic Landmark.

SPECIFICATIONS

Flag: Portugal
Rig: Barque
Homeport: Lisbon, Portugal
Normal cruising waters:
Worldwide
Sparred length: 293' 6"
Draft: 17'
Beam: 39' 6"
Hull: steel

Photo by MAX

SAGRES

Sagres II sails under the Portuguese flag as a naval training ship. She was built in 1937 at the Blohm & Voss shipyard in Hamburg, Germany, and is virtually a sister ship to *Eagle*, *Mircea*, *Tovarishch*, and *Gorch Fock II*. Originally named *Albert Leo Schlageter*, she served under American and Brazilian flags before being acquired by Portugal in 1962. At that time she replaced the first *Sagres*, which was built in 1896 as the *Rickmer Rickmers*. The original *Sagres* has now been restored and serves as a museum ship in Hamburg, Germany. The name *Sagres* is derived from the historic port that sent forth many famed Portuguese explorers and navigators. It served as the home and base for Prince Henry the Navigator (1394-1460). His court in *Sagres* was responsible for the geographic studies and practical explorations that made Portugal master of the seas in the early 15th century. A bust of Prince Henry serves as the figurehead on the bow of *Sagres II*, and the ship is easily identified by the traditional Portuguese crosses of Christ (Maltese crosses) that mark the square sails on her fore- and mainmasts.

Who sails: Cadets of the Portuguese Navy
Program type: Training vessel for the Portuguese Navy
Season: Year-round
Built: 1937: Hamburg, Germany, Blohm & Voss Shipyard
Contact: Portuguese Defense and Naval Aftaché, Embassy of Portugal, 2012 Massachusetts Ave., NW, Washington, DC 20008 USA
Tel: 202-232-7632
Fax: 202-328-6827
E-mail: ponavnir@mindspring.com

SPECIFICATIONS

Flag: USA
Rig: Ketch
Homeport: Portland, Maine
Sparred length: 63'
LOD: 53'
LWL: 45'
Draft: 7'
Beam: 16'
Rig height: 85'
Freeboard: 4'
Sail area: 1,500 square feet
Tons: 34 GRT
Power: Ford Lehman
Hull: steel

SAMANA

Who sails: Individuals of all ages
Program type: Sail training for paying trainees; ocean sailing, celestial navigation, offshore passage making
Designer: Van de Wiele
Built: 1975: The Netherlands
Crew: 2 **Trainees-passengers:** 6
Contact: Captain Larry Wheeler, School of Ocean Sailing, TLC #1, 5600 Royal Dane Mall, Suite 12, St. Thomas, VI 00802
Tel: 207-321-9249
E-mail: svsamana@sailingschool.com
Website: www.sailingschool.com

The instructional mission for the School of Ocean Sailing is to teach offshore ocean sailing and ocean navigation in a live-aboard setting. In our sailing school we offer seven and eight-day courses. Your classroom and sailing school home is a modern, well-founded, romantic, beautiful, fast, and very sea-kindly sailing vessel. *Samana*, a 52-foot steel offshore sailing ketch, was built in 1975 in Holland. The School of Ocean Sailing operates winters out of Saint Thomas, USVI, sailing the Atlantic Ocean and the Caribbean Sea surrounding the USVIs and BVIs. During the summers, the sailing school operates in the North Atlantic Ocean off the coast of Maine. The curriculum is a rich blend of technical skill, confidence building, and common sense coupled with a spirit of adventure and romance. Instruction centers on the principal objectives underlying the knowledge of ocean sailing, coastal navigation, or celestial navigation. The School of Ocean Sailing is able to accommodate beginners just learning to sail a large ocean vessel, and to students interested in advanced ocean navigation or celestial navigation.

SPECIFICATIONS

Flag: USA
Rig: Staysail schooner
Homeport: Sausalito, California / San Francisco Bay
Normal cruising waters: Northern California to Mexico
Sparred Length: 82'
LOA: 82'
LOD: 65'
Draft: 8' 6"
Beam: 17'
Rig Height: 75'
Freeboard: 4'
Tons: 59 GRT
Power: 210 HP Cummins 6BT
Hull: steel

SEAWARD

Call of the Sea and the schooner *Seaward's* mission is to inspire people of all ages and backgrounds, and especially youth, to connect with the sea, San Francisco Bay, and seafaring. Our hands-on programs focus on the ocean and bay environment, our nautical heritage, seamanship, teamwork, and leadership. *Seaward* is well-suited to both the 'inside' waters of the bay and the 'outside' waters beyond the Golden Gate and our programs range from three hour Bay sails for all ages to challenging week-long coastal voyages with teenagers. We offer wintertime voyages along the Mexican coast for adults and youth groups. *Seaward* is also available for collaborative programs with educational partners as well private charters and public sails.

Who sails: elementary schools, teenagers, & adults
Program type: maritime and environmental education through hands-on programs ranging from 3 hours to week-long voyages
Season: April through November in San Francisco Bay and Northern California coastal waters; December to March in coastal waters of California and Mexico
Designer: Russ Woodin
Built: 1988: Paul Bramsen, St. Augustine, Florida
Coast Guard certification: Passenger Vessel (Subchapter T) for Ocean waters
Crew: 4-5 **Trainees-passengers:** 40 daysails, 14 overnight
Contact: Call of the Sea, 3020 Bridgeway, #278, Sausalito, CA 94965 USA
Tel: 415 331-3214 **Fax:** 415 331-1412
E-mail: info@CalloftheSea.org
Website: www.CalloftheSea.org

SPECIFICATIONS

Flag: Russia
Rig: Barque, 4-masted
Homeport: Murmansk, Russia
Normal cruising waters:
Worldwide
Sparred length: 386'
Draft: 27'
Beam: 48'
Hull: steel

Photo by Thad Koza

SEDOV

Who sails: Students of the Murmansk State
Technical University
Program type: Sail training vessel
Designer: 1921: Friedr. Krupp, A.G.
Germaniawerft, Kiel, Germany
Crew: 70 crew, 120 cadets **Trainees-
passengers:** 50 guest passengers
Contact: Murmansk State Technical University
Website: http://eng.mstu.edu.ru/

Sedov is the world's largest tall ship still in service and
was one of the last barques built for deepwater cargo
carrier service from South America and Australia to the
German ports of Bremen and Hamburg. Constructed in
1921 as *Magdalene Vinnen* in Kiel, Germany, she sailed
for the Bremen firm of F. A. Vinnen. Following the German
commercial tradition, she was christened in honor of one of
the owner's female family members. After being sold to the
shipping conglomerate Norddeutscher Lloyd in 1936, she
was renamed *Kommodore Johnson* and served as a sail
training vessel. After World War II, she was appropriated
by the Russian Ministry of Fisheries and was renamed
for the Soviet polar explorer and oceanographer Georgij
Sedov (1877 – 1914). *Sedov* is the largest square-rigger
still in service from the days of deepwater cargo sailing.
She is ten feet longer than the other giant Russian barque,
Kruzenshtern. Besides her physical statistics, such as
masts that rise 184 feet above the deck and a length of
386 feet, *Sedov* boasts its own bakery, workshop, and first-
aid station.

SPECIFICATIONS

Flag: Sultanate of Oman
Rig: Barquentine
Homeport: Muscat, Oman
Sparred length: 171'
Draft: 15'
Beam: 28'
Hull: wood

Photo by Thad Koza

SHABAB OF OMAN

Built in Scotland in 1971 as a sail training vessel, *Shabab of Oman* was acquired by the Sultanate of Oman in 1979. *Shabab of Oman*, which means "youth of Oman," serves as a training ship for the royal navy of Oman and also trains young men from other Omani government bureaus. The sculptured figurehead on her bow is a replica of the fifteenth-century Omani mariner Ahmed bin Majed, who helped the Portuguese sailor Vasco da Gama explore Africa and India. The turban-clad Majed cuts a rakish figure, wearing a green sash and red "khunjar," a traditional dagger. The red coat-of-arms of the sultanate is recognizable on the sails of *Shabab of Oman* and consists of a khunjar superimposed on a pair of crossed scimitars.

Program type: Sail training vessel of the Royal Navy of Oman
Contact: Embassy of the Sultanate of Oman, 2535 Belmont Road, NW Washington, DC 20008 USA
Tel: 202-387-1980
Fax: 202-745-4933

SPECIFICATIONS

Flag: USA
Rig: Square topsail schooner, 2-masted
Homeport: Vineyard Haven, Massachusetts
Normal cruising waters: Southern New England
Sparred length: 152'
LOA: 108'
LWL: 101'
Draft: 11'
Beam: 23'
Rig height: 94'
Freeboard: 3' (amidships)
Sail area: 7,000 square feet
Tons: 85 GRT

SHENANDOAH

Who sails: School groups from elementary through college and individuals of all ages
Program type: Sail training for paying trainees ages 9-16; private charters and day sails are also available
Season: June to September
Coast Guard certification: Passenger Vessel (Subchapter T)
Crew: 9 **Trainees-passengers:** 35 daysails, 30 overnight
Contact: Captain Robert S. Douglas, The Black Dog Tall Ships, PO Box 429, Vineyard Haven, MA 02568 USA
Tel: 508-693-1699 **Fax:** 508-693-1881
Website: www.theblackdogtallships.com

While the *Shenandoah* is not a replica, the vessel's design bears a strong resemblance to that of the US Revenue Cutter *Joe Lane* of 1851. For her first 25 years, the rakish square topsail schooner was painted white, but she now wears the black and white checkerboard paint scheme of the 19th century Revenue Service. She is the only non-auxiliary power square-rigged vessel operating under the American flag. Her hull form and rig, anchors, and all materials of construction adhere closely to mid-19th century practice. Every summer, *Shenandoah* plies the waters of southern New England visiting the haunts of pirates and the homeports of whaling ships. *Shenandoah* runs six-day sailing trips for kids ages 9-16 from mid-June through mid-September. She is also available for day sailing and private charter.

SPECIFICATIONS

Flag: USA
Rig: Sloop
Homeport: Newport, Rhode Island
Normal cruising waters:
Narragansett Bay, Rhode Island
Sparred length: 46'
LOA: 46'
LOD: 42'
LWL: 40'
Draft: 6' 6"
Beam: 11' 1"
Rig height: 63'
Freeboard: 3' 6"
Sail area: 961 square feet
Power: 47 HP diesel
Hull: aluminum

SIGHTSAILER

Fast and fun! *Sightsailer* has a towering sail plan allowing her to sail in the lightest of winds and give a lively sailing experience once the wind pipes up! *Sightsailer* sails with a maximum of 14 guests for daysails and 16 for private charters. There is a large, comfortable cushioned cockpit complete with back and footrests and two stern seats. When the wind is light to moderate, guests may also sit up on deck. Guests may take the wheel and experience the thrill of sailing a very light, highly responsive boat or simply sit back and relax. Guests board *Sightsailer* at historic Bowen's Wharf in downtown Newport, RI. Shortly after departure the sails are raised and *Sightsailer* sails through Newport Harbor, past Goat Island and Fort Adams and into Narragansett Bay. The scenery is stunning-yachts, seaside estates, the Pell-Newport Bridge, and the sailing is generally first rate. The crew is more than happy to answer guests' questions or get them involved in sailing the boat. *Sightsailer* is also available for private charters.

Who sails: Ages 6 and over
Program type: Public daysails and private charters
Season: May - October
Coast Guard certification:
Crew: 2
Trainees-passengers: 14 daysails, 16 private charters
Contact: Contact: John Hirschler, Sightsailing, Inc., 32 Bowen's Wharf, Newport, RI 02840 USA
Tel: 800-709-7245 or 401-849-3333
E-mail: info@sightsailing.com
Website: www.sightsailing.com

SPECIFICATIONS

Flag: USA
Rig: Sloop
Homeport: Baltimore, Maryland
Normal cruising waters:
Chesapeake Bay and the Delaware
River
Sparred length: 76'
LOD: 50'
Draft: 3' 5"
Beam: 16'
Rig height: 68'
Freeboard: 2' 5"
Sail area: 1,767 square feet
Tons: 14 GRT
Power: 150 HP diesel

SIGSBEE

Who sails: Students and other organized groups, individuals, and families
Program type: Sail training with paying trainees; sea education in marine and nautical science, maritime history, and ecology for school groups from elementary through college
Season: March through September
Built: 1901: Deale Island, Maryland
Coast Guard certification: Passenger Vessel (Subchapter T)
Crew: 4 **Trainees-passengers:** 30 daysails, 15 overnight , age: 13+; Dockside visitors: 30
Contact: Christine Truett, Director of Education, Living Classrooms Foundation, 802 South Caroline Street, Baltimore, MD 21231-3311 USA
Tel: 410-685-0295 **Fax:** 410-752-8433
Website: www.livingclassrooms.org

The skipjack *Sigsbee* was built in 1901 in Deale Island, Maryland and worked as an oyster dredge boat until the early 1990s. She was named after Charles D. Sigsbee, who was the Commanding Officer of the battleship *Maine.* The vessel was rebuilt by the Living Classrooms Foundation in 1994, and now sails Chesapeake Bay with students on board. While sailing on board the *Sigsbee*, students learn the history of skipjacks and the oyster industry, marine and nautical science, and gain an appreciation of Chesapeake Bay and the hard work of the watermen of a bygone era.

SPECIFICATIONS

Flag: Canada
Rig: 3-masted schooner
Homeport: Halifax, Nova Scotia, Canada
Normal cruising waters: Halifax Harbour, Nova Scotia Coast
Sparred length: 130'
LOA: 115'
Draft: 9'
Beam: 24'
Rig height: 75'
Freeboard: 4'
Tons: 199 GRT
Power: 350 Cummins

SILVA

Silva was built at Karlstads Mekaniska, Verksta, Sweden as a 3-masted steel schooner. During the first two decades of her life, she was used in the Scandinavian fishing industry, with regular trips to Iceland. In the 1960s, *Silva* was refitted as a bulk freighter, and had her sailing rig removed. *Silva* continued coastal trading until 1994 and remained in Sweden until the summer of 2001 when Canadian Sailing Expeditions bought and delivered her, for the first time, to North America. She now offers sailing tours of Halifax Harbour. She runs educational programs for students, day trade for general public, and private and corporate charters. Canadian Sailing Expeditions is dedicated to providing opportunities for people of all ages to experience and explore our seacoast the traditional way.

Who sails: Groups and individuals of all ages
Program type: Sail training for paying trainees; passenger day sails; private charters
Season: April through October
Built: 1939: Verksta, Sweden, Karlstads Mekaniska
Certification: Transport Canada
Trainees-passengers: 150 daysails
Contact: Captain Doug Prothero, Owner/operator, Canadian Sailing Expeditions, PO Box 2613, Halifax, NS B3J 3N5 Canada
Tel: 902-429-1474 **Fax:** 902-429-1475
E-mail: doug@canadiansailingexpeditions.com
Website: www.canadiansailingexpeditions.com

SPECIFICATIONS

Flag: Venezuela
Rig: Barque
Homeport: La Guaira, Venezuela
Normal cruising waters: Worldwide
Sparred length: 270'
Draft: 14' 6'''
Beam: 35'
Hull: steel

Photo by Thad Koza

SIMON BOLIVAR

Program type: Training vessel of the Venezuelan Navy
Contact: Embassy of the Bolivarian Republic of Venezuela, 1099 30th Street, NW Washington, DC 20007 USA
Tel: 202-342-2214 **Fax:** 202-342-6820

Simon Bolivar was one of four barques built in Spain for Latin American countries. Similar in design and rigging, the four ships are nearly identical sister ships: *Gloria* from Columbia, *Guayas* from Ecuador, *Cuauhtemoc* from Mexico, and *Simon Bolivar*. All four are frequent visitors to the United States and at major tall ship gatherings. The 270-foot *Simon Bolivar* was completed in 1980 and named for the "great liberator" of northern South America. Bolivar (1783-1830) was instrumental in the independence of Columbia, Ecuador, Panama, Peru, and Venezuela. *Simon Bolivar* embodies the spirit of idealism and freedom of her namesake. Her figurehead is an allegorical depiction of Liberty and was designed by the Venezuelan artist Manuel Felipe Rincon.

SPECIFICATIONS

Flag: Norway
Rig: Full-rigged ship
Homeport: Kristiansand, Norway
LOA: 210'
LOD: 186'
LWL: 158'
Draft: 15'
Beam: 29'
Rig height: 112'
Freeboard: 17'
Sail area: 6,500 square feet
Tons: 499 GRT
Power: 560 HP engine
Hull: steel

Photo by Thad Koza

SORLANDET

The *Sørlandet* was built as a schoolship for the merchant marine in 1927 in Kristiansand, Norway, and served this purpose up until 1974. She was named *Sørlandet,* meaning "the Southland", after the southern region of Norway of which Kristiansand is the capital. Thousands of young men have received their first seagoing experience onboard the *Sørlandet*. During the war, the German occupation force took her undercommand and she was used as a recreation ship for German U-boat crew. Later she was used as a prison camp for Russian prisoners of war. During one of the many air-raids, she sunk in the Kirkenes Bay far up North in Norway with only her masts above water. She was later brought afloat and towed back to her homeport heavily damaged. In 1947 she was restored and once again able to welcome young cadets. In the early seventies the Government of Norway had different ideas on how to educate young seamen and the schoolship era in Norway came to an end. A new administrative organization was established which offers people of all ages a tall ship experience as paying trainees for short or longer trips.

Who sails: 15-80 year old trainees accepted.
Program type: Sail training ship, tall ship adventures
Season: May through September
Desiner: Hoivold Shipyard
Built: 1927: Hoivold Shipyard, Kristiansand, Norway
Crew: Up to 20 **Trainees-passengers:** 70
Contact: Leif Brestrup, Director, Stiftelsen Fullriggeren Sorlandet, Gravane 6, Kristiansand, N-4610 Norway
Tel: +47 38 02 98 90 **Fax:** +47 38 02 93 34

SPECIFICATIONS

Flag: USA
Rig: Gaff schooner, 3-masted
Homeport: Stamford, Connecticut
Normal cruising waters:
Long Island Sound
Sparred length: 80'
LOD: 65'
Draft: 3' (centerboards up),
8' (centerboards down)
Beam: 14'
Rig height: 60'
Freeboard: 3' 6"
Sail area: 1,510 square feet
Tons: 32 GRT
Power: diesel
Hull: steel

SOUNDWATERS

Who sails: School groups from elementary through college; individuals and families
Program type: Sea education in marine science and ecology in cooperation with accredited institutions and other groups, and as informal, in-house programming
Season: April to November
Designer: William Ward
Built: 1986: Norfolk, Virginia, Marine Metals, Inc.
Coast Guard certification: Passenger Vessel (Subchapter T)
Crew: 3 - 5 instructors **Trainees-passengers:** 42 daysails, 15-20 overnight
Contact: SoundWaters Inc., Cove Island Park, 1281 Cove Road, Stamford, CT 06902 USA
Tel: 203-323-1978 **Fax:** 203-967-8306
E-mail: connect@soundwaters.org
Website: www.soundwaters.org

SoundWaters, Inc. is a non-profit education organization dedicated to protecting Long Island Sound and its watershed through education. *SoundWaters* offers shipboard and land-based programs to 35,000 children and adults from Connecticut and New York. The schooner *SoundWaters* is the platform for a variety of programs includes seamanship, navigation, helmsmanship, and field exploration of marine ecosystems. *SoundWaters* crew includes environmental educators, biologists, naturalists, and a licensed captain. In addition, *SoundWaters*, Inc. operates the *SoundWaters* Community Center for Environmental Education, featuring educational exhibits and displays, classroom and community meeting space, a wet lab, and cutting-edge "green" construction. The organization also conducts many free outreach programs, which are offered through public schools and community centers.

SPECIFICATIONS

Flag: Bermuda
Rig: Bermudian
Homeport: Hamilton, Bermuda
Normal cruising waters: Bermuda waters and Western Atlantic
Sparred length: 112'
LOA: 112'
LOD: 88'
LWL: 75'
Draft: 9' 6"
Beam: 23'
Rig height: 93'
Freeboard: 5'
Sail area: 4,437 square feet
Tons: 92 GRT
Power: Cat 3126 Mechanical 385 HP diesel
Hull: cold-moulded epoxy

SPIRIT OF BERMUDA

The purpose-built sail training vessel is based on civilian Bermudian-type schooners built between 1810-1840. Bermudians, enslaved and free, built the schooners in the period prior to the Emancipation of Slavery in the British Empire (August 1, 1834). The original hull shape was adapted from the Bermuda-built RN "Shamrock" class, fast dispatch and patrol vessels that ran from the RN Dockyard, Bermuda, northwest to Halifax and Southwest to Jamaica to contain the rebel colonies. The Bermuda rig was innovated on the coastal Bermuda sloops that abounded in the 17th, 18th and early part of the 19th century. Faced with impassable pathways by land, locals had evolved the lateen rig to short-tack up(wind) the island and up to the fishing banks to windward of Bermuda.

Who sails: 14+ years
Program type: Extra-curricular team (high school) and curricular learning expeditions (middle school 3)
Season: Year-round
Designer: Bill Nash / Langan Design Associates, Newport, RI
Built: 2006: Rockport, ME, Rockport Marine
Coast Guard certification: Passenger vessel (Subchapter T)
Crew: 3 professional, 8 volunteer **Trainees-passengers:** 40 inside the reef, 26 coastal
Contact: Mr. Malcolm Kirkland, Executive Director, Bermuda Sloop Foundation, Suite 1151, 48 Par-la-Ville Road, Hamilton HM11 Bermuda
Tel: 441-737-5667 **Fax:** 441- 297-5776
E-mail: malcolm.kirkland@bermudasloop.org
Website: www.bermudasloop.org/

SPECIFICATIONS

Flag: USA
Rig: Schooner
Homeport: Dana Point, California
Normal cruising waters:
Southern California
Sparred length: 118'
LOD: 86'
LWL: 79'
Draft: 10'
Beam: 24'
Rig height: 100'
Freeboard: 6'
Sail area: 5,000 square feet
Power: HP diesel
Tons: 64 GRT
Hull: wood

SPIRIT OF DANA POINT

Who sails: School groups from elementary school through college; adult education groups; families and individuals of all ages
Program type: Sail training for volunteer crew or trainees; sea education in marine science, maritime history, and ecology based on informal in-house programming and in cooperation with other organizations; day sails and overnight passages
Season: Year-round
Designer: Howard Chapelle **Built:** 1983: Costa Mesa, California, Dennis Holland
Coast Guard certification: Passenger Vessel (Subchapter T)
Crew: 7 **Trainees-passengers:** 75 daysails, 30 overnight
Contact: Karin Wyman, Maritime Director, Ocean Institute, 24200 Dana Point Harbor Drive, CA 92629 USA
Tel: 949-496-2274 **Fax:** 949-496-4715
E-mail: kwyman@ocean-institute.org
Website: www.ocean-institute.org

A young colony, in a new land, dreamed of independence and built some of the fastest and best sailing ships in the world. These ships were the result of ingenuity, independence and a strong desire to accomplish something. It was Dennis Holland's life dream to build an accurate replica from the period when America fought for independence and world recognition. Armed with talent, determination, a little money and plans he purchased from the Smithsonian Institute, he laid the keel in his yard on May 2, 1970. Thirteen years later, this fast privateer was launched and his vision became reality. Today at the Ocean Institute this dream continues as young students step aboard and back in time. During their voyages, students relive the challenges and discoveries of early ocean exploration. Through a series of national, award-winning living history programs, the *Spirit of Dana Point* serves as an excellent platform for our youth to directly experience life at sea, as it has been for hundreds of years. She sails throughout Southern California for more than 150 days a year.

SPECIFICATIONS

Flag: USA
Rig: Gaff tops'l schooner, 2-masted
Homeport: Boothbay Harbor, Maine
Normal cruising waters: North Atlantic Ocean and Caribbean Sea, Canada to South America
Sparred length: 125'
LOA: 98'
LOD: 95'
LWL: 88'
Draft: 10' 6"
Beam: 24'
Rig height: 103'
Freeboard: 5'
Sail area: 7,000 square feet
Tons: 90 GRT
Power: 235 HP diesel
Hull: wood

SPIRIT OF MASSACHUSETTS

Owned by the Ocean Classroom Foundation, the schooner *Spirit of Massachusetts* offers programs of education under sail to the youth of America. Programs range from four month semesters-at-sea to week-long programs with schools and youth groups. Trainees sail the ship and learn traditional seamanship skills under the Captain and crew, and they explore maritime subjects with the onboard academic staff. Ocean Classroom's Discovery™ program is a semester-at-sea for qualified high school students, fully accredited by Proctor Academy. The voyage covers more than 6,000 nautical miles, connecting South American shores to the Canadian Maritimes. Students live and work as sailors on a true voyage of discovery, while they study maritime history, maritime literature, marine science, applied mathematics,and navigation. Discovery™ is offered Fall and Spring Terms. Other programs include SEAmester™, OceanBound and Summer Seafaring Camps. The Ocean Classroom Foundation also owns and operates the schooners *Harvey Gamage* and *Westward*.

Who sails: Individuals and school groups from middle school through college; affiliated institutions include Proctor Academy, University of Maine, Center for Coastal Studies, Outward Bound, and other schools
Program type: Traditional seamanship training combined with accredited academic studies
Season: Year-round
Designer: Melbourne Smith and Andrew Davis
Built: 1984: Boston, MA, New England Historic Seaport
Coast Guard certification: Sailing School Vessel (Subchapter R), Passenger Vessel (Subchapter T)
Crew: 8 - 11 including instructors **Student-trainees:** 22 overnight
Contact: Executive Director, Ocean Classroom Foundation, 29 McKown Street, Boothbay Harbor, Maine 04538 USA
Tel: 800-724-7245
E-mail: mail@oceanclassroom.org
Website: www.oceanclassroom.org

SPECIFICATIONS

Flag: USA
Rig: Schooner
Homeport: Charleston, South Carolina
Normal Cruising Waters: North Atlantic, Caribbean Sea, and the Canadian Maritimes
Sparred length: 140'
LOD: 91'
LWL: 88'
Draft: 10' 5"
Beam: 24'
Rig Height: 125'
Freeboard: 3' 9"
Sail Area: 6,462 square feet
Tons: 94 GRT
Power: two 230 HP Cummins diesel
Hull: wood

SPIRIT OF SOUTH CAROLINA

Who sails: South Carolina students and educators
Program type: Under-sail educational programs in marine science, maritime history, and seamanship, including both day trips and live-aboard programming
Season: Year-round
Designer: Tri-Coastal Marine
Built: 2007: Sea Island Boat Builders
Coast Guard certification: Passenger Vessel (subchapter T) Sailing School Vessel (subchapter R) pending
Crew: 9 **Trainees-passengers:** 40 daysails, 21 overnight
Contact: South Carolina Maritime Foundation (SCMF), PO Box 22405, Charleston, SC 29413 USA
Tel: 843-722-1030
E-mail: info@scmaritime.org
Website: www.scmaritime.org

The *Spirit of South Carolina*, owned and operated by the South Carolina Maritime Foundation, was launched in March 2007. Her lines are reminiscent of an 1870s pilot schooner that was built in Charleston, SC. The *Spirit of South Carolina* operates mainly as a sailing school vessel offering a unique education platform for the students of the Palmetto State. The hands-on programs conducted aboard are designed to challenge and engage students while promoting responsibility, teamwork, and stewardship for both their community and their environment. Programs vary in duration from day sail programs to multi-day and multi-week voyages. When not sailing in South Carolinas waters, the vessel also serves as the states floating 'Goodwill Ambassador' promoting the resourcefulness and vibrancy of South Carolinians.

SPECIFICATIONS

Flag: Canada
Rig: Brigantine
Homeport: Kingston, Ontario, Canada
Normal cruising waters: Lake Ontario and adjacent waters
Sparred length: 72'
LOA: 60'
LOD: 57'
LWL: 46'
Draft: 8' 6"
Beam: 15'
Rig height: 54'
Freeboard: 4' 6"
Sail area: 2,560 square feet
Tons: 34 GRT
Power: 165 HP diesel
Hull: steel

ST. LAWRENCE II

The *St Lawrence II* is a purpose built sail training vessel in operation since 1957, primarily on the Great Lakes. She was designed to be manageable by a young crew, yet complex enough with her brigantine rig to introduce teenagers to the challenge of square-rig sailing. The ship is owned and operated by Brigantine, Inc., a nonprofit charity staffed by local volunteers who share the conviction that the lessons of responsibility, self-reliance, and teamwork provided by sail training are especially applicable to teenagers. Brigantine, Inc. is one of the pioneering sail training programs in North America. Cruises in this hands-on program range from six to ten days or more in length. *St. Lawrence II*'s crew complement of 28 is comprised of 18 new trainees, plus a crew of watch officers, petty officers, cook, and bosun, all aged 13 to 18. The captain is usually the only adult onboard. The ship's teenage officers are graduates of Brigantine, Inc.'s winter training program, involving lessons in seamanship, navigation, and ship's systems, as well as the ongoing maintenance of the ship.

Who sails: School groups and individuals of all ages
Program type: Sail training with paying trainees
Season: April to November (sailing); October to March (winter program)
Designer: Francis McLachlan/Michael Eames
Built: 1953: Kingston, Ontario, Canada, Kingston Shipyards
Crew: 10   **Trainees-passengers:** 36 daysails, 18 overnight
Contact: Brigantine, Inc., 53 Yonge Street, Kingston, Ontario K7M 6G4 Canada
Tel: 613-544-5175 **Fax:** 613-544-9828
E-mail: briginc@kos.net
Website: www.brigantine.ca

SPECIFICATIONS

Flag: USA
Rig: Barque, 3-masted
Homeport: San Diego, California
Normal cruising waters: Coastal waters between San Diego, California and northern Baja California, Mexico
Sparred length: 278'
LOD: 210'
LWL: 200'
Draft: 21' 6"
Beam: 35'
Rig height: 148'
Freeboard: 15'
Sail area: 18,000 square feet
Tons: 1,197 GRT
Hull: iron

STAR OF INDIA

Who sails: Selected volunteers, permanent crew, and invited passengers
Program type: Sail training for crew and apprentices; sea education in maritime history; dockside interpretations
Designer: Edward Arnold
Built: 1863: Ramsey, Isle of Man, UK, Gibson, McDonald & Arnold
Coast Guard certification: Museum Attraction Vessel
Contact: Scott Baldwin, San Diego Maritime Museum, 1492 N. Harbor Drive, San Diego CA 92101 USA
Tel: 619 234 9153 x 120
E-mail: sbaldwin@sdmaritime.org
Website: www.sdmaritime.org

The *Star of India* is the world's oldest active ship. She was built at Ramsey shipyard on the Isle of Man and launched as the *Euterpe* in 1863. She began her working life as a cargo ship in the India trade and was nearly lost on her first two voyages, surviving a mutiny, collision, cyclone and the death of her captain. In 1871, she embarked on a quarter century of hauling emigrants to New Zealand. She circumnavigated the globe 21 times during this service. She was sold to American owners in 1898 and renamed the *Star of India* in 1906. By 1923, steam power had replaced sails on merchant ships and the *Star of India* was laid up in Oakland. A group of San Diegans purchased the ship and had her towed to San Diego in 1927. Depression and war delayed the beginning of her restoration until the late 1950s. In 1976, with her restoration complete, she sailed on San Diego Bay for the first time in 50 years. The *Star of India* is now the pride of the Maritime Museum of San Diego's fleet of historic ships. She is maintained by a dedicated group of volunteers and skilled craftsman and sails at least once a year.

SPECIFICATIONS

Flag: Norway
Rig: Barque
Homeport: Bergen, Norway
Sparred length: 321' 6"
Draft: 17'
Beam: 41'
Hull: steel

Photo by Thad Koza

STATSRAAD LEHMKUHL

Statsraad Lehmkuhl is Norway's largest and oldest square-rigged sailing ship. She is a 3-masted barque built in 1914 at the J. C. tecklenborgwerft yard in Bremerhaven, Germany, as a training ship for the German merchant navy and originally christened *Grossherzog Fridrich August*.
In 1923, she was purchased by agents in Bergen for the Norwegian Shipowners Association on the initiative of secretarty of state Kristoffer Lehmkuhl. For his work in promoting the cause of cadet ships and for his contributions to the creation of an independent Norwegian government in 1905, the ship was renamed in his honor.
In 1924 the training ship was transferred to the Bergen Schoolship Association, which operated the vessel through difficult years until 1979 under the direction of Hilmar Reksten. In 1979, the ship was donated to the Statraad Lehmkuhl Foundation. The board of directors of this foundation comprises representatives of national and local governments, the Maritime Museum of Bergen, the firm of Hilmar Reksten, and the City of Bergen. Today she carries young people across oceans to discover the romance of the sea and the adventure of sailing.

Who sails: Norwegian Navy, schools, companies, public institutions, organizations or large groups of friends
Program type: Sail training for paying trainees, 5-7 hour day cruises and 4-10 day sailing cruises
Built: 1914: Johann C. Tecklenborg AG, Bremerhaven-Geestemünde
Crew: 17 **Trainees-passengers:** 350 daysails, 150 overnight
Contact: Statsraad Lehmkuhl, Skur 7 Bradbenken 2 NO- 5003 Norway
Tel: 55 30 17 00 **Fax:** 55 30 17 01
E-mail: lehmkuhl@lehmkuhl.no
Website: www.lehmkuhl.no

SPECIFICATIONS

Flag: United Kingdom
Rig: Brig
Homeport: Portsmouth, England
Normal cruising waters: United Kingdom, Europe, Mediterranean, Canaries, Azores and Caribbean
Sparred length: 195'
LOA: 159'
LOD: 159'
LWL: 133'
Draft: 15'
Beam: 33'
Rig height: 148'
Sail area: 12,503 square feet
Tons: 493 GRT
Power: 2x MTU 33OKW
Hull: steel

STAVROS S. NIARCHOS

Who sails: Groups and individuals aged 14-75
Season: Year-round
Program type: Sail training for paying trainees
Designer: Burness, Corlett & Partners & Captain Mike Willoughby
Built: 2000: North Devon, United Kingdom, Appledore Shipbuilders
Crew: 6 pemanent, 13 volunteer   **Trainees-passengers:** 44 daysails, 48 overnight
Contact: Tall Ships Youth Trust, 2A The Hard, Portsmouth, Hampshire P01 3PT England
Tel: +44 (0) 23 9283 2055
Fax: +44 (0) 23 9281 5769
E-mail: info@tallships.org
Website: www.tallships.org

Stavros S Niarchos is a purpose built sail training vessel owned by the Tall Ships Youth Trust. She is a 200-foot, steel hulled, square-rigged brig built in Appledore, Devon, and was launched in 2001. She is named after a very generous Greek benefactor. The Tall Ships Youth Trust, incorporating the Sail Training Association, is a registered charity founded in 1956 and is dedicated to the personal development of young people aged 14-25 through the crewing of ocean-going vessels. Every year, thousands of people aged 14 to 75 from all over the world sail on either *Stavros S Niarchos* or the Trust's fleet of four 72-foot Challenger Yachts. *Stavros S Niarchos* operates all year round. In the summer months she frequents European and Mediterranean waters, and during the winter she may head south for the Canaries, Azores and Caribbean. Youth voyages for 14-25 year olds last from 7-14 nights whereas 18+ voyages range from day sails to a 24 night trans-Atlantic.

SPECIFICATIONS

Flag: USA
Rig: Square topsail schooner, two-masted
Homeport: Chestertown, Maryland
Normal cruising waters: Chesapeake Bay
Sparred length: 97'
LOD: 53'
LWL: 53'
Draft: 8'
Beam: 17'
Rig height: 72'
Freeboard: 5'
Tons: 43 GRT
Power: Single screw diesel
Hull: wood

SULTANA

The schooner *Sultana* is a full scale reproduction of a 1767 vessel of the same name used by the British Royal Navy to enforce the notorious "Tea Taxes" on the North American coastline in the years preceding the American Revolution. *Sultana* is notable as one of the most thoroughly documented vessels from the American Colonial period. The schooner's original logbooks, crew lists, correspondence, and design drawings have all survived intact to the present day. Owned an operated by Sultana Projects, Inc., a non-profit, 501(c)(3) organization based in historic Chestertown, Maryland, the new *Sultana* sails as a floating classroom; providing unique, hands-on educational opportunities for children and adults that focus on the history and environment of the Chesapeake Bay and its watershed. *Sultana's* educational programs are designed to compliment and support national, state and local curriculum goals - but just as importantly, they are meant to excite students about the process of learning. Again and again teachers have found that a trip on *Sultana* can help to bring subjects like history, science, math and reading to life.

Who sails: School & adult groups as well as individuals of all ages
Program type: Under-sail educational experiences in environmental science and history, including both day trips and live-aboard programming
Season: April to November
Designer: Benford Design Group, St. Michael's, Maryland
Built: 2001: Chestertown, Maryland, Swain Boatbuilders, LLC
Coast Guard certification: Passenger Vessel (Subchapter T)
Crew: 5 **Trainees-passengers:** 32 daysails, 11 overnight
Contact: Drew McMullen, President, Sultana Projects, Inc., P.O. Box 524, Chestertown, MD 21620 USA
Tel: 410-778-5954 **Fax:** 410-778-4531
E-mail: dmcmullen@sultanaprojects.org
Website: www.sultanaprojects.org

SPECIFICATIONS

Flag: USA
Rig: Full-rigged ship
Homeport: San Diego, Californian
Normal cruising waters:
San Diego Bay
LOA: 179'
LOD: 135'
Draft: 13'
Beam: 30'
Rig Height: 130'
Sail Area: 13,000 square feet
Tons: 263 GRT
Hull: wood

HMS SURPRISE

Who sails: Museum vessel at this time
Program type: No programs as yet
Designer: Admiralty
Built: 1970: John Fitzhugh Millar, Lunenburg, Nova Scotia
Contact: Scott Baldwin, San Diego Maritime Museum, 1492 N. Harbor Drive, San Diego CA 92101 USA
Tel: 619-234-9153 x120
E-mail: sbaldwin@sdmaritime.org
Website: www.sdmaritime.org

"HMS" *Surprise* is a 179' full rigged ship. Her designers and builders made painstaking efforts to recreate a 24 gun frigate of Great Britains' Nelson era Royal Navy. The result is a replica vessel unmatched in its authenticity and attention to detail. Originally christened "HMS" *Rose* when she was launched in 1970, she served as a sail training vessel operating out of several east coast ports for over 30 years. The ship underwent extensive modifications for the production of the film "Master and Commander: The Far Side of the World" in 2002. The Maritime Museum of San Diego purchased "HMS" *Surprise* from 20th Century Fox in October, 2004. Plans include restoring the ship to seaworthy condition.

SPECIFICATIONS

Flag: USA
Rig: Barque, 3-masted (lateen mizzen)
Homeport: Jamestown Settlement, Virginia
Normal cruising waters: Chesapeake Bay
Sparred length: 116'
LOA: 96'
LOD: 83'
LWL: 77'
Draft: 11' 6"
Beam: 24' 10'
Rig height: 95'
Freeboard: 11'
Sail area: 3,902 square feet
Tons: 180 GRT
Power: twin 135 HP diesels
Hull: wood

SUSAN CONSTANT

Susan Constant is a full-scale re-creation of the flagship of a small fleet that brought America's first permanent English colonists to Virginia in 1607. Together with the smaller *Godspeed* and *Discovery*, *Susan Constant* is on exhibit at Jamestown Settlement, a living history museum of 17th-century Virginia. Jamestown Settlement is administered by the Jamestown Yorktown Foundation, an agency of the Commonwealth of Virginia. While no plans or renderings of the original *Susan Constant*, *Godspeed*, and *Discovery* have ever been located, the replicas are based on the documented tonnages of the 17th century ships, and *Susan Constant's* design incorporates research information that emerged after the first replicas were built. With a crew of staff and volunteers, *Susan Constant* and *Godspeed* periodically sail to other ports in the Chesapeake Bay region to participate in commemorative and community events and host educational programs.

Who sails: Crew consisting of Jamestown Settlement staff and volunteers age 18 years and older
Program type: Sail training and dockside interpretation.
Designer: Stanley Potter
Built: 1991: Jamestown Settlement, VA, Allen C. Rawl
Crew: 25
Contact: Captain Eric Speth, Maritime Program Manager, Jamestown Settlement, PO Box 1607, Williamsburg, VA 23187 USA
Tel: 757-253-4838
Fax: 757-253-7350
Website: www.historyisfun.org

SPECIFICATIONS

Flag: USA
Rig: Square topsail schooner
Homeport: Los Angeles, California
Normal cruising waters: Coastal California and offshore islands
Sparred length: 92'
LOA: 70'
LOD: 66'
LWL: 62'
Draft: 10'
Beam: 18'
Rig height: 74'
Freeboard: 5'
Sail area: 4,000 square feet
Tons: 46 GRT
Power: Diesel
Hull: wood

SWIFT OF IPSWICH

Who sails: Youth/school groups from diverse communities, especially pre-teens and other youth and adult groups seeking character-building/team-building sailing adventures
Program type: Educational sailing adventures
Season: Year-round
Designer: Howard I. Chappelle
Built: 1938: Ipswich, MA, William A. Robinson
Coast Guard certfication: Passenger Vessel (Subchapter T)
Crew: 6 **Trainees-passengers:** 49 daysails, 31 overnight - Age: 10+
Contact: Captain Jim Gladson, Los Angeles Maritime Institute, Berth 84, Foot of Sixth Street, San Pedro, CA 90731 USA
Tel: 310-833-6055 **Fax:** 310-548-2055
Website: www.LAMItopsail.org

The Los Angeles Maritime Institute is currently making a major investment in the restoration of the square topsail schooner *Swift of Ipswich*. Once completed, she will return to the TopSail Youth Program, alongside the twin brigantines, *Irving Johnson* and *Exy Johnson*, providing character building sail training adventures for youth. As LAMI's original vessel, *Swift of Ipswich* is a learning environment that nurtures the development of knowledge, skills and attitudes that are necessary for the education of today's youth, but difficult to teach in a traditional classroom. About two thirds the size of one of LAMI's twin brigantines, *Swift* is especially well suited for working with smaller, younger groups who might be overwhelmed by the size and complexity of the LAMI brigantines. Built to the lines of an historic Revolutionary War privateer, *Swift of Ipswich* was once the personal yacht of actor James Cagney and has been known as a floating landmark mostly serving youth in Southern California for over 60 years.

SPECIFICATIONS

Flag: USA
Rig: Gaff schooner, 2-masted
Homeport: Marion, Massachusetts
Normal cruising waters:
Coastal New England (summer),
offshore Atlantic Ocean (school year)
Sparred length: 115'
LOA: 92' 10"
LOD: 84' 6"
LWL: 78' 8"
Draft: 10' 4"
Beam: 21' 8"
Rig height: 95'
Sail area: 3,540 square feet
Tons: 100 GRT
Power: 300 HP diesel
Hull: iron

TABOR BOY

Tabor Boy has been engaged in sail training as a seagoing classroom for Tabor Academy students since 1954. Offshore voyaging and oceanographic studies go together in the curriculum, with cruises to destinations as distant as Mexico and Panama adding adventure to the experience. Many Tabor Academy graduates go on to the US Merchant Marine, Naval, or Coast Guard academies. The schooner also offers seven summer orientation voyages for newly enrolled freshmen and sophomore students. During this time, trainees are fully involved in sail handling while studying Gulf of Maine marine wildlife and ecology. Winter programs feature sailing and snorkeling in the US and British Virgin Islands to observe and study coral reef ecosystems.

Who sails: Enrolled students at Tabor Academy
Program type: Seamanship and oceanography for high school students
Built: 1914: Amsterdam, The Netherlands, Scheepswerven & Machinefabrik
Coast Guard certification: Sailing School Vessel (Subchapter R)
Crew: 6 **Trainees-passengers:** 23 - Age: 14-18
Contact: Captain James E. Geil, Master, Tabor Boy, Tabor Academy, 66 Spring Street, Marion, MA 02738 USA
Tel: 508-748-2000 **Fax:** 508-291-6666
E-mail: jgeil@taboracademy.org
Website: www.taboracademy.org

SPECIFICATIONS

Flag: India
Rig: Barque, 3-masted
Homeport: Kochi, India
Normal cruising waters:
Worldwide
Sparred length: 177'
Draft: 15'
Beam: 28'
Sail area: 10,392 square feet
Power: twin 320 HP diesels
Hull: steel

Photo by MAX

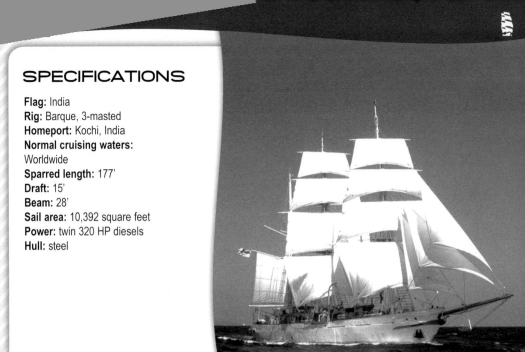

TARANGINI

Who sails: Officer cadets of the First Training Squadron and officers of the Indian Navy
Program type: Sail training and seamanship for cadets and officers of the Indian Navy
Season: Year-round
Design: Colin Mudie
Built: 1997: Goa, India, Goa Shipyard Limited
Crew: 37   **Trainees:** 30
Contact: CDR S Shaukat Ali, C/O Fleet Mail Office, Kochi, India

Tarangini is a 3-masted barque designed by the world famous sail ship designer Mr. Colin Mudie. The name *Tarangini* comes from the Hindi word, "Tarang", which means waves. Besides being an ideal platform for basic seamanship, *Tarangini* provides character building and sail training capsule for officer cadets of the First Training Squadron and officers/sailors of Indian Navy. *Tarangini* provides an ideal setting for first hand experience of the natural elements to the cadets embarking on a Naval career. The training imparted onboard *Tarangini* includes general points and terms used in sailing, parts of sails and rigging, setting and furling of sails, watch-keeping, safety, and sail maneuvers such as tacking, veering and boxhauling. INS *Tarangini* fosters the old fashioned and time-tested virtues of courage, camaraderie, and endurance. She instills among the trainees the indefinable "sea sense", which encompasses the qualities of humanity and prudence which are inseparable from safe and successful seafaring.

SPECIFICATIONS

Flag: United Kingdom
Rig: Barque, 3-masted
Homeport: Southampton, United Kingdom
Normal cruising waters:
United Kingdom (summer)
Caribbean and Southern
Europe (winter)
Sparred length: 213' 3"
LOA: 177' 2"
Draft: 15' 9"
Beam: 34' 9"
Rig height: 137' 9"
Freeboard: 6' 7"
Sail area: 12,917 square feet
Power: twin 400 HP
Hull: wood/epoxy

TENACIOUS

The 213-foot, 3-masted barque *Tenacious* is the Jubilee Sailing Trust's (JST) second and newest ship. She is the largest wooden tall ship of her kind to be built in Great Britain this century. JST promotes the integration of able-bodied and physically disabled people though the challenge of tall ship sailing. Such had been the success of the JST's first ship, *Lord Nelson*, that JST decided to build *Tenacious*. Like the *Lord Nelson*, *Tenacious* enables all members of her crew to sail together on equal terms. Features include signs in Braille, power-assisted hydraulic steering, and points throughout the ship that enable wheelchairs to be secured during rough weather. Voyages are open to anyone between 16 -70+ and no previous experience is required. The crew of 40 is split 50/50 between able bodied and physically disabled people, with eight wheelchair users. There is a permanent crew of ten, including a medical purser and cook.

Who sails: Physically disabled and able-bodied people, aged 16 to 70+
Program type: Sail training for paying trainees; integration of physically disabled and able-bodied people through the challenge of tall ship sailing
Season: Year-round
Designer: Tony Castro, Ltd.
Built: 1996-2000: Woolston, Southampton, United Kingdom
Crew: 10 Trainees-passengers: 40
Contact: Ms. Amanda Butcher, Jubilee Sailing Trust, Jubilee Yard, Hazel Road, Woolston, Southampton, Hampshire, S019 7GB United Kingdom
Tel: 44-23-8044-9108 **Fax:** 44-23-8044-9145
E-mail: jst@jst.org.uk
Website: www.jst.org.uk

SPECIFICATIONS

Flag: USA
Rig: Square topsail schooner, 3-masted
Homeport: Long Beach, California
Normal cruising waters: Channel Islands and beyond
Sparred length: 156'
LOD: 123'
LWL: 101'
Draft: 13' 6"
Beam: 31'
Rig height: 110'
Freeboard: 6'
Sail area: 8,500 square feet
Tons: 229 GRT
Power: 575 HP Deutz diesel
Hull: steel

TOLE MOUR

Who sails: School groups 4th grade through college; educational adult groups; individuals
Program type: Live-aboard educational voyages focusing on sail training and marine science
Designer: Ewbank, Brooke, and Associates
Built: 1988: Whidbey Island, WA, Nichols Brothers
Coast Guard certification: Sailing School Vessel (Subchapter R)
Crew: 13 **Trainees-passengers:** 53 daysails, 36 overnight
Contact: CIMI Tall Ship Expeditions, PO Box 1360, Claremont, CA 91711 USA
Tel: 1-800-645-1423 **Fax:** 909-625-7305
Website: www.guideddiscoveries.org or www.tolemour.org

Tole Mour is a 156-foot, 3-masted square topsail schooner owned and operated by the non-profit organization, Guided Discoveries. With her incredibly seaworthy construction, 15 sails, hands-on science equipment, professional crew dedicated to teaching, and close proximity to Southern California's biologically rich Channel Islands, she is the ultimate platform for sail training and marine science education. The *Tole Mour* has been carrying out the work of Catalina Island Marine Institute (CIMI) since 2001. CIMI Tall Ship Expeditions, founded in 1998, is a Guided Discoveries program that is dedicated to "taking young people to sea in order to build character and minds." CIMI Tall Ship Expeditions offers live-aboard voyages during the school year, summer, and winter, that focus on sail training and marine science education and range from 2 to 21 days in length. *Tole Mour* accommodates groups of up to 36 and ages ten to adult. She sails the waters of Southern California's eight off-shore islands and beyond.

SPECIFICATIONS

Flag: USA
Rig: Gaff schooner
Homeport: Newport, Rhode Island
Sparred length: 93'
LOA: 70'
LOD: 70'
LWL: 58'
Draft: 8' 5"
Beam: 18' 6"
Rig height: 85'
Freeboard: 4' 5"
Sail area: 4,800 square feet
Tons: 83 GRT
Power: diesel
Hull: wood/epoxy

TREE OF LIFE

The Schooner *Tree of Life*, launched in 1991, was built in Nova Scotia, Canada. She sleeps 12 in three cabins and the foc'sle. Her hull is a composite of strip planked clear fir and Kevlar saturated in epoxy and sheathed in fiberglass. Her deck is fir, spars are spruce, and brightwork is Honduran Mahogany. The interior is paneled in koa and teak. The *Tree of Life*, her owners, a crew of four plus two trainees, sailed out of Newport Oct. 2002 on a three year circumnavigation. In 2003, *Tree of Life* spent five months in Auckland, New Zealand via Bora Bora, the Southern Cooks and Fiji for the America's Cup. She sailed the Indian Ocean to Capetown, South Africa, the Atlantic to Antigua for Classic Race Week, St Barth's, St Martin, Turks & Caicos, the Bahamas, Palm Beach and home to Newport, RI. The owners were on board for the duration of the voyage. The *Tree of Life*, at home in Newport Harbor, now sails throughout New England waters as she awaits prospective owners to return her to the world's oceans.

Who sails: Adult individuals and families
Program type: Sail training for volunteer and trainees; sea education in marine science and maritime history
Designer: Ted Brewer
Built: 1991: Covey Island, Canada
Crew: 4 **Trainees-passengers:** 2
Contact: Sheri & John Laramee, Owners, 443 Bellevue Avenue, Newport, RI 02840 USA
Tel: 401-640-9777 or 401-732-6464
E-mail: JohnOnTree@aol.com
Website: www.schoonertreeoflife.com

SPECIFICATIONS

Flag: USA
Rig: Topsail schooner
Homeport: Bridgeport, Connecticut
Normal cruising waters: East Coast, Long Island Sound, New England and Great Lakes
Sparred length: 118'
LOD: 90'
LWL: 83'
Draft: 9' 6"
Beam: 22'
Rig height: 96'
Freeboard: 3' 6"
Sail area: 9,688 square feet
Tons: 98 GRT
Power: 350 HP diesels
Hull: steel from German U-Boats

UNICORN

Who sails: Girls age 13 – 21; male and female executives
Program type: Sail training vessel for teenage girls, women, executive teams, private groups and film work
Built: 1947: Alphen, The Netherlands
Crew: 6 - 10 **Trainees-passengers:** 12 daysails, 6 overnight
Contact: Dawn Santamaria, 2 Gravel Hill Road, Asbury, NJ 08802 USA
Tel: 908-713-1808
E-Mail: dawn@tallshipunicorn.com
Website: www.tallshipunicorn.com

From metals of old German submarines to majestic tall ship, STV *Unicorn* sails the sea with proven on-board leadership and development programs for teenage girls, executive women and executive teams. Holland-built in 1947, STV *Unicorn* partners with Sisters Under Sail Corp. to deliver a non-profit leadership development program for teenage girls, whose mission is to build confidence, enhance self-esteem, develop social conscience and teach the value of sisters working together towards a common goal. The vessel welcomes young women from around the globe to sail aboard with *Unicorn's* all-female professional crew. *Unicorn* also partners with BeamPines, Inc., a human resources consulting firm in New York City, to offer on-board executive development and team building programming. HR consultants work closely with *Unicorn's* crew to create an effective learning environment that drives results.

SPECIFICATIONS

Flag: Netherlands
Rig: Ketch
Homeport: Den Helder, Netherlands
LOA: 76'
Draft: 8' 6"
Beam: 18'
Hull: steel

Photo by Thad Koza

URANIA

Urania is the flagship of the Royal Netherlands Naval College. Every executive officer who has graduated from the naval college over the past 40 years trained on the *Urania*. Generally she sails with three officers, two petty officers, and 12 cadets. She is a very active ship and has been the recipient of the prestigious Friendship Trophy four times, which is awarded by Sail Training International annually to a ship that best demonstrates the spirit of sail training. Her original wishbone rig was modified to her present Bermudian ketch rig in the late 1950s.

Program type: Training vessel of the Royal Netherlands Naval College
Built: 1928
Crew: 5 **Trainees-passengers:** 12
Contact: Royal Netherlands Embassy, 4200 Linnean Avenue, NW, Washington, DC 20008 USA
Tel: 202-244-5300 **Fax:** 202-362-3430

SPECIFICATIONS

Flag: USA
Rig: Gaff topsail knockabout schooner, 2-masted
Homeport: Norfolk, Virginia
Normal cruising waters: Worldwide
Sparred length: 126'
LOA: 121' 10"
LOD: 114'
LWL: 84'
Draft: 12' 3"
Beam: 24"
Rig height: 112"
Freeboard: 6' 6"
Sail area: 6,538 square feet
Tons: 97 GRT
Power: twin diesels 205 BHP each
Hull: wood

VIRGINIA

Who sails: Youth Sail Training program for students ages 13-17 years of age and adult voyages which feature celestial navigation training and winter passages in the Caribbean.
Program type: Sail training for volunteer crew and trainees; sea education in marine science, maritime history, and ecology in cooperation with accredited institutions; dockside interpretation during port visits
Season: Spring, summer & fall
Designer: Tri-Coastal Marine, Inc. **Built:** 2004: Norfolk, VA, Tri-Coastal Marine, Inc.
Coast Guard certification: Sailing School Vessel (Subchapter R), Passenger Vessel (Subchapter T)
Crew: 12   **Trainees-passengers:** 42 daysails, 12 overnight
Contact: Jon Gorog, Executive Director, Virginia Maritime Heritage Foundation, 500 East Main Street, Suite 600, Norfolk, VA 23510 USA
Tel: 757-627-7400 **Fax:** 757-627-8300
E-mail: info@schoonervirginia.org
Web site: www.schoonervirginia.org

Schooner *Virginia* is a re-creation of its namesake vessel, the *Virginia*, which was the last pure sailing vessel used by the Virginia Pilot Association. Almost entirely handmade, Schooner *Virginia* is the first tall ship built on the Norfolk waterfront in nearly 80 years. After nearly two-and-a-half years under construction, the vessel was launched and christened on December 10, 2004. Schooner *Virginia* was designed using the blueprints drafted to build the original *Virginia*, which was designed along the lines of an America's Cup defender. Traditionally, pilot schooners in the area were built for speed. Through pilot service, smaller ships like schooners would assist larger vessels in navigating the notorious bay channels and waterways. Schooner *Virginia* is owned and operated by the Virginia Maritime Heritage Foundation. Her mission is three-fold and education is the primary focus. She is also a goodwill ambassador for the Commonwealth of Virginia, and is used as an economic development vehicle by providing a unique and historic venue as she visits ports up and down the Eastern seaboard.

SPECIFICATIONS

Flag: USA
Rig: Full-rigged ship
Homeport: New York, New York
Sparred length: 325'
LOD: 263'
Draft: 11' (min.), 22' (max.)
Beam: 40'
Rig height: 167'
Sail area: 31,495 square feet
Tons: 2,170 GRT
Hull: iron

WAVERTREE

Wavertree was built in Southampton, England in 1885. She was first employed to carry jute for use in making rope and burlap bags, voyaging between India and Scotland. Within two years she entered the tramp trade, taking cargoes anywhere in the world. After 25 years, she limped into the Falkland Islands in 1911, having been almost dismasted in a gale off Cape Horn. Rather than rerigging her, her owners sold her for use as a floating warehouse at Punta Arenas, Chile. *Wavertree* was converted into a sand barge at Buenos Aires, Argentina in 1947, and was acquired there by the South Street Seaport Museum in 1968 for eventual restoration to her appearance as a sailing vessel. By the time *Wavertree* was built, she was nearly obsolete, being replaced by ocean crossing steam ships. At the same time iron, long the choice of ship builders in iron-producing countries such as England, was giving way to steel. *Wavertree* was one of the last large sailing ships built of wrought iron and today is the largest afloat.

Program type: Sea education in marine science, maritime history, and ecology in cooperation with accredited schools and other groups; other education programs focused toward restoration
Built: 1885: Southampton, England, Oswald Mordaunt & Co.
Contact: South Street Seaport Museum, 12 Fulton Street New York, NY 10038 USA
Tel: 212-748-8594
Website: www.southstseaport.org

SPECIFICATIONS

Flag: USA
Rig: Square topsail sloop
Homeport: Traverse City, Michigan
Normal cruising waters:
Great Lakes
Sparred length: 87'
LOA: 55'
LWL: 49'
Draft: 7'
Beam: 16'
Rig height: 96'
Freeboard: 6'
Power: diesel
Hull: wood, plank on frame

WELCOME

Who sails: Families and adults of all ages
Program type: Sail training for volunteer crew and trainees; sea education in maritime history; overnight
passages; dockside interpretation
Season: June – October
Designer: Fred Ford
Built: 1976: Mackinaw City, MI, State of Michigan
Coast Guard certification: Moored Attraction Vessel
Crew: 5
Contact: Maritime Heritage Alliance, 322 Sixth, Traverse City, MI 49684 USA
Tel: 231-946-2647 **Fax:** 231-946-6750
E-mail: mark@MaritimeHeritageAlliance.org
Website: www.MaritimeHeritageAlliance.org

The *Welcome* is a 55-foot armed sloop, a replica of the original *Welcome* built in 1775 at Fort Michimackinac during the Revolutionary War, which later became a British military vessel. The Mackinac Island State Park Commission built *Welcome* for the 200th anniversary of Independence Day. The vessel sailed the Great Lakes for a number of years before serving as a dockside museum in Mackinac City. In December of 1992 the Maritime Heritage Alliance (MHA), a nonprofit organization located in Traverse City, MI, was awarded the vessel for reconstruction. Volunteers of the MHA, having built the schooner *Madeline*, used traditional boat building skills to restore this magnificent vessel. In 2009, *Welcome* returned to the Straits of Mackinac for the first time in 20 years, providing dockside tours and historical interpretation.

SPECIFICATIONS

Flag: USA
Rig: Staysail schooner, 2-masted
Homeport: Rockland, Maine
Normal cruising waters: North Atlantic Ocean and Caribbean Sea, Canada to South America
Sparred length: 125'
LOD: 94'
LWL: 82'
Draft: 12'
Beam: 22'
Rig height: 105'
Freeboard: 7'
Sail area: 7,000 square feet
Tons: 138 GRT
Power: 500 HP diesel
Hull: steel

WESTWARD

Owned by the Ocean Classroom Foundation, the schooner *Westward* offers programs of education undersail to the youth of America. Programs range from four month semesters-at-sea to week-long programs with schools and youth groups. Trainees sail the ship and learn traditional seamanship skills under the Captain and crew, and they explore maritime subjects with the onboard academic staff. Ocean Classroom's Discovery™ program is a semester-at-sea for qualified high school students, fully accredited by Proctor Academy. The voyage covers more than 6,000 nautical miles, connecting South American shores to the Canadian Maritimes. Students live and work as sailors on a true voyage of discovery, while they study maritime history, maritime literature, marine science, applied mathematics, and navigation. Discovery™ is offered Fall and Spring Terms. Other programs include SEAmester™, OceanBound and Summer Seafaring Camps. The Ocean Classroom Foundation also owns and operates the schooners *Harvey Gamage* and *Spirit of Massachusetts*.

Who sails: Individuals and school groups from middle school through college; affiliated institutions include Proctor Academy, University of Maine, Center for Coastal Studies, Outward Bound, and other schools
Program type: Traditional seamanship training combined with accredited academic studies
Season: Year-round
Designer: Eldridge McInnis
Built: 1961: Lemwerder, Germany, Abeking & Rasmussen
Coast Guard certification: Sailing School Vessel (Subchapter R)
Crew: 8-11 including instructors **Trainees-passengers:** 24 overnight
Contact: Executive Director, Ocean Classroom Foundation, 29 McKown Street, Boothbay Harbor, Maine 04538 USA
Tel: 800-724-7245
E-mail: mail@oceanclassroom.org
Website: www.oceanclassroom.org

SPECIFICATIONS

Flag: USA
Rig: Gaff schooner,
2-masted
Homeport: Abaco, Bahamas
Normal cruising waters:
Biscayne Bay, Florida Keys,
and Bahamas
Sparred length: 70'
LOA: 60'
LOD: 56'
LWL: 49'
Draft: 6'
Beam: 14'
Rig height: 64'
Freeboard: 6'
Sail area: 2,100 square feet
Tons: 24 GRT
Power: 140 HP GM Diesel
Hull: wood

WILLIAM H. ALBURY

Who sails: School and other groups and individuals; Affiliated institutions include Boy Scouts and schools in Abaco, Bahamas
Program type: Sail training with crew, apprentices, and paying trainees; sea education in maritime history and ecology in cooperation with accredited schools and colleges and other groups; passenger day sails and overnight passages
Built: 1964: Man o' War Cay, Abaco, Bahamas, William H. Albury
Certification: Certified by the Bahamian Port Authority
Crew: 3 **Trainees-passengers:** 30 daysails, 14 overnight
Contact: Captain Joseph A. Maggio, Marine Superintendent, Inter-Island Schooner, 3145 Virginia St., Coconut Grove, FL 33133 USA
Tel: 305-461-1938 **Fax:** 305-442-0563
E-mail: 1schooner@att.net

In an era when the Atlantic crossing is measured in hours rather than weeks and most people's occupations anchor them to a desk, counter, or workbench, Sea Exploring offers a learning-by-doing environment. Lessons of character building and teamwork apply to all facets of one's life. The Sea Explorer program requires that each trainee exerts and extends him or herself physically, morally and mentally to perform duties which contribute to the ship. The reward, over and above the experience of a world of beauty and challenge, is the satisfaction and self assurance that contributes to self-discipline. The *William H. Albury*'s Sea Explorer Program offers lessons in ecology and international cooperation, as well as history, science, literature, and art. Subject to the dictates of nature, the Sea Explorer program is adventuresome while also a developer of character and a molder of lives. The *William H. Albury* is now in its 34th year of sailing under the command of Captain Joe Maggio (recipient of the 2006 ASTA Lifetime Achievement Award) and was co-winner of the 1999 ASTA Sail Training Program of the Year Award.

SPECIFICATIONS

Flag: USA
Rig: Gaff topsail schooner, 4-masted
Homeport: Chicago, Illinois
Normal cruising waters: Great Lakes, Eastern Seaboard, and Caribbean
Sparred Length: 148'
LOA: 109'
LOD: 109'
LWL: 95'
Draft: 8' 6"
Beam: 25'
Rig height: 85'
Freeboard: 8'
Sail area: 4,839 square feet
Power: Cummins 6CTA-M 300 HP
Hull: steel

WINDY

Built as a modern interpretation of the last days of commercial sail, the *Windy* is true to function while using modern materials and safety features. In 1996, *Windy* was the first 4-masted commercial sailing vessel built since 1921. She has many features not found on older tall ships like hot showers, private bunks, a great cabin, furling topsails, as well as bowthruster, shoal draft, and wing keel. With her divided and easily managed multi-sail design, there are ample opportunities for persons of all walks of life to participate in the sailing experience. During the summer at Navy Pier, Chicago, *Windy* offer hands on sailing experiences to the public as well as private charters for corporations, weddings, team building, and private parties. *Windy* was the dockside ship used as the Schooner *Rouse Simmons*, in "The Christmas Tree Ship" documentary which was first aired on the Weather Channel in December 2004.

Who sails: 5th grade and up, adults and seniors of all ages
Season: Spring and Fall
Designer: R. Marthai
Built: 1996: Detyens Shipyard/Southern Windjammer, Ltd.
Coast Guard certification: Passenger Vessels (Subchapter T)
Crew: 4 **Trainees-passengers:** 150 daysails, 26 overnight
Contact: Captain Bruce Randall, Lakeshore Maritime Collective / Tall Ship Adventures Of Chicago, 401 E. Illinois St. Ste 332, Chicago IL 60611 USA
Tel: 312-731-9689 **Fax:** 312-222-9048
E-mail: tallshipwindy@aol.com
Website: www.tallshipwindy.com

SPECIFICATIONS

Flag: USA
Rig: Staysail Schooner
Homeport: Annapolis, Maryland
Normal cruising waters:
Chesapeake Bay
Sparred length: 74'
LOA: 61'
LOD: 61'
LWL: 51'
Draft: 7'
Beam: 16'
Rig height: 65'
Freeboard: 5'
Sail area: 1,800 square feet
Tons: 25 GRT
Power: 100 HP diesel Volvo
Hull: wood and epoxy

WOODWIND

Who sails: School groups from elementary through college, individuals of all ages
Program type: Sail training for paying trainees; informal sea education; team building (including match racing); passenger day sails and group charters; special sailing packages available
Season: April through November
Designer: John Scarano, Scarano Boat Builders **Built:** 1993: Albany, NY, Scarano Boat Builders
Coast Guard certification: Passenger Vessel (Subchapter T)
Crew: 10 **Trainees-passengers:** 48 daysails, 8 overnight
Contact: Jennifer Brest, Captain and Director of Marketing, Running Free, Inc., 1930 A Lincoln Drive, Annapolis, MD 21401 USA
Tel: 410-263-7837 **Fax:** 410-280-6952
E-mail: info@schoonerwoodwind.com
Website: www.schoonerwoodwind.com

The Schooner *Woodwind* and her sister ship the *Woodwind II* are identical 74-foot wooden schooners that sail out of Annapolis, Maryland and can accommodate up to 48 passengers each. These staysail-rigged schooners do a variety of different activities based out of the Annapolis Marriott Waterfront Hotel. The *Woodwind's* offer two hour public cruises that depart up to four times daily from downtown Annapolis and sail into the Chesapeake Bay. These schooners also offer private charters for special events, family gatherings and corporate events. One of our specialties is our team building program where the clients match race both schooners and really learn what it is like to work as a team to get around the race course (hopefully first). *Woodwind* has four staterooms where couples can stay aboard on Friday & Saturday nights including a sunset sail, accommodations, and breakfast in the morning.

SPECIFICATIONS

Flag: USA
Rig: Staysail Schooner
Homeport: Annapolis, Maryland
Normal cruising waters:
Chesapeake Bay
Sparred length: 74'
LOA: 61'
LOD: 61'
LWL: 51'
Draft: 7'
Beam: 16'
Rig height: 65'
Freeboard: 5'
Sail area: 1,800 square feet
Tons: 25 GRT
Power: 100 HP diesel, Volvo
Hull: wood and epoxy

WOODWIND II

The Schooner *Woodwind II* and her sister ship the *Woodwind* are identical 74-foot wooden schooners that sail out of Annapolis, Maryland and can accommodate up to 48 passengers each. These staysail-rigged schooners do a variety of different activities based out of the Annapolis Marriott Waterfront Hotel. The *Woodwind's* offer two hour public cruises that depart up to four times daily from downtown Annapolis and sail into the Chesapeake Bay. These schooners also offer private charters for special events, family gatherings and corporate events. One of our specialties is our team building program where the clients match race both schooners and really learn what it is like to work as a team to get around the race course (hopefully first). In mid-October, there are four cabins available to cruise the Chesapeake for five days on a one-way cruise from Norfolk, Virginia to Annapolis, Maryland. All meals, instruction, accommodations, sailing lore and plenty of lighthouse history are included on this 130-mile journey.

Who sails: School groups from elementary through college, individuals of all ages
Program type: Sail training for paying trainees; informal sea education; team building (including match racing); passenger day sails and group charters; special sailing packages available
Season: April through November
Designer: John Scarano, Scarano Boat Builders **Built:** 1998: Albany, NY, Scarano Boat Builders
Coast Guard certification: Passenger Vessel (Subchapter T)
Crew: 10 **Trainees-passengers:** 48 daysails, 8 overnight
Contact: Jennifer Brest, Captain and Director of Marketing, Running Free, Inc., 1930 A Lincoln Drive, Annapolis, MD 21401 USA
Tel: 410-263-7837 **Fax:** 410-280-6952
E-mail: info@schoonerwoodwind.com
Website: www.schoonerwoodwind.com

SPECIFICATIONS

Flag: USA
Rig: Topsail schooner
Homeport: Miami, Florida
Sparred length: 78'
LOD: 62' 6"
LWL: 50'
Draft: 6'
Beam: 17' 6"
Rig height: 64'
Sail area: 2,500 square feet
Tons: 44 GRT
Power: Ford Lehman 120
Hull: steel

YANKEE

Who sails: All aboard
Program type: Sailing Charters in Miami, FL, corporate charters, teambuilding, pirate cruising. Arrg!!, sight sailing, weddings, family gatherings, parties, hands-on sail training, overnight cruises.
Coast Guard certification: Passenger Vessel (Subchapter T)
Crew: 3 Trainees-passengers: 48 daysails, 20 overnight
Contact: John Watson, 830 Euclid Ave #1 Miami Beach, FL 33139 USA
Tel: 401-862-9101
E-mail: coolschooner@yahoo.com
Website: www.coolschooneryankee.com

Yankee is a replica of a 1880s privateer. She is a 78-foot topsail schooner, with wide decks and comfortable seating. Her motion on the bays around Miami is gentle, but she really sails. Food and drinks are easily prepared in her large galley. *Yankee* is also available for overnight charters. She has many private staterooms and bathrooms. She is Coast Guard certified to take out 48 passengers for the day and 20 overnight. Customize your party or experience around us.

SPECIFICATIONS

Flag: USA
Rig: Ketch
Homeport: Seattle, Washington
Normal cruising waters:
Puget Sound and the San Juan and
Gulf Islands
Sparred length: 54'
LOD: 44'
LWL: 42'
Draft: 4' 6"
Beam: 11'
Rig height: 50'
Freeboard: 2'
Sail area: 1,000 square feet
Tons: 14 GRT
Power: Cummins J-130, 100
Hull: wood

YANKEE CLIPPER

A familiar sight through Puget Sound and the San Juan Islands, the Gaff Ketch *Yankee Clipper* has been training young men and women in the ways of the sea since 1950. Based out of West Seattle, the *Yankee Clipper* carries on the Sea Scout program started in 1930 and its new year-round youth maritime training program. Youth in the Sea Scout Program meet weekly to learn basic seafaring skills and take part in the Scout program. The *Yankee Clipper* has been a supporter of the ecology of the Duwamish River by providing historical and environmental interpretive tours on the river, emphasizing water quality pollution, and shoreside industry. During the tours, emphasis has been placed on protecting fish and wildlife while educating and collecting scientific data. Participants in the program learn about water safety and the opportunity to handle several types of small boats. Confidence is gained by experience and many find lifetime careers and a deep love and respect for the sea.

Who sails: Youth in the Sea Scout program
Program type: Sail training and maritime history, environmental education
Season: Year-round
Designer: US NAVY / Carl Nyberg
Built: 1941
Crew: 4 **Trainees-passengers:** 18 daysails, 10 overnight
Contact: Daniel Joram, Executive Director, Yankee Clipper Foundation, 2226 Eastlake Ave. East, # 97, Seattle, WA 98102 USA
Tel: 206-947-6199
E-mail: info@tallshiptraining.org
Website: www.tallshiptraining.org

SPECIFICATIONS

Flag: Australia
Rig: Brigantine
Homeport: Sydney, Australia
Sparred length: 144' 6"
Draft: 13'
Beam: 25' 6"
Hull: steel

YOUNG ENDEAVOUR

Program type: Sail training vessel
Built: 1987
Crew: 9 **Trainees-passengers:** 24
Contact: Embassy of Australia, 1601
Massachusetts Avenue, NW, Washington, DC
20036 USA
Tel: 202-797-3000 **Fax:** 202-797-3168

Given by the United Kingdom to the government and people of Australia in celebration of that country's bicentenary, *Young Endeavour* serves as Australia's national sail training vessel. She was dedicated with the words of Prime Minister Robert Hawke, "This ship – *Young Endeavour* – bears a name imperishably linked with Captain Cook's great voyage of discovery. And the name itself expresses a great deal of our aspirations for our country." For a land surrounded by the sea, this brigantine is a reminder of the country's maritime heritage. *Young Endeavour's* arrival in Sydney also heralded the start of a new era of sail training in Australia. *Young Endeavour* sails with a permanent crew of nine from the Royal Australian Navy and hosts a coeducational crew of 24 young people. Each year *Young Endeavor* provides hundreds of youngsters with the opportunity to participate in one of twenty ten-day voyages off the Australian coast.

SPECIFICATIONS

Flag: Cook Islands
Rig: Gaff ketch with a yard for square sail and raffee
Homeport: Avatui, Rarotonga, Cook Islands, South Pacific Ocean
Normal cruising waters: Cook Islands and central South Pacific
LOA: 130'
Draft: 14'
Beam: 26'
Rig height: 115'
Freeboard: 6'
Sail area: 7,500 square feet
Tons: 298 GRT
Cargo: General goods, foodstuffs, frozen goods, building and gardening supplies, marine supplies, fishing gear, dry goods, medical and educational supplies.
Power: 900 HP Deutz Diesel
Hull: steel

ZEBROID

The *Zebroid* is an auxiliary-sail passenger/cargo trading vessel established to carry cargo, freight, inter-island passengers, trade in supplies and goods, and carry out medical and government missions in the South Pacific Islands and other remote tropical routes. In addition to her staff crew and passengers, this ship will reserve berths for six apprentices training to become advanced professional seafarers. In their extended period aboard, the apprentices will receive instruction and experience in all ship's departments, learn about all aspects of ship's operations applicable to this and other ships, and become well-rounded and broadly-experienced mariners. This apprenticeship is specifically aimed at young people who have sailed previously in sea education programs or who have had a start in other vessels or other marine experiences and can also benefit those seeking an increase in tonnage or scope. Voyage routes will primarily be within the Cook Islands in the mid South Pacific, sailing from Rarotonga for Aitutaki, Mangaia, Atiu, Puka Puka, Manihiki, Mauke,Tongareva, Rakahanga, Mitiaro, Palmerston and Suwarrow with occasional voyages to Samoa, Fiji and Tahiti.

Who sails: Young mariners seeking to advance and increase their skill levels and broaden their deep-sea and tropical island sailing experience.
Program type: professional vocational maritime training under sail
Season: Year-round
Designer: Hull: George T. Davie & Sons Ltd, Quebec; Rig and layout: D. Moreland - Master Steam, Motor and Sail, any gross tons, oceans
Built: 1963
Crew: 8 **Apprentices:** 6 **Passengers:** 29
Contact: Dawson Moreland & Associates, P.O. Box 1076, Lunenburg, Nova Scotia, B0J 2C0 Canada
E-mail: tradingundersail@gmail.com

SPECIFICATIONS

Flag: Belgium
Rig: Bermuda ketch
Homeport: Zeebruge, Belgium
Sparred length: 93'
Draft: 8' 6"
Beam: 22' 6"
Rig height: 105'
Hull: wood

ZENOBE GRAMME

Program type: Training vessel of the Belgian Navy
Built: 1961
Contact: Embassy of Belgium, 3330 Garfield Street, NW, Washington, DC 20008 USA
Tel: 202-333-6900 **Fax:** 202-333-3079

Serving first as a coastal survey ship, *Zenobe Gramme* is now a training ship for the Belgian Navy. She is a frequent participant in sail training races and gatherings and is easily recognizable when she set her spinnaker which displays the Belgian royal coat-of-arms. *Zenobe Gramme* is named for the Belgian inventor who perfected the technology for alternating-current motors and generators in the 1860s and 1870s.

SPECIFICATIONS

Flag: USA
Rig: Gaff schooner, 2-masted
Homeport: Seattle, Washington
Normal cruising waters: Puget Sound, San Juan Islands, Canadian Gulf Islands
Sparred length: 160'
LOA: 127'
LWL: 101'
Draft: 16'
Beam: 26'
Rig height: 127'
Freeboard: 5'
Sail area: 7,000 square feet
Tons: 147 GRT
Power: diesel
Hull: wood

ZODIAC

Listed on the National Register of Historic Places since 1982, the *Zodiac* is the largest working schooner on the West Coast. Lovingly restored, she now sails with up to 49 passengers through the waters of Puget Sound, the San Juan Islands, and on international trips to Canada (SOLAS certified). A variety of one to ten day cruises include education and recreation and provide passengers with hands-on sail training, maritime programs, and shore explorations. There is an emphasis on natural resources, the environment and recycling. Built 1924 in Maine, the *Zodiac* was a luxury yacht for the Johnson and Johnson pharmaceutical heirs. She explored the Arctic and sailed in the 1928 transatlantic race. The San Francisco Bar Pilots bought her in 1931, renamed her *California,* and sailed her off the Golden Gate for more than 40 years. Retired in 1972, the schooner has been restored to her original sail plan and given back her maiden name. Her mission is now to help young sailors advance with their Coast Guard licenses, maintain herself as a national maritime treasure, and introduce traditional sailing skills to the public.

Who sails: Schools; families, groups, and adults of all ages
Program type: Sail training for schools, groups and individuals; deckhand internships; private charters; some day-sails.
Season: March to November
Designer: William Hand, Jr.
Built: 1924: East Boothbay, ME, Hodgdon Brothers
Coast Guard certification: Passenger Vessel (Subchapter T)
Crew: 8 **Trainees-passengers:** 49 daysails, 26 overnight
Contact: Captain Tim Mehrer, Vessel Zodiac Corporation, 3 Strawberry Point, Bellingham WA 98229 USA
Tel: 206.696.4556
E-mail: richard@schoonerzodiac.com
Website: www.schoonerzodiac.com

Affiliate Members

Non-profit organizations which do not own or operate vessels but do offer sail training or sea education programs (Scouts, schools, colleges, museums etc.)

ActionQuest/ActionSail Programs

For over 30 years, ActionQuest has been providing high quality, expedition-based summer programs for teenagers. ActionQuest voyages focus on sailing, scuba diving, cultural immersion, marine biology and global exploration – all in a live-aboard environment unlike any other. Through hands-on experiential learning and exceptional global expeditions, ActionQuest challenges young adults with high action, life-changing adventures that promote personal growth, teamwork and leadership. Choose from voyage offerings in the British Virgin Islands, the Caribbean's Leeward Islands, the Mediterranean, Galapagos, Australia or Tahiti and French Polynesia.

ActionQuest also offers Lifeworks community service summer programs for teens and Sea-mester Programs for college students and high school graduates. Living full-time aboard our traditional schooners and sailing through extraordinary destinations that span the globe, Sea-mester teaches accredited academics unconfined by the four walls of a traditional classroom.

ActionQuest
Mike Meighan and Captain James M. Stoll
PO Box 5517, Sarasota, FL 34277 USA
Tel: 941-924-6789 or 800-317-6789
Fax: 941-924-6075
E-mail: info@actionquest.com
Website: www.actionquest.com

Algonac-Clay Township Historical Society

The "Hospitality Port" of the Great Lakes
N.42 deg. 37' 09.43", W 82 deg 31' 45.50"

Algonac is on the St. Clair River between Lake St. Clair and Lake Huron. Our museum is located in the Waterfront Park that features more than 2,200 feet of riverside boardwalk.

Tall ships have enjoyed our Hospitality Port with sufficient water depth, easy docking and convenience of stores within walking distance. We can arrange fueling, pump outs, fresh water, land showers, boat repair, transportation. A Port of Entry is located next to the museum.

In 2001, we hosted 17 tall ships at our boardwalk at one time as part of the American Sail Training Association's Great Lakes TALL SHIPS CHALLENGE® Race Series. We have welcomed the *Bluenose II, Picton Castle, Niagara, Pride of Baltimore II, Europa, Nina*, Coast Guard Cutters and many others. If dock side tours or day cruising are available, we will advertise and sell tickets. Some ships have stopped in for a quick trip to the grocery store or a Dairy Queen across the street, changing of crewmembers or passengers, or a safe haven for inclement weather.

Algonac-Clay Township Historical Society
1240 St. Clair River Drive, Algonac, MI 48001 USA
Tel: 810-794-9015
E-mail: achs@algonac-clay-history.com
Website: www.algonac-clay-history.com

Golden Gate Tall Ships Society

The Golden Gate Tall Ship Society (GGTSS) is a California nonprofit organization dedicated to educating people in nautical skills and supporting the preservation and operation of traditional sailing vessels, particularly tall ships.

Goals and strategies include:
• Provide opportunities for sail training experiences for young people
• Provide sailing and shipboard education for members
• Support shore-side education
• Support tall ship visiting San Francisco Bay

Golden Gate Tall Ships Society provides scholarships for young people aboard tall ships, including high school students in San Francisco.

Golden Gate Tall Ship Society
PO Box 926, Sausalito, CA 94966 USA
Tel: 415-332-6990
E-mail: info@ggtss.org
Website: www.ggtss.org

Istanbul Turkish Chamber of Shipping

" Maritime Nation Maritime Country "

Turkish Chamber of Shipping is an important professional institution of the Turkish maritime sector established with a view to improving the maritime business for the public benefit in compliance with the national transportation and maritime policies as well as to meeting the mutual needs and ensuring the further development of this line of business.

Turkish Chamber of Shipping
Meclis-i Mebusan Cad. No:22 Fındıklı / Istanbul, Turkey
Tel: +90 212 252 01 30 (8 Line) Fax: +90 212 293 79 35
E-Mail: dto@denizticaretodasi.org or dto@chamber-of-shipping.org.tr
Website: www.denizticaretodasi.org

Landing School of Boatbuilding and Design

Established in 1978 and located in Kennebunkport, Maine, The Landing School of Boatbuilding and Design is a non-profit post-secondary career school dedicated to providing the highest quality vocational education in boatbuilding, yacht design, and marine systems technology available. The School was created to provide a gateway to the marine industry for students seeking career opportunities in the marine trades focusing on both recreational and commercial watercraft in both power and sail. The Landing School's ability to reinforce and preserve traditional skills and knowledge while advancing the art and science of boat design, construction, outfitting and repair through the integration of modern techniques and contemporary materials is recognized and valued throughout the marine industry. Our school has earned an international reputation for program quality, and, as an educational institution, is considered by many in the marine industry to be unequaled. The graduates and hundreds of alumni of the school are highly sought after for their craftsmanship, productivity, work ethic, and passion for their chosen careers in, on, and around boats.

Landing School of Boatbuilding and Design
PO Box 1490, Kennebunkport, Maine 04046 USA
Tel: 207-985-7976 Fax: 207-985-7942
E-mail: landingschool@cybertours.com
Website: www.landingschool.org

Lewes Chamber of Commerce

Welcome to "the First Town in the First State!"

Lewes, Delaware is located where the Delaware Bay and the Atlantic Ocean meet, which is referred to as Cape Henlopen. The beauty of Cape Henlopen is vast abroad Lewes. From the Cape Henlopen State Park, to the Historic District to the beautiful beaches, trails and sanctuaries, the shore beauty and charm exists.

Lewes is a quaint, charming walking town, that contains a beautiful Historic district, historical museums, historic inns and bed and breakfasts, refined restaurants, and a variety of fine shops.

Lewes County Chamber of Commerce
120 Kings Highway. Lewes, DE 19958 USA
Tel: 302-645-8073 Toll-Free 877-465-3937
Fax: 302-645-8412
Website: www.leweschamber.com

Manhattan Sailing School

Manhattan Sailing School is the largest and most respected such organization operating in the New York Harbor. Our instructors are trained professionals who specialize in communicating the concepts of sailing in a relaxed and informative manner. It's easy and fun to learn to sail!

Manhattan Sailing School
385 South End Ave #7G, New York, NY 10280 USA
Tel: 212-786-0400 Fax: 212-786-1743
E-mail: info@sailmanhattan.com
Website: www.sailmanhattan.com

Maritime Pirates

Founded in the mythological year of 1699.... In reality was created in 1998 in the little seaside port of Greenport, Long Island, New York. This is a theatrical family friendly enterprise. The motto of the Maritime Pirates is "The Greatest Treasure Of All Is A Heart Of Gold". Programs include: invasions, stage shows, interactive kids shows, seasonal shows, sails programs and educational "camp" style curriculums. Core materials are of all original content, songs, scripts and themes. The purpose of the franchise is to present ideas which promote good character development, social values and elements of maritime culture. All are Boces approved for Arts In Education and PARP Parents And Reading Partnership. Now a proud member of ASTA - American Sail Training Association. We are also host to the Pirate Day Festival on Long Island. AND REMEMBER: It takes honesty, faith, love, humility, courage and a heart of gold to be a good hearted pirate... to be a Maritime Pirate!

Maritime Pirates
P.O. Box 863, Southold, NY 11971 USA
Tel: 631-765-6235
E-mail: info@maritimepirates.com
Website: www.MaritimePirates.com

 # Maryland School of Sailing & Seamanship

The Maryland School of Sailing & Seamanship offers a full range of courses from Basic Sailing through Ocean Training Cruises on Island Packet yachts in Chesapeake Bay, Virgin Islands and the Atlantic Ocean between Mystic, CT, Bermuda, Norfolk, VA, and the Caribbean. Also Celestial and Coastal Navigation classes and Docking Practice classes. Students can earn certification from the American Sailing Association (ASA). The Maryland School of Sailing & Seamanship boasts an impressive staff of offshore-savvy instructors and is notable for its high level of organization and dedication to real ocean sailing.

Maryland School of Sailing & Seamanship
PO Box 6, Railroad, PA 17355 USA
Tel: 410-639-7030 Fax: 717-235-0908
E-mail: office@mdschool.com
Website: www.mdschool.com

Northwest School of Wooden Boatbuilding

The Northwest School of Wooden Boatbuilding, located on the Olympic Peninsula of Washington State, has been teaching the marine trades since 1981. Nationally accredited by ACCSCT, the School grants diplomas and degrees in both traditional and modern wooden boatbuilding techniques, with specialization in yacht interiors and restoration work. Other marine trades taught at the school include sailmaking, rigging, blacksmithing, boat design, and systems. Many tall ship crew members have attended the school and remain active members of our alumni. A boat school education can make you an even more valuable member of your crew and will be one of the most memorable years of your life.

Northwest School of Wooden Boatbuilding
42 N. Water Street Port Hadlock, WA 98339 USA
Tel: 360-385-4948 Fax: 360-385-5089
Website: www.nwboatschool.org

Save the Bay - Narragansett Bay, RI

Save The Bay was founded on the community's desire to protect our most precious resource - Narragansett Bay. To do that, Save The Bay has focused on the development of a committed constituency for the Bay. Children and adults throughout this region have learned the tremendous value the Bay brings to our economy, our environment and our quality of life.

Save The Bay has watched over the activities and programs of the government and the citizenry that degrade the environmental quality of the Bay, basin, and watershed, providing educational opportunities for children and adults to explore the Bay and, fostering understanding and a sense of personal responsibility for the resource.

Save The Bay's history is one of accomplishment. Once choked by raw sewage and dying a slow death from industrial toxins, the Bay is now making a comeback. There is still room for vast improvement, but more people than ever before are able to swim, fish, sail and enjoy the waters of Narragansett Bay.

Save The Bay Center
100 Save The Bay Drive, Providence, RI 02905 USA
Tel: 401-272-3540 or 1-800-NARRBAY Fax: 401-273-7153
Website: www.savebay.org

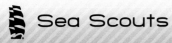 Sea Scouts

Sea Scouting promotes better citizenship and improves members' boating skills and knowledge through instruction and practice in water safety, outdoor, social, and service experiences, and knowledge of our maritime heritage. The program fosters self-esteem as the youth share responsibility for the upkeep of boats and equipment; and the value of teamwork, an important life lesson, receives emphasis every time the boats are underway where the actions of one impacts the safety and well-being of all. Each ship has a unique program designed and implemented by its youth members. Basically, if it is an activity about, on, in, under or through the water, Sea Scouts are involved.

Sea Scouts were organized in 1912 as a "new branch of Boy Scouts of America." The purpose was to serve older boys who were interested in the lore of the sea. Sea Scouting became co-ed in 1968, and since that time, the program has continued to grow nationally and internationally. Today's program provides adventure on land and sea and serves youth ages 14 to 21.

Charles Holmes
National Director Venturing Division
Boy Scouts of America
1325 Walnut Hill Lane, Irving, Texas 75015-2079 USA
Tel: 972-580-2425
Website: www.seascout.org

SeaStar Society

The SEASTAR Society is a Nova Scotia based, non-profit society established to advance young Nova Scotia's through the development of life skills and experience aboard tall ships.

The society is committed to fostering inclusiveness and diversity in its activities, through engaging youth from varied social, economic, ethnic and ability backgrounds.

E-mail: info@seastarsociety.ca
Website: www.seastarsociety.ca

Tall Ship Education Academy

TSEA combines an exciting curriculum with the challenges of living at sea and learning to sail. Our students have sailed within San Francisco Bay, along the coast of Baja, and through the Caribbean while developing life skills and engaging in studies that earn them high school credit. Our cornerstone program, the Tall Ship Semester for Girls is an innovative high school program that combines a strong academic curriculum with experiential learning.

The semester breaks into three six-week phases: first, students attend academic classes in our classroom on the San Francisco State University campus. Second, students sail aboard a traditionally rigged sailing vessel and visit foreign countries and third, students participate in internships in San Francisco businesses.

In addition to the semester program, we offer other sail training experiences for youth of all ages.

Tall Ship Education Academy
c/o RLS Dept, 1600 Holloway Ave., San Francisco, CA 94132-4161 USA
Tel: 415-405-3703 Fax: 415-338-0543
E-mail: info@tallshipsemester.org
Website: www.tallshipsemester.org

Yorktown Foundation

Riverwalk Landing is a beautiful waterfront development designed in the spirit of colonial architecture reflected in the town's historic buildings. It features a variety of fine retail shops as well as a conveniently located two-tier 270-space parking terrace. The restored historic Freight Shed may be reserved for small receptions and meetings. The waterfront also features a performance area, an inviting beach and two floating piers – one to support larger vessels such as regional cruise ships and visiting tall ships, and the other for smaller personal watercraft. The pier has more than 1,000 feet of dock frontage and electrical, water, telephone, and sewer pump out hookups all provided pier side. A mile-long pedestrian riverwalk links Yorktown's major attractions and provides exquisite views of the York River. Benches lining the walk offer visitors the chance to sit and admire the natural beauty of the York River. A free trolley runs daily, spring through fall, offering many stops throughout town and arrives approximately every 20 minutes to each stop. On many weekends throughout the year, visitors can enjoy live entertainment.

The Yorktown Foundation is a non-profit organization dedicated to preserve and perpetuate the special historic character of Yorktown (site of the last major battle of the American Revolutionary War in 1781).

Dennis Nate, Dockmaster
Riverwalk Landing, 425 Water Street, PO Box 219, Yorktown, VA 23690 USA
Tel: 757-890-3370
E-mail: dockmaster@yorkcounty.gov
Website: www.riverwalklanding.com

US Naval Sea Cadets of RI

The U.S. Naval Sea Cadets of Rhode Island is a federally-sponsored association for teenagers and pre-teens (age 11 through 17), who have or desire ambition, self-discipline, and a strong academic background. Our primary mission is to instill in Rhode Island youth a desire to succeed as individuals and citizens, beginning with a solid foundation for building academic and social skills, teamwork, and critical thinking.

Our goals include:
- Develop in our youth an appreciation for Naval History, traditions, customs, and their role in national defense.
- Develop in our youth a sense of pride in our nation, positive qualities of patriotism, courage and self-reliance, confidence and strong moral character, and good citizenship traits.
- Develop in our youth an interest and skill in seamanship, seagoing, and aviation subjects. Increase the advancement potential of Cadets who may later elect to serve in the Navy, Marine Corps, Coast Guard or Merchant Marines.

US Naval Sea Cadets of Rhode Island
David R. Kerwood, President
35 Belver Avenue, Suite 001, North Kingstown, RI 02852 USA
Tel: 401-932-2396 Fax: 206-666-3422
E-mail: contact@riseacadets.org
Website: www.riseacadets.org

Business Partner Members

Organizations, corporations, businesses and ports which do not own or operate a vessel or offer sail training or sea education programs but which do support sail training and the ASTA mission.

Allen Agency

Navigate the complexities of marine insurance with help from the professionals at Allen Insurance/Financial in Camden, Maine. The Marine Division custom tailors insurance programs for vessels of all sizes.

Allen Insurance/Financial's Gene McKeever and Rick Bagnall are among the world's leaders in tall ship insurance. We are the exclusive endorsed insurance agency of ASTA, providing new, unique and improved coverages for ASTA members and their crews, including crew health insurance. Meeting your Marine insurance needs is what we do.

You lead an independent lifestyle. You want things done well, and done right, the first time. Pride of place and pride of profession: that's the Allen Insurance/Financial way.

Global expertise. Hometown service. Allow us to navigate life's risk & rewards with you, to the port you call home.

Established in 1866, Allen Insurance/Financial is an independent, employee-owned company with 64 employees.

Contact us:

Eric (Rick) Bagnall: rbagnall@allenAFG.com
Barbara Murray: bmurray@allenafg.com
Gene McKeever: gmckeever@allenagency.com
Rebecca Robinson: brobinson@allenagency.com
Toll free # 800-439-4311
Website: www.allenagency.com/insurance/

Artinium Design, Inc.

Artinium Design, Inc. is a full service creative communications company, that offers the services, talent, and skills you need to drive your business forward. Our marketing and creativity is on target, because we use strategies developed in partnership, by working with and listening to our clients. We're energetic, fun and versatile, which enables us to get any project done, just the way you want it, in the right amount of time.

Founded in 2002 by Head Honcho Darren Marinelli, Artinium's offices are located at 1525 Old Louisquisset Pike, Lincoln, RI, in the heart of Lincoln Woods. With a BFA in Graphic Design from Rhode Island College, Darren brings over 12 years of design experience to Artinium.

Since its inception, Artinium has provided unique and professional advertising, graphic design and web development services to numerous clients in the Northeast, Mid-Atlantic and on the West Coast. Some of our exciting clients are Consumer Reports Magazine, Babson College, Dartmouth College, The City of Warwick, American Sail Training Association and the Department of Fish and Wildlife Marine Fisheries.

Our services include:

~Advertising~logos~brochures~website design & development~
~email marketing~banner ads~trade show graphics~

Artinium Design, Inc.
Darren Marinelli
1525 Old Louisquisset Pike, Building C . Suite 205, Lincoln, RI 02865 USA
Tel: 401.729.1997
E-mail: darren@artiniuminc.com
www.artiniuminc.com

Blue Ocean Events

Formed in 2008, Blue Ocean Events works with communities in Atlantic Canada and along the New England Coast to develop their inherent maritime heritage and culture for sustainable economic development. Long a fan of Tall Ships and Heritage Vessels, company principal David Jones was inspired by his experience project managing TALL SHIPS CHALLENGE® 2007 in Halifax and seven other ports in Nova Scotia. Services offered include strategic planning, program development and vessel readiness review for ports; Canadian Government Regulation consultation for both ports and vessels; and Coasting Trade license applications for vessels in Canada.

David Jones
Blue Ocean Events
Tel: (902) 483-8515
E-mail: davidjones@ns.sympatico.ca

Boothbay Harbor Shipyard

Boothbay Harbor Shipyard, formerly Sample's Shipyard, was founded more than 135 years ago. Continuing a local shipbuilding tradition, the yard specializes in the maritime skills and trades that made New England famous. Its 700-ton marine railway has braced tall ships, tugboats, fishing trawlers, Coast Guard vessels and other service craft such as passenger boats and ferries. The 150-ton railway has accommodated sailing yachts, workboats, schooners and motor vessels. Conveniently located at the head of Boothbay Harbor in mid-coast Maine, the shipyard offers a complete range of marine-related repairs and services for all vessel types. The 700-ton railway can haul vessels up to 200-feet, and our skilled labor is available for new building, restoration and repairs in steel and wood. We take pride in doing top-quality work quickly and efficiently.

Boothbay Harbor Shipyard
120 Commercial Street, PO Box 462,
Boothbay Harbor, Maine 04538
Tel: 207-633-3171 Fax: 207-633-3824
E-mail: info@boothbayharborshipyard.com
Website: www.bbhshipyard.com

Channel Islands Harbor Department

The Channel Islands Harbor, owned by the County of Ventura, is located 60 miles north of Los Angeles, halfway between Los Angeles and Santa Barbara. The harbor is best known for it's year round events and gateway to a wilderness playground, the Channel Islands National Park. Called the "gateway" to the Channel Islands because of its proximity, the harbor is the perfect location from which to take day or extended trips. Located in a picturesque setting, the harbor is home to nine full-service marinas with more than 2,600 boat slips, three nautically themed shopping centers, yacht clubs, more than a dozen restaurants with spectacular views, a year round water taxi, a weekly Farmers' Market, a waterfront hotel and a variety of shops and services. The harbor is home to one of the country's finest maritime collections housed at the Ventura County Maritime Museum located at Fisherman's Wharf. The museum is a cultural center dedicated to the interpretation of maritime history through interactive exhibits and educational outreach.

The Channel Islands hosts several annual events including Celebration of the Whales, Fireworks by the Sea, Concerts by the Sea, Ventura County Boat Show, Ventura Vintage Rods Harbor Run, Channel Islands Harbor Seafood Festival and Parade of Lights.

The Channel Islands Harbor was proud to become a host port for the ASTA TALL SHIPS CHALLENGE® Race Series in 2005 and 2008.

Michele Gilmour, Marketing Director, County of Ventura
Channel Islands Harbor Department
3900 Pelican Way, Oxnard, CA 93035 USA
Tel: 805-382-3013 Fax: 805-382-3015
E-mail: michele.gilmour@ventura.org
Website: www.channelislandsharbor.org

Classic Yacht Models

Rob Eddy has been building models all his life. Starting with building Revelle plastic models, to die-cast automobiles kits, and later on constructing custom models of yachts and architectural display models. Aside from the many self-taught skills, Rob's work focuses on the overall job, documentation of the vessel, drafting, computer design, and wood and metal working.

Flawlessly detailed and perfectly scaled, the custom boat models of Robert H. Eddy have earned him a place among the masters of a most demanding art. A skilled draftsman, Eddy spends thousands of hours on each one of his recreations, first personally examining a client's vessel inch by inch, then meticulously recapturing its every nuance in wood, silver, and gold. The results are museum-quality models with an elegance and flair that make them works of art.

Robert H. Eddy & Associates
19 Neillehaven Drive, Camden, Maine 04843 USA
Tel: 207-236-6579
E-mail: reddy@yachtmodels.com
Website: www.yachtmodels.com

Eastern Salt Company

Eastern Salt is a family-owned business operating on Boston Harbor in the City of Chelsea. We are Massachusetts' leading importer of road salt, and are able to accommodate all sizes and types of vessels, from tall ships to tankers. Located in a designated port area, our facility is a five-acre site with a low-water depth of 40 feet. The City of Chelsea has always played an important role in the maritime history of Massachusetts, and we at Eastern believe in continuing to connect the citizens of Chelsea with her working ports. To celebrate the relationship of community to ocean, Eastern Salt welcomes tall ships to our dock each summer for community groups, schools, and neighbors to tour.

Paul Lamb
Eastern Salt Company, 37 Marginal Street, Chelsea, Massachusetts, USA
Tel: 617-884-5201

Great Lakes Marketing Group

Great Lakes Marketing Group, works to bring both ships to ports and ports to ships throughout the Great Lakes. Our goal is to provide ships with a constant audience, while helping the community to develop long-term waterfront programs. These opportunities may include student, community and environmental education programs, waterfront festival development, grants and sponsorship recruitment. Through strategic marketing and communications, and as liaison between ships and ports, Great Lakes Marketing integrates mutually successful port visits.

Since 1998, Great Lakes Marketing has worked with over 25 vessels including the U.S. Brig *Niagara* (2002, 2004, 2008), HMS *Bounty* (2004, 2007 (England)) and *Pride of Baltimore II* (2008). We have produced or co-produced maritime festivals throughout the Great Lakes including Chicago (1998, 2000, 2007), Kenosha, WI (2003, 2004), Cleveland, OH (2000, 2001, 2003, 2007) and Green Bay (2007).Great Lakes Marketing has been an integral participant in the American Sail Training Association's Great Lakes TALL SHIPS CHALLENGE® Series, recruiting local and international vessels, ship hosting, volunteer training, and port festival development.

Patricia Lock
Marketing Strategist for Ports & Ships
Great Lakes Marketing Group
Tel: 847-274-2475
E-mail: pattilock@aol.com

Great Lakes United

Great Lakes United is an international coalition dedicated to preserving and restoring the Great Lakes-St. Lawrence River ecosystem. Great Lakes United is made up of member organizations representing environmentalists, conservationists, hunters and anglers, labor unions, community groups, and citizens of the United States, Canada, and First Nations and Tribes.

Great Lakes United develops and promotes effective policy initiatives, carries out education programs, and promotes citizen action and grassroots leadership to assure clean water and clean air for all, better safeguards to protect the health of people and wildlife and a conservation ethic that will leave a healthy Great Lakes.

Great Lakes United
c/o Daemen College
4380 Main Street, Amherst, NY 14226 USA
Tel: 216- 886-0142 Fax: 716-204-9521
E-mail: glu@glu.org
Website: www.glu.org

Kenosha Days of Discovery

Kenosha Days of Discovery is made possible through collaborative efforts between the City of Kenosha and two local, not-for-profit organizations:

The Kenosha Days of Discovery Foundation was established in 2002. The foundation is a 501(c)(3) corporation dedicated to developing resources to provide Kenosha's youth with sail-training opportunities leading to increased nautical and scientific knowledge, increased self-esteem, development of teamwork and leadership skills, and greater intercultural understanding.

The Kiwanis Club of Western Kenosha also dedicates its fund raising efforts to provide a better quality of life for our area's youth, elderly and disadvantage through programs such as Terrific Kids, Babe Ruth Baseball Program, and the Shalom Center. Club members play a vital role in the planning and staffing of Kenosha Days of Discovery.

Kenosha Days of Discovery is proud to have the support of the Kenosha Yacht Club. The KYC plays an essential role in providing port services to the ships and crew, as well as volunteer staff to assist visitors boarding the ships.

Kenosha Days of Discovery
P.O. Box 594, Kenosha, WI 53141-0594 USA
Tel: 262-653-4460 Fax: 262-654-0882
E-mail: Info@kenoshadaysofdiscovery.com
Website: www.kenoshadaysofdiscovery.com

MedAire

When an illness or injury strikes, MedAire is there. We train crews to recognize and manage events, ensure your vessel is outfitted with life-saving equipment and offer the MedLink service, a 24/7 medical lifeline. Sailing, on holiday, or preparing for a trip, we offer attentive account service and unmatched capabilities:

Assistance:
Medical advice/direction from emergency care doctors
Referrals to 44,000 credentialed doctors and dentists
Access International SOS clinics
Evacuation and repatriation assistance
Online travel/medical information for 200 destinations

Equipment:
Medical kits are continuously enhanced, based on data gleaned from more than 120,000 emergency medical cases
Flexible refurbishment or replacement options for managing expirables

Training:
Learn to prevent, recognize and manage medical incidents
Train on the vessel or at approved training centers per regulations
Practice CPR, using an AED, contacting MedLink and accessing MedAire kits

An International SOS company, MedAire is the only maritime specialist in the world that provides a complete in-house medical solution. ASTA members will receive these special discounts:
- 20% off MedLink remote medical advisory
- 15% off MedAire's Maritime Medical Kits

Let us customize a solution for you!
E-mail: MedLinkYachts@MedAire.com
Tel: 480-333-3700

Norfolk Festevents

Founded in 1977, Norfolk Festevents originated as an all volunteer organization dedicated to producing an annual waterfront and maritime festival - Norfolk Harborfest. Since then, Norfolk Festevents has evolved into a major East Coast event production company, producing over 80 waterfront events, festivals and concerts annually, as well as serves as the managing agency for the City of Norfolk for tall ship visits and related maritime projects.

Norfolk Festevents, Ltd
Karen Scherberger, Executive Director
120 W. Main Street, Norfolk, VA 23510 USA
Tel: 757441-2345 Fax: 757441-5198
E-mail: scherbergerk@festevents.org
Website: www.festevents.org

 # Piscataqua Maritime Commission

The PMC is a non-profit community organization dedicated to promoting awareness and education of the New Hampshire seacoast's rich maritime history through tall ship port calls. Proceeds from ship tours and marketing fund a variety of sail training scholarships for area students and other educational programs. Ships visit for at least a three day weekend anytime between April and October.

With over two decades of experience successfully hosting tall ships annually, the PMC Board and hundreds of PMC members and volunteers make a port call not only a regional event for residents, but also the ship, captain, and crew. Vessels are berthed with the enthusiastic support of the NH Dept. of Ports and Harbors, at docks with full facilities and 24 hour security.

The PMC encourages tall ships whose course takes them near New England to contact us to discuss a visit - and discover why captains recommend Portsmouth as "one of their best port calls ever".

Larry Job, Vice Chairman
Tel: 603-929-4472.
E-mail: lrjob@comcast.net

R & W Traditional Rigging & Outfitting

R & W is a family owned and operated distributor of rope and cordage. Started in 1985 as a "one man" operation out of the trunk of a hand-me-down car, we've grown into one of the most diverse stocking warehouses in the industry.

We've got rope - whether it's small 50 lb test braided line for ice fishing, brightly colored rope for trying your hand at tying a rope halter or a fancy knot, a safety line for a school's challenge course, or a full set of custom spliced docklines, chances are we have it and have it in stock.

We know rope – both the technical side of how it's made and the application side of how its used, and enjoy helping you find just the right product for your needs. And we sell our rope at some of the best prices you'll find anywhere. QUALITY, VALUE & SERVICE - it's what we expect and it's what you can expect from us.

Distributors of:
• Davey & Co. Marine Hardware
• Meissner Winches
• Ording Wooden Blocks and Rope of all descriptions.

Choose the best gear from the age of classic yachting and working sail.

R & W Traditional Rigging & Outfitting
39 Tarkiln Place, New Bedford MA 02745 USA
Tel: 866-577-5505 or 508-995-1114
E-mail: mainstay@csolve.net
Website: www.RWrope.com

Sailing Ship Adventures

Sailing Ship Adventures is a specialty travel service that represents sailing ship owners and operators, including some of the sailing world's best-kept secrets. We book voyages for our customers on a wide variety of sailing ships ranging from the largest full rigged tall ship in the world (The Royal Clipper, at over 400 feet in length) to smaller vessels (ranging from 60 to 100 feet in length), as well as aboard crewed chartered yachts.

Unlike your local travel agent we do not represent just a few ships and tour providers, but a wide variety of ships in many different destination areas. We have researched tall ships and sailing ship vacations the world over. Our extensive knowledge of sailing ships and the resulting roster of vessels in our fleet means that, no matter where you would like to spend your next vacation or what you would like to do there, we can find the perfect voyage for you.

Our fleet is comprised of more than 100 full rigged tall ships, brigantines, barkentines, schooners, and smaller vessels. This range of ships, from the most luxurious to the more spartan, offers you the widest range of choice available.

Our ships sail to destinations through the world, ranging from popular itineraries in the Caribbean and Mediterranean Seas, to ocean crossings, to exotic areas such as the fjords of Patagonia, the Andaman Sea, and the Queen Charlotte Islands. Sailing to these destinations offers opportunities to experience exotic locations in an up-close and intimate way that is not possible on traditional cruises. Smaller vessels are able to stop at smaller, out-of-the-way ports of call not accessible to large cruise liners.

Climb aboard one of these majestic sailing ships and set sail to exotic locations!

Dexter Donham
Sailing Ship Adventures
Tel: 781-237-4395 or toll free 877-882-4395
Fax: 781-237-3141
E-mail: ddonham@sailingshipadventures.com
Website: www.sailingshipadventures.com

ASTA
ASTA
ENDORSED

Seven Corners, Inc.

Seven Corners is one of the industry's most experienced travel health insurance providers. The company serves leisure, student, business, government and missionary/volunteer travelers. It offers an extensive selection of international medical and travel insurance policies to U.S. citizens traveling overseas or foreign nationals visiting the United States.

Seven Corners has thousands of policy holders and a worldwide network of 30,000 agents. The company created and maintains the industry's most comprehensive network of international health care providers that includes thousands of doctors, pharmacies and hospitals around the globe.

Seven Corners is a member of the United States Travel Insurance Association, is GSA certified and is currently pursuing a SAS 70 Type II compliant designation. In addition to travel medical insurance, Seven Corners also offers health care administration to the government sector. The company is privately held and headquartered just north of Indianapolis in Carmel, IN.

Seven Corners Inc.
303 Congressional Boulevard, Carmel, IN 46032 USA
Tel: 800-335-0611
Website: www.sevencorners.com

Tall Ship Celebration Bay City

Tall Ship Celebration is a non-profit organization producing award-winning maritime festivals in Bay City, Michigan. With a reputation for providing exceptional support and hospitality to visiting vessels and their crews, Bay City was twice named "Port of the Year" by ASTA. Bay City is proud to again serve as Michigan's "Port of Call," the only official host port in the state for the 2010 Great Lakes United TALL SHIPS CHALLENGE®. From July 15—18, 2010, Tall Ship Celebration: Bay City will welcome thousands of people to the banks of the Saginaw River for a world-class event featuring ship tours, an international Maritime Music Festival, fine art show, interactive craft activities, small boat building, storytellers, pirate shows and much more. Tall Ship Celebration: Bay City has been named one of the Top 100 Events in North America for 2010 by the American Bus Association.

Shirley Roberts, Event Coordinator
Tall Ship Celebration: Bay City
1712 Center Avenue, Bay City, MI 48708 USA
Tel: 989-225-7856
E-mail: Shirley.Roberts@charter.net
Website: www.tallshipcelebration.com

Village of Greenport, New York

Located in the beautiful, deep and superbly protected waters of the Gardiners/ Peconic Bay system of eastern Long Island, Greenport Harbor has been a uniquely appealing destination for mariners since the dawn of American history. Modern-day Greenport remains true to this heritage.

Deep water dockage for large and small vessels is available at a municipally owned marina in the heart of a downtown waterfront listed on the National Register of Historic Places. Stores, galleries, and services including those catering to mariners, such as welding, hauling, carpentry and marine hardware, even a hospital, are but steps away. A waterfront park has been developed upland of the marina which boasts a vintage carouse', an outdoor amphitheater and boardwalk. Additional board-walk will soon connect the marina to a transportation center where bus, rail, and ferry connections are available to Shelter Island, New York City, and destinations throughout Long Island. Greenport is keenly interested in visits by tall ships and sail training vessels and will make special arrangements to host traditional sailing vessels, their crews and trainees.

Mayor David Nyce
236 Third Street, Greenport, NY 11944 USA
Tel: 631-477-0248 Fax: 631-477-2488
E-mail: David_Nyce@greenportvillage.org
Website: www.greenportvillage.com

 Whitworth Marine

Meeting the modern needs of traditional vessels.

Specializing in:
• Diesel Engines • High and Low Voltage DC Electrical Systems
• Chargers, Inverters, Ac & DC Panels • Electrical Wiring and Electronics
• Pumps and Piping • Water Makers • Fuel Systems • Sewage Systems

*** Over ten years experience as Chief Engineer on off-shore vessels ***

Nobby Peers
Tel: 631-804-3077
E-mail: knobby@whitworthmarine.com
Website: www.whitworthmarine.com

Associate Members

A very important factor in our growth over the years has been the strength of our membership. Without the support of our members, the development and implementation of all of our programs, publications, and resources, would not be possible.

Board Members & Commodores

Henry H. Anderson, Jr.	Norman Lemley
Raymond Ashley	Paul Madden
Daveneet Bakhshi	Ken Neal
Les Bolton	David Neibuhr
Michael Brown	Caleb Pifer
Terry Davies	Doug Prothero
Dexter Donham	Michael J. Rauworth
Bart Dunbar	Nancy H. Richardson
Kevin Dykema	Bert Rogers
Robert Frost	Christopher Rowsom
Susan Geiger	Eric Shaw
James Gladson	Dan Stetson
Jen Haddock	Alix T. Thorne
Richard H. Hawkins	Barclay 'Tim' Warburton
Deborah Hayes	Thomas R. Weschler
Karen Helmerson	F. C. 'Bunky' Wichmann
James W. Hiney	David V. V. Wood
John Jamian	Meghan Wren
James Kerr	

 # Advisory Board Members

Richard Bailey	Thad Koza
Hal G. Barstow	Perry Lewis
Beth Bonds	James Lyons
Alice Cochran	Joseph Maggio
Chuck Fowler	Jeffrey Parker
Chris Freeman	Jed Pearsall
Tom Gochberg	Nigel Rowe
Andrew A. Hammond	Walter Rybka
Michael Jehle	Chris Sinnett
	Howard Slotnick

Individual Members

Alexander M. Agnew	R. Bruce Carruthers
Mike Albertson	Julia Carter
Constance Allen	Casey Charkowick
Jay Amster	G. AndyChase
Anthony Audrieth	Frederick Christian
Christopher Avildsen	Michael Cicalese
Sandra Aylesworth	Theophilos Collins
Terese Ayre	Sym Colovos
Rick Bagnall	Stephen Connett
Richard Bailey	H. Joseph Coughlin
Thomas E. Baker	Lori Crace
Shannon Ball	Hank Cramer
Mike Bancroft	Peter L. Crew
Katrina Barnes	Rebecca Cutting
Roland Baroni	Blythe Daly
Clive Beasley	Morgan Davis
Robert Bein	Beth Deal
David Bell	Gerard DeModena
Erik Berliner	Bob Dollar
Paul Berta	Amanda Doren
Arthur Birney	Debbie Doucette
James A. Bising	Loraine DuBeau
David H. Blomberg	Michael F. Dugan
Jonathan Boulware	Bart Dunbar
Peg Brandon	Kevin Dykema
Mark K. Branse	Margaret Eifert
George & Anne Brengle	Collette Emanuel
Robert Brittain	Elaine Eno
Paulina Brooks	Peter Equi
David Brown	John Evans
Edward Burns	Peter Favelle
John Cameron	Kip Files

Individual Members (continued)

Ron Finney
Douglas T. Fischer
David E. Fleenor
Iver C. Franzen
Philip Galluccio
Stephen K. Galpin
Steve Garrity
Darlene Godin
Elizabeth Graves
Hannah Gray
Robert Green
Donald Grosse
Mark Haller
Jennifer Hammond
Richard H. Hawkins
John Healey
Matt Heffron
Karen Helmerson
Jill Helterline
E.A. Hank Hibbard
Jeffrey Hicks
James E. Hilyard
James Hinde
James W. Hiney
David Hirzel
H. Jochen Hoffmann
Robert P. Hofmann
Tido Holtkamp
Jennifer Holtsclaw
Kathryn Hunter
Magdalena Jablonowska
Andrew Jagger

Patricia Jernigan
Robert A. Johnson
Robert P. Johnson
Thomas Kastle
Jessie Kehr
Carole Keller
Michael Kellick
John E. Kelly
Arthur M. Kimberly
Brian Kiracofe
Kevin Koob
Roy H. Kruse
Amoah Kwaku
Wil Langdon
Monica Larimer
Risa Lax
Vic Leanza
Audrey Lee
Emile Legault
Norman Lemley
Jesse Leonard
Richard Levine
Nancy Linden
John Link
J. Eric Little
Richard C. 'Chad' Loebs
Otto Loggers
Patricia R. Longan
Sally H. Lunt
Paul Madden
Grace Malolepszy
Peter Marcucci

Individual Members (continued)

Christopher Martin

Paul H. Martinez

Carol Mason

Theodore Mason

Dennis C. Mayhew

Michael McAllister

Peter McCracken

Neil McManus

Brian S. McNamara

John D. McShane

Jan Miles

Tim Miller

Robert Miorelli

Vincent Mocini

Wilfred P. Moore

Charles Nelson III

Daniel Nemsdale

Lee Newberry

Paul C. Nicholson

Donald L. Nock

Deborah Novachick

John T. O'Brien

Cindy Olivier

Ed Olivier

Brian Olson

Lynn Ann Oschmann

Richard S. Palmer

Robert Papp

Slavek Pardo

Megan Patterson

Edward V. Pietka

Maia Pilzer

Oscar Pott

John Prescott

Donna Prieur

Joyce Pucino

Andrew Radel

Octavia Randolph

Andrew Reay-Ellers

Bruce Reeh

Nick Remlinger

Alan Rice

Richard 'Rusty' E. Rice, Jr.

Nancy H. Richardson

Alden T. Ring

Stephanie Robb

J. Catherine Roberts

George Rockwood

Leslie Rosenblatt

Mark Rosenstein

Greg R. Rossi

Christine Rybak

Walter Rybka

James D. Salmon

Clyde Sanadi

Jesse Schaffer

Gary Schwarzman

Ann Sera

Richard Shannon

Eric Shaw

Paul H. Sheehan

Zachary Simonson-Bond

Horatio Sinbad

Chris Sinnett

Individual Members (continued)

Kathy Sinnett

Robert Siragusa

Cassandra Sleeper

David Slocum

Amelia Smith

Donald Smith

Karla M. Smith

Ronald Smith

Tiffany Smith

Doran E. Smout

Sally Somsel

David Southworth

Jay Spence

Jennifer Spring

Scott Spring

M. Jeremy Steele-Perkins

Michele Stevens

Ron Straub

Luise Strauss

Kaari Sullivan

Jean Taber

Donald F. Teal

Dave Thompson

Llewellyn Toulmin

Russell Tryder

Thompson Tully

Nelly Turley

Kurt Voss

Toby Walker

Spencer Warren

Christopher Weiss

F. Bradley Wellock

Keith Weyrick

John C. Wigglesworth

Kit Williams

Christian Winter

Tracy Wolfe

Woody Wright

Peter C. Wylie

Karin Wyman

Brady Young

William F. Young

Crew Members

Mary Acton-Bond

Amy Albrecht

Matthew Bale

Claudia Bankert

Brandi Bednarik

Michael Biggie

Les Bolton

David Bonner

Thomas Briggs

Michael Campbell

Crew Members (continued)

Beau Churchill	Ardrey Manning
Jennifer Clark	Glenn Mariano
Mike Cohen	Wayne Marquardt
Orion Couling	Malcom Martin
Brad Crooks	Patricia McLaren
Christopher Cusson	Michael McLaughlin
Richard Dorfman	James McManus
Laura Dyro	Jason McNaught
Margaret Flanagan	Denise Meagher
Joe Follansbee	Karl Messerschmidt
Matthew Francis	Ashlee Mitchell
Simon A. F. Fuller	J.B. Morrison
Jeremiah Gempler	Kerry Nolan
Matt Gempler	David Nowlan
Sara Gempler	Bruce Randall
Roxanne Hadler	William Rudek
Darryl Hall	William Sabatini
Dave Haslam	Duffy Sabella
Gabriel Heninger	Deon Sandoval
Shevawn Innes	Sasha Schoennemann
Michael Jacobson	Mark Scibinico
Claire Kirby	David Sheldon
John A. Kraus	Reasa Shuck
Dennis LaKomski	Sam Sikkema
Stacey Lary	Inez Wall
Dylan Leach	Kent Wall
Ryan LeMar	Lawrence Woods
Laura Levin	Kathleen Wroblewski
Eric Lindholm	Isaiah Young
Drew Little	

Junior Members

Blake Cannino	Theresa O'Byrne
Stephen Fick	Susanna Ordway
Geoffrey Frank	Kwesi Phillips
Aaron Gralnik	Nicholas Rivelle
Thomas Green	Jon Roberson
Arielle Knuttel	Zachary Strassberg
Patrick Maher	Brian Turnbull
Tyler Nemsdale	Peter Walters

 # Supporting Members

Hal G. Barstow	Bill Munger
Anne Beaumont	Hisakazu Nakayama
John Beebe-Center	David Niebuhr
Paul Bonge	Jeffrey N. Parker
John W. Braitmayer	Christopher Rowsom
David Hayes	Stan Selden
Frank Klimas	Alix T. Thorne
Doug & Pat McKenzie	Thomas R. Weschler

 # Lifetime Members

John Benson	Frederic S. Sater
Joseph M. Davis	Cornelius Vanderstar
Robert S. Douglas	Robin Wallace
Ronald V. Gallo	Robert W. Wrathall
John M. Hopkins	Arthur W. Young
Thor H. Ramsing	

Family Members

Edward M. & Bernadette Andrews

Steven H. Baker

Daveneet Bakhshi & Paula Silva

John B. & Beth Bonds

Nick & Wendy Bowen

William and Deborah Cooper

Vivian Coxe

David R. Damon

George Dow

Chuck Fowler

Robert Frost

Deborah Hayes
   & John Beebe-Center

Steven Hertz

Cameron Hinman

Ken & Kim Howard

Eric Jones

Jonathan T. Kabak

Thomas & Phyllis Kelly

Michael Lachance

Ivan T. Luke

Stanley Martin

Hank & Kaia Moseley

Steve Moulton

Mark & Susan Nusall

Darren & Misty O'Brien

Aaron Paolino

Jed Pearsall

Caleb Pifer

Cynthia & Monty Pifer

Dana & Carolyn Rexford

Bert & Donna Rogers

Don & Chad Russell

Robert D. Rustchak

Glenn & Linda Short

Howard Slotnick

Colby Smith

Robert A. Smith

Johanna & William Strassberg

Jonathan & Christian Thomas

Robert Wheeler

David V. V. Wood

Stanley Young

Paul Zambianco

Sail Training International

Sail Training International is a registered charity (not for profit organization) with worldwide membership and activities whose purpose is the development and education of young people of all nationalities, cultures, religions and social backgrounds through the sail training experience.

Sail Training International offers a range of activities and services including conferences and seminars, races and other events for sail training tall ships, publications and DVD presentations, international research and the Class A Tall Ships Forum (for the operators of big square-rigged sail training ships). Members are made up of the national sail training organizations of Australia, Belgium, Bermuda, Canada, Denmark, Finland, France, Germany, Greece, India, Ireland, Italy, Latvia, Lithuania, Netherlands, New Zealand, Norway, Poland, Portugal, Russia, South Africa, Spain, Sweden, UK and USA. The American Sail Training Association is a founder member of Sail Training International.

www.sailtraininginternational.org

Member Organizations

AUSTRALIA - Australian Sail Training Association

Founded in 1996, AUSTA represents the interests of 16 sail training organizations and tall ship operators in Australia and New Zealand. Its purpose is to promote the development of sail training with an emphasis on adventure training for young people at sea under sail in Australia and elsewhere. AUSTA also plays a key role in the development (for sail training vessel operators) of safety-related codes of conduct and on-board management systems, trainee and professional crew training programs and other related programs.
www.sailtrainingaustralia.com

BELGIUM - Sail Training Association Belgium

Founded in 1994, STA Belgium is a registered charity with national membership. It restored, owns and operates the T/S Williwaw and promotes sail training for young people on many other Belgian vessels.
www.sailtraining.be

BERMUDA - Sail Training Association Bermuda

Formed in 2001 following the success of the Tall Ships® 2000 transatlantic race, STA Bermuda promotes and helps to fund the participation of young Bermudians in sail training programs internationally. It is also working with The Bermuda Sloop Foundation to support the construction of its own unique Bermudian sloop for sail training.
stabermuda@logic.bm

CANADA - Canadian Sail Training Association

Founded in 1984, its membership now includes the owner/operators of 18 vessels ranging in size from a six meter open sloop to an 80 meter barquentine and providing sail training programs as diverse in scope as the vessels themselves. A key priority for the organization now is to ensure a regulatory environment that is consistent with the goals and activities of sail training operators and their programs.
www.sailtraining.ca

Denmark - Danish Sail Training Association

Founded in 1996, DSTA represents the interests of 30 members in Denmark, the Faroe Islands and Greenland, including ten sail training vessels (ranging in size from an 18 meter ketch to three Class A full rigged ships) and five ports. The organization operates a grant scheme to assist trainees taking part in The Tall Ships' Races.
www.dsta.dk

Member Organizations

FINLAND - Sail Training Association Finland

STA Finland member sail training vessels have taken more than 16,800 young people to sea since the organization's foundation in 1973. These young trainees have also formed their own organization (The Sail Trainees of Finland Association) which provides opportunities for continuing contact between the trainees and also helps to promote sail training in Finland.
www.staf.fi

FRANCE - Sail Training Association France

Amis des Grands Voiliers: Founded in 1990, STA France represents the interests of around 40 vessels and about 400 members (individuals - associations - charities - vessels operators) in promoting sail training for young persons through exhibitions at various maritime festivals and other events. Through its quarterly publication "Grands Voiliers Infos" and its monthly newsletter, it helps potential young trainees in finding opportunities to embark on sail training vessels around the world.
www.amisdesgrandsvoiliers.org

GERMANY - Sail Training Association Germany

Founded in 1984 as a not-for-profit organization, STAG's main purpose is the education, development and support of young people of all nationalities through sail training. Its members include 50 sail training vessels and over 5,000 individual members. The organization operates a bursary program for sail training vessels and individual trainees.
www.sta-g.de

IRELAND - Coiste an Asgard

Formed in 1968, Coiste an Asgard operates the state owned Class A sail training vessel *Asgard II* and promotes offshore sail training for young people generally in the Republic of Ireland. Coiste an Asgard provides the communications link for offshore sail training interests in Ireland with Sail Training International pending the development of a national sail training organization (as defined by Sail Training International).
www.irishsailtraining.com

Member Organizations

ITALY - Sail Training Association Italy

Founded in 1976 by a partnership of the Italian Navy and the Yacht Club Italiano, its charter is to develop and promote sea training for young people as a means to further their personal development and education. Through the co-operation of the Navy and many owner/operators of other vessels, STA Italy offers a variety of sail training opportunities to young people, including berths at no charge or highly subsidized. The organization also operates an international trainee exchange program which is currently expanding.
www.sta-italia.it

LATVIA - Sail Training Association Latvia

Founded in 2002 by 23 sail training enthusiasts in Latvia, the organization also has three members who own/operate vessels, two yacht clubs and three maritime companies. STA Latvia's principal goals are to develop sail training for young people in Latvia by encouraging other vessel owners to participate in sail training activities and events, and through an international trainee exchange program.
www.sta-latvia.lv

NETHERLANDS - Sail Training Association Netherlands

Founded in 1985, STAN's goals are to encourage and develop sail training off-shore for young people in the Netherlands. In pursuit of this, STAN organizes maritime events and races for sail training and tall ships in the Netherlands.
www.stanetherlands.nl

NEW ZEALAND - Spirit of Adventure Trust

Established in 1972 by Lou Fisher, The Spirit of Adventure Trust was formed to offer equal opportunity to young New Zealanders to gain qualities of independence, leadership and community spirit through the medium of the sea. The Spirit of Adventure Trust is dedicated to the youth of New Zealand. Each year it brings together 1,200 young people throughout the country.
www.spiritofadventure.org.nz

NORWAY - Norwegian Sail Training Association

Founded in 1999, NSTA has four membership categories: sail training vessels, past and prospective host ports for The Tall Ships' Races, individuals and organizations supporting NSTA ideals, and corporate entities. The organization promotes sail training for young people and international friendship through sail training.
www.nsta.no

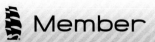 # Member Organizations

POLAND - Sail Training Association Poland

Established in 1993, STA Poland has more than 100 individual (voting) members and is co-owner and sole operator of the Class A sail training tall ship, *Pogoria*. Supporting (non-voting) members include the Maritime Academy of Gdynia (*Dar Mlodziezy*), the Polish Navy (ORP *Iskra*) the Polish Scouts Union Sea Training Centre (*Zawisza Czarny*) and the Polish Yachting Association (*Kapitan Glowacki*).
www.pogoria.pl

PORTUGAL - Portuguese Sail Training Association

Aporvela – Portuguese STA was founded in 1980 as a registered charity. It has three categories of membership and owns three sail training vessels including the Caravel *Vera Cruz*. The organization's main objectives are to promote off-shore sail training mainly for young people.
www.aporvela.pt

RUSSIA - Admiral Makarov State Maritime Academy

This institution represents the interests of sail training in Russia and operates the 100-metre sail training ship *Mir*. The Academy provides the communications link for all sail training activities in Russia with Sail Training International, pending the development of a national sail training organization (as defined by Sail Training International).
smamir@lek.ru

SPAIN - Sail Training Association España

Created in 2003, STA España membership includes all sail training vessels in Spain, the Spanish Navy and a number of ports.
www.sta-espana.org

SWEDEN - Sail Training Association Sweden

STA Sweden was founded in 1998, initially to support the Tall Ships' Races. Today its members include a number of Swedish ports, the Swedish Navy and some 60 vessels engaged wholly or occasionally in sail training activities.
www.stas.nu

UNITED KINGDOM - Association of Sea Training Organisations

Founded in 1972, ASTO represents the interests of UK sail training organizations. It has 25 full members and 10 associate members operating 55 sail training vessels ranging in size from a 10-metre sloop to a 65-metre barque. The organization grants bursary funding towards the costs of more than 80,000 berth days for young people, including disabled trainees each year.
www.asto.org.uk

Member Organizations

USA - American Sail Training Association

Founded in 1973, the organization represents the interests in the US of 200 member sail training vessels from more than 20 countries. There are also 100 affiliate members including museums, schools and universities, and close to 500 individual members who support the organization's mission. ASTA raises funds and administers several scholarship programs as well as a professional development grant program to support the continuing education of professional sail trainers and marine educators.
www.sailtraining.org

Recent Additions to the Membership Include:
Greece, India, Lithuania, South Africa

Sail Training International
5 Mumby Road
Gosport
Hampshire PO12 1AA
UK

Telephone: +44 (0)23 9258 6367
Fax: +44 (0)23 9258 4661
Email: office@sailtraininginternational.org

www.sailtraininginternational.org

Programs and Services

ASTA Programs foster youth education, leadership development and the preservation of North American maritime heritage. ASTA organizes the TALL SHIPS CHALLENGE® annual series of sail training races, rallies and maritime festivals, hosts an annual conference on sail training and tall ships, and publishes SAIL TALL SHIPS! A Directory of Sail Training and Adventure at Sea. ASTA also raises money for scholarships, and administers grants directly supporting youth education and leadership development programs that shape young people's lives and build tomorrow's leaders.

ASTA's Annual Conference on Sail Training and Tall Ships

ASTA's Annual Conference on Sail Training and Tall Ships gathers ships' masters, port representatives, public officials, marine suppliers, naval architects, program administrators, festival managers, preservationists, environmentalists, crewmembers, and educators. Topics concerning vessel operations, regulatory issues, management, educational programming, and safety at sea are addressed each year, as are sessions on media relations, marketing, funding, communications, and port event organization. Held annually during the first or second week in November, the ASTA Conference on Sail Training and Tall Ships is both fun and informative and offers oceans of networking opportunities.

ASTA's Biennial Education Under Sail Forum

The ASTA Education Under Sail Forum made its grand premiere in Chicago in 2000. The first of what has now become a program-focused complement to the Safety Under Sail Forum biennial series. The Education Under Sail Forum is held during even-numbered years, in conjunction with the Annual Conference on Sail Training and Tall Ships. The forum is designed to inform and inspire excellence in the development and delivery of educational experiences under sail, and overflows with creative exchanges among captains, crew, administrators, teachers, program developers, curriculum designers, and others.

ASTA's Biennial Safety Under Sail Forum

Initiated in 1992, the Safety Under Sail Forum expands the international dialogue among professional mariners by presenting case studies of actual incidents at sea, discussing emerging technologies, and sharing "best practices" so as to constantly insure a high level of safety and professionalism in the sail training industry. Professionals engaged in sail training, sea education, vessel operations, and tall ship events from throughout the world participate in this biennial symposium. Topics covered have included preparing for heavy weather, hypothermia, technology and forecasting, survival gear and much more. The American Sail Training Association hosts the Safety Forum during odd-numbered years, in conjunction with the Annual Conference on Sail Training and Tall Ships.

The ASTA Sail Training Rally

In the 1980s, ASTA developed the concept of the Sail Training Rally; a competition among crews, both at sea and ashore. These rallies provide trainees with an opportunity to demonstrate their seamanship skills in a friendly but competitive format by participating in shoreside events such as knot tying, tug-of war, bucket brigade, rowing, walk the plank, and heaving line toss/hawser pull. Most often held in conjunction with the TALL SHIPS CHALLENGE® Race Series, ASTA Sail Training Rallies allow the general public to observe the sort of teamwork and maritime skills that are learned on board sail training vessels at sea.

ASTA's Annual Regional Meetings

Regional-Atlantic, Pacific and Great Lakes-meetings are held late winter and early spring. These meetings are less formal than our annual conference, but like the conference, we encourage our members to submit ideas for locations and topics. The regional meetings offer an opportunity for the host organization to showcase their facility and programs while providing an intimate setting for attendees to network.

A typical regional meeting may include a tour, special presentation, workshops, discussion groups, safety demonstration, day sail, luncheon and reception. Planning usually starts in November at the annual conference with meetings held in February, March or April. If your organization would like to host a regional meeting, please send a letter of interest along with a proposed agenda to ASTA.

The ASTA Website

The ASTA website, www.sailtraining.org, links you to the world of sail training and Tall Ships. The website combines many exciting features with a fresh look and easy to navigate pages.

A searchable listing of ASTA Member Vessels makes it easy to learn more about opportunities under sail, the ships that can take you to sea, and shore-based programs. The ASTA website also provides information about Tall Ships® events such as the TALL SHIPS CHALLENGE® Race Series and international sail training associations and resources around the world.

The ASTA Billet Bank

ASTA BILLET BANK

Filter Positions By:

SHOWING ALL POSITIONS

HMS Bounty Organization, LLC www.tallshipbounty.org based in Palm I Florida, operates Bounty and invites applications for the post of **Engine Bosun, mates, deckhands**.

The Bounty Organization is looking for crew to be on board for the winter maintenance months of Bounty in Florida. The duties will include tours, daily maintenance and possible sailing for private functions. All positions are open. Those who are hired for the winter will have first choice for positions during our 2010 sailing season.

This post is Seasonal.

Apply by email to
Contact Name: Margaret Ramsey
Tel: 1 (631) 584-7900
Fax: 1 843 280-6856
email: mramsey@tallshipbounty.org
2806 Ship Wheel Drive , North Myrtle Beach SC 29582 US

An online Billet Bank provides notice of positions available aboard ASTA member vessels.

The Billet Bank is the most visited section of the ASTA website all year long and is the most effective service available for matching professional sail trainers and open positions.

ASTA does not endorse any specific program or individual, but simply shares information as it becomes available.

# ASTA's Crew Membership Program

ASTA's Crew Membership program allows ASTA Sail Training Organization members to purchase blocks of 10 membership vouchers at a reduced rate, for distribution to their staff, crew, volunteers and trainees.

Crew memberships must be purchased by the member Sail Training Organization and are sold in blocks of 10 for US $250. Membership application forms are sent to the member STO who then distributes them to staff and crew. The memberships are valid for one year from the time ASTA receives the completed application form and carry all the same benefits as an individual membership (US $50) plus some added benefits.

ASTA's Marine Insurance Program

The Allen Agency of Camden, Maine is ASTA's officially-endorsed insurance agency. Established in 1866, the Allen Agency is an independent, employee-owned company with 55 employees specializing in providing vessel owners from around the world with choices in coverage from a variety of the industry's best insurance companies.

The Allen Agency has insured tall ships for decades. The company's tradition of exemplary service and competitive rates is now available to both new customers and returning ones.   The Allen Agency's marine insurance experts, back up these offerings with the utmost attention to detail and an emphasis on customer service.

The Allen Agency offers these products to ASTA members who qualify: Hull, P&I and related vessel insurance for U.S.-flagged member vessels; hull, P&I and related vessel insurance for foreign-flagged member vessels; non-profit directors and officers liability insurance; events cancellation insurance and events liability insurance; and general business insurance for land-based operations of ASTA members.

For more information on the ASTA Marine Insurance program contact Gene McKeever at the Allen Agency 800-439-4311 or gmckeever@allenagency.com

ASTA's Marine Medical Coverage Program

ASTA Mariners require a medical program they can depend on to protect them as they travel throughout the world. Coverage that provides security, flexibility and benefits unique to today's marine industry demands. Now ASTA members can sail and travel anywhere with the confidence that they are protected with comprehensive, marine-specific medical coverage.

The Allen Agency and Allen Financial Group of Camden, the ASTA-endorsed insurance company, are pleased to offer a brand new health/medical program for both crew and individuals. This special health/medical product protects ASTA members with full coverage, 24/7, while onboard the vessel and when signed off or on personal leisure time.

ASTA membership is required to participate, through the ASTA Crew Membership Program (pg 341) or as an individual ASTA member (pg 394).

For more information on the ASTA Marine Medical Coverage program contact Rick Bagnall at the Allen Financial Group 207-236-8376 X 540 or rbagnall@ allenfg.com

Scholarships and Grants

Henry H. Anderson, Jr. Sail Training Scholarships
ASTA Crew Development Grants
Ernestine Bennett Memorial Sail Training Scholarships
Ted Cochrane Memorial Sail Training Scholarships

Henry H. Anderson, Jr. Sail Training Scholarship Program

The Henry H. Anderson, Jr. Sail Training Scholarship was established in 1999 and is designed to assist young people between the ages of 14 and 19 achieve a sail training experience aboard a USCG (or national equivalent) inspected ASTA member vessel. Scholarships are available to both individuals and groups. Scholarships are awarded to individuals and groups who are genuinely interested in experiencing sail training and education under sail. Applicants must show a demonstrated need for financial assistance and must describe, in writing, what they feel they will achieve by participating in the sail training experience.

For details contact the ASTA office or visit the ASTA Website at www.sailtraining.org.

The ASTA Crew Development Grant Program

The ASTA Professional/Crew Development Grant has been established to provide financial assistance to professional crewmembers of ASTA vessels in order to meet new and existing requirements for maintaining as well as advancing their USCG licenses, and to encourage the highest possible standards of safety training for individuals or groups of ASTA members. Applicants must be an ASTA Associate or ASTA Crew Member in good standing.

For details contact the ASTA office or visit the ASTA Website at www.sailtraining.org.

Ernestine Bennett Memorial Sail Training Scholarship Program

The Ernestine Bennett Memorial Sail Training Scholarship is designed to assist people to achieve a sail training experience aboard a USCG (or national equivalent) inspected ASTA member vessel. Scholarships are available to people ages 14 and above with special consideration going to female applicants from the Pacific Northwest. Scholarships are awarded to individuals who are genuinely interested in experiencing sail training and education under sail. Applicants must show a demonstrated need for financial assistance and must describe, in writing, what they feel they will achieve by participating in the sail training experience.

For details contact the ASTA office or visit the ASTA Website at www.sailtraining.org.

Ted Cochran Memorial Scholarship For CLASS AFLOAT™

Class Afloat™, in conjunction with the American Sail Training Association, offers an annual memorial scholarship in the name of former friend and supporter Ted Cochran. Covering one semester of tuition costs, this scholarship is awarded to a Class Afloat™ applicant who is affiliated with an ASTA member organization.

For details contact Class Afloat™ at 800-301-7245 or www.classafloat.com.

ASTA Publications

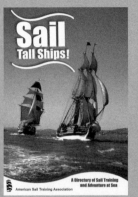

Sail Tall Ships! A Directory of Sail Training and Adventure at Sea, is a comprehensive guide featuring hundreds of ASTA member tall ships and shore-based programs offering a diverse range of sail training opportunities throughout North America and around the globe. A must for those planning their own adventure and for tall ship enthusiasts alike.

ASTA Publications

Sail Tall Ships! A Directory of Sail Training and Adventure at Sea

Sail Tall Ships! A Directory of Sail Training and Adventure at Sea first appeared in 1980, and is now in its eighteenth edition. The directory provides program and contact information for ASTA member vessels and sail training associations throughout the world. To help fulfill ASTA's mission, the directory is also distributed through maritime museums and their affiliated shops, marinas, maritime events, and sail training programs, as well as bookstores, libraries, high school guidance counselors, university career resource centers, and education conferences throughout the United States and Canada. 436 pages. Soft cover, 9 by 6 inches. US $14.95

18th Edition

Sail Tall Ships!
American Sail Training Association

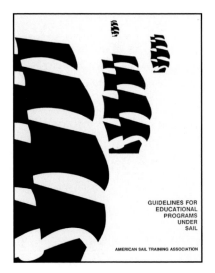

GUIDELINES FOR
EDUCATIONAL
PROGRAMS
UNDER
SAIL

AMERICAN SAIL TRAINING ASSOCIATION

Guidelines for Educational Programs Under Sail

Guidelines for Educational Programs Under Sail defines ASTA standards for sail training and sea education within the framework of the Sailing School Vessels Act. This manual defines criteria and indicators of effectiveness for the design, delivery, and evaluation of curricula, instruction, and program administration. In addition to the core of safe seamanship education, the guidelines apply to all aspects of sail training: adventure, education, environmental science, maritime heritage, and leadership development. US $12.00

ASTA Publications

Tall Ships: The Fleet for the 21st Century

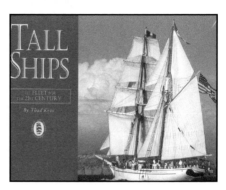

Tall Ships The Fleet for the 21st Century by Thad Koza, is published by TideMark Press and now in it's fourth edition. With brilliant color photographs on each page, Thad Koza's collection of the world's most majestic sailing vessels will undoubtedly take its place in the libraries of ship aficionados. From fighting ships like USS Constitution to the Sedov, a Russian training ship that is the largest sailing vessel afloat, this soft cover book includes scantlings and a description for each of (more than) 150 featured ships. 231 pages. 210 plus full-color photographs. Soft cover, sewn binding, 12 by 9 inches. US $24.95

Tall Ships Calendar

There are few things on the high seas more dramatic than the great clouds of sail raised by traditional full-rigged ships. Thad Koza, a renowned tall ships lecturer, photographer, and author, photographs these vessels at events in the United States and in Europe. Sales benefit the American Sail Training Association. Wall hanging, full color, 12 months, 14 x 22 inches, open. US $13.95

The ASTA Training Logbook

The ASTA Training Logbook enables trainees to keep a personal log of their sea time and to document their progress in sail training, and records a progression of skill-building activities in nautical science, safety, seamanship, and navigation. Completion of course work and sea time must be certified by either the instructor or the ship's master. US $5.00 (Quantity discounts available)

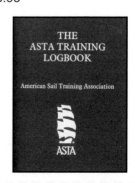

2008/2009 ASTA Events

ASTA Conferences, Fundraisers, Receptions and other events

2008 International Sail Training and Tall Ships Conference

400 DELEGATES FROM 28 COUNTRIES... CONFERENCE RATED 'EXCELLENT'

Four hundred delegates from 28 countries around the world converged on Halifax, Nova Scotia, (14-15 November) for the International Sail Training and Tall Ships Conference 2008. Organized by Sail Training International in collaboration with the American Sail Training Association (the biggest of STI's 25 member national organizations), the conference had an overall rating from delegates of close to 'Excellent'. Sail training vessel operators from Australia, New Zealand, South Africa, and throughout both Europe and North America attended, along with representatives of host ports from Europe, the Caribbean and North America. The conference comprised a mix of plenary sessions for all delegates and an á la carte menu of 16 workshops. These covered a range of topics from dealing with the current 'economic tsunami' and navigating the regulatory seas, to recruiting trainees, the development of a successful sail training program, and the ingredients of a successful Tall Ships event. The conference also included a session for the Sail Training International Youth Forum, attended by 36 young sail trainers.

The Rt Hon Rodney MacDonald, Premier of Nova Scotia opened the conference and welcomed the delegates, followed by Nigel Rowe (President and Chairman, Sail Training International) and Mike Rauworth (Chairman of the American Sail Training Association). The premiére of a dramatic new two-minute film aimed at attracting young trainee crews to participate in Tall Ships events preceded an inspirational key-note address by Peter Neill, Director, World Ocean Observatory. He talked about the value and importance of sail training in changing the lives of young people, the imperative of exemplary safety standards, and the perils of organizational complacency in the sail training industry.

2008 International Sail Training and Tall Ships Conference

The conference was preceded by a full session of the Class A Tall Ships Forum, an organization created by Sail Training International in 2004 to address the needs and interests of the big square-rigged ships. The delegates to this meeting made considerable progress on the codification of a modular training program to meet the demands of the new IMO Code for Special Purpose Ships, and on a process for developing new ideas to improve the economics of participating in Tall Ships events. In parallel with this, representatives from host ports met for a separate seminar.

2008 International Sail Training and Tall Ships Conference

The Allen Agency, ASTA's endorsed insurance agency, sponsored a Welcome Reception at the conference hotel on Thursday evening. On Friday evening the delegates were given the opportunity to tour the local maritime museum during

2008 International Sail Training and Tall Ships Conference

a reception sponsoroed by the official host ports of the 2009 TALL SHIPS® ATLANTIC CHALLENGE Race Series. The conference concluded on Saturday evening with a GALA dinner dance and awards ceremony.

2009 "A Taste of Tall Ships" Boston Reception

While the ships were in Boston for the Sail Boston port event of the TALL SHIPS® ATLANTIC CHALLENGE Race Series, ASTA held their annual fundraiser and reception on board the barkentine *Concordia,* the sail training vessel which is part of the West Island College - Class Afloat program (www.classafloat.com).

The theme for the reception was "A Taste of Tall Ships" and the evening included amazing performances from vessels representing eight nations. The crowd of 150 people enjoyed traditional dancing and singing from Russia, Tango and percussion from Uruguay, rhythmic gymnastics and national songs from Romania, cockney rhyming slang from the UK, folk music from Argentina, Bosa Nova and jazz from Brazil, rope tricks from the Netherlands, and Bluegrass music from the USA. All of the entertainment was performed by sailors from the visiting tall ships. It was a beautiful evening, a great event, and a wonderful celebration of international goodwill.

2009 "A Taste of Tall Ships"
Boston Reception

Indices

Geographical
and
Alphabetical

Photo by Matthew Cohen

Directory Sponsors

The American Sail Training Association would like to thank our sponsors. Their support made the production of this Directory possible.

Allen Agency
BaySail
Canadian Sailing Expeditions
Epifanes
Great Lakes Marketing Group
Great Lakes United TALL SHIPS CHALLENGE® 2010
MedAire
Navy Pier/Tall Ships® Chicago
Northeast Maritime Institute
Oceanus Sailcloth
Picton Castle
R & W Traditional Rigging & Outfitting
Sailing Ship Adventures
Scarano Boat
Sea Education Association (SEA)
Sea History Magazine
Star Clippers
Tall Ship Celebration Bay City
The Spar Shop
Tidemark Press
US Brig Niagara
Village of Greenport, NY
West Indies Management Company (WIMCO)

Photo by Matthew Cohen

Geographical Index

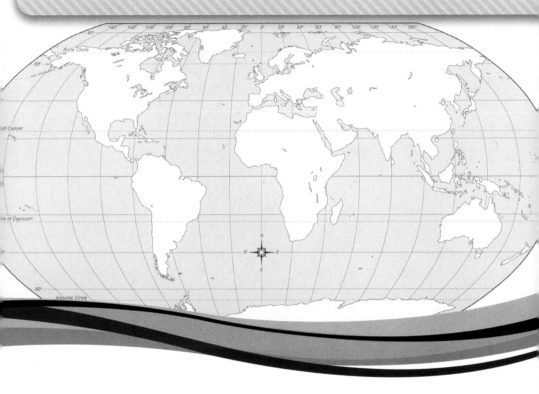

New England
Mid-Atlantic
Florida/Gulf of Mexico
California
Pacific Northwest
Great Lakes USA and Canada
Canadian Maritimes and St. Lawrence Seaway
Mexico
South America and Caribbean
Asia and South Pacific
Europe

New England

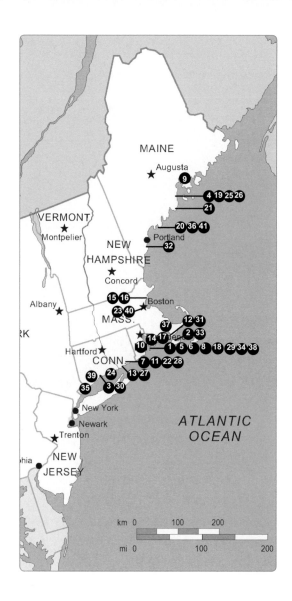

⚓ New England

Mid Atlantic

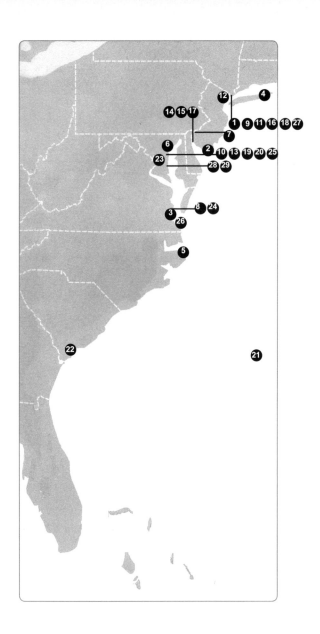

Mid Atlantic

Florida/Gulf of Mexico

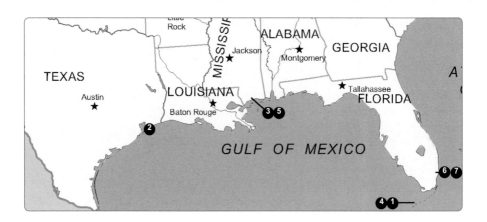

California

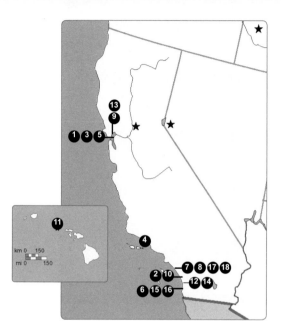

	Vessel Name	Homeport	Page #
1	ALMA	San Francisco, CA	116
2	AMERICAN PRIDE	Long Beach, CA	118
3	BALCLUTHA	San Francisco, CA	130
4	BILL OF RIGHTS	Oxnard, CA	131
5	C.A.THAYER	San Francisco, CA	139
6	CALIFORNIAN	San Diego, CA	140
7	EXY JOHNSON	Los Angeles, CA	164
8	IRVING JOHNSON	Los Angeles, CA	187
9	KAISEI	Sausalito, CA	192
10	LYNX	Newport Beach, CA	204
11	MAKANI OLU	Kaneohe Bay, HI	206
12	PILGRIM	Dana Point, CA	233
13	SEAWARD	Sausalito, CA	248
14	SPIRIT OF DANA POINT	Dana Point, CA	259
15	STAR OF INDIA	San Diego, CA	263
16	HMS SURPRISE	San Diego, CA	267
17	SWIFT OF IPSWICH	Los Angeles, CA	269
18	TOLE MOUR	Long Beach, CA	273

Pacific Northwest

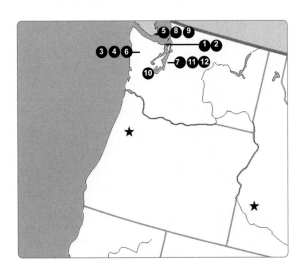

Great Lakes USA and Canada

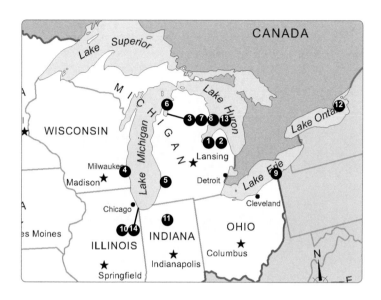

Canadian Maritimes and St. Lawrence Seaway

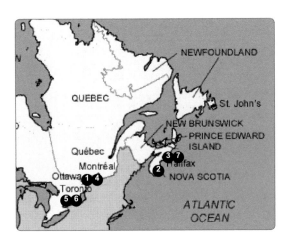

	Vessel Name	Homeport	Page #
1	BLACK JACK	Ottawa, ON, Canada	132
2	BLUENOSE II	Lunenburg, NS, Canada	133
3	CALEDONIA	Halifax, NS, Canada	138
4	FAIR JEANNE	Ottawa, ON, Canada	165
5	PATHFINDER	Toronto, ON, Canada	229
6	PLAYFAIR	Toronto, ON, Canada	236
7	SILVA	Halifax, NS, Canada	254

Mexico

	Vessel Name	Homeport	Page #
1	CUAUHTEMOC	Puerto de Acapulco, Mexico	151

South America and Caribbean

	Vessel Name	Homeport	Page #
1	ARGO	Road Harbor, British Virgin Islands	127
2	CAPITAN MIRANDA	Montevideo, Uruguay	141
3	CISNE BRANCO	Rio de Janeiro, Brazil	145
4	CONCORDIA	Bridgetown, Barbados	146
5	ESMERALDA	Valparaiso, Chile	161
6	GLORIA	Cartegena, Columbia	176
7	GUAYAS	Guayquil, Ecuador	180
8	LIBERTAD	Buenos Aires, Argentina	200
9	OCEAN STAR	Road Town, Tortola	222
10	ROSEWAY	St. Croix, US Virgin Islands	245
11	SIMON BOLIVER	La Guaira, Venezuela	255

Asia and South Pacific

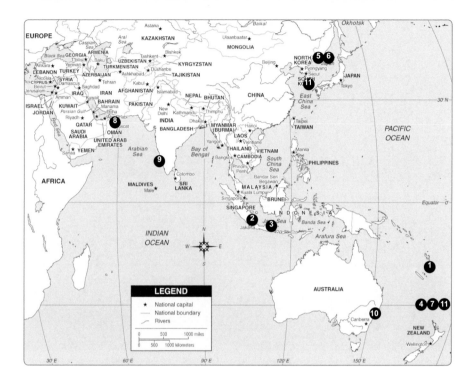

	Vessel Name	Homeport	Page #
1	ALVEI	Port Vila, Republic of Vanuatu	117
2	ARUNG SAMUDERA	Jakarta, Indonesia	128
3	DEWARUCI	Surabaya, Indonesia	155
4	KWAI	Rarotonga, Cook Islands	195
5	NADEZHDA	Vladivostok, Russia	217
6	PALLADA	Vladivostok, Russia	227
7	PICTON CASTLE	Avatiu, Rarotonga, Cook Islands	232
8	SHABAB OF OMAN	Muscat, Oman	250
9	TARANGINI	Kochi, India	271
10	YOUNG ENDEAVOUR	Sydney, Australia	287
11	ZEBROID	Avatiu, Rarotonga, Cook Islands	288

Europe

1. LIECHTENSTEIN
2. SAN MARINO
3. BOSNIA AND HERZEGOVINA
4. MACEDONIA
5. YUGOSLAVIA
6. TURKEY

Europe

Photo by Matthew Cohen

Alphabetical Index

From A - Z
everything you always
wanted to know about
tall ships and sail training

A

I (continued)

J

K

L

S (continued)

T

U

Membership Opportunities

Associate and Organizational Memberships

Associate Membership

Associate memberships are renewable on date of anniversary.

Individual - $50 per year

Benefits:
- Complimentary copy of Sail Tall Ships! A Directory of Sail Training and Adventure at Sea.
- Subscription to e-Running Free, ASTA's monthly e-mail newsletter covering tall ships news and events.
- Discounts to attend ASTA's Annual Conference
- Discounts to attend ASTA's Regional Meetings, Education and Safety Forums
- Invitations to attend ASTA special events and friendraisers.

Junior - $25 per year
Open to sailors 22 years of age or younger

Benefits:
- All of the benefits of Individual Membership above

Family - $75 per year
Open to two members at the same address

Benefits:
- All of the benefits of Individual Membership above

Supporting - $250 per year

Benefits:
- All of the benefits of Membership above
- An autographed copy of Tall Ships – The Fleet for the 21st Century by Thad Koza, a beautiful coffee table book featuring color photographs of 150 sail training vessels in the international fleet. (New members only)

Patron - $1,000 per year
For individuals wishing to express a greater commitment to ASTA's mission

Benefits:

- All of the benefits of Supporting Membership above

Oranizational Membership

Dues are based on a calendar year January 1 – December 31

Business Partners - $475 per year
For ports, businesses, and associates of sail training and tall ships.

Corporate - $1000 per year
For ports, businesses and associates of sail training and tall ships wishing to express a greater commitment to ASTA's mission.

Affiliate Membership - $300 per year
Open to non-profit organizations which do not operate their own sail training vessel, but do offer sail training, sea education or maritime history programs (Scouts, schools, colleges, etc.)

Benefits:
- A 150-word listing in the ASTA directory Sail Tall Ships! *
- A listing of your Organization on the ASTA website. We provide a hot link to your website and appreciate reciprocity.
- The opportunity to post help wanted ads in the very popular Billet Bank on the ASTA website. The Billet Bank is the most visited section of the ASTA website all year long and is the most effective service for matching professional sail trainers and open positions.
- 10 complimentary copies of Sail Tall Ships! for your staff and volunteers.
- Subscription to e-Running Free, ASTA's monthly e-mail newsletter covering tall ships news and events.
- Discounts for staff to attend ASTA's Annual Conference on Sail Training and Tall Ships.
- Discounts for staff to attend ASTA Regional Meetings, educational and safety forums.
- Invitations to attend ASTA special events and friendraisers
- 15% discount on sponsorship displays in Sail Tall Ships!*
- Additional copies of Sail Tall Ships! at production cost (plus shipping) for resale.**

 * In those membership years when a printed directory is produced.
**We anticipate production cost to be less than $6.00 per book. Therefore, when you sell them at the suggested retail price of $14.95 you will not only be raising revenue for your program but equally important, you will be assisting us in spreading the word about the power of sail training.

Organizational Membership (continued)

Sail Training Organizations/ Historic/Educational Vessels
Open to those organizations operating vessels. Membership dues are based on the organization's annual budget. STO1: Less than $250,000 / $450 per year, STO2: $250,000-$500,000 / $600 per year, STO3: Over $500,000 / $700 per year.

Benefits:
- Sail Training Organizations/ Historic / Educational Vessels - A full page listing, including a photo of your vessel, in the ASTA directory Sail Tall Ships! (additional vessel listings are available for additional charges.) Distribution is 7,500 copies.*
- A listing of your vessel(s) on the ASTA website. During the TALL SHIP CHALLENGE® Series in the summer the ASTA website receives over 650,000 hits. We provide a hot link to your website and appreciate reciprocity.
- Eligibility for the Henry H. Anderson, Jr. Sail Training Scholarship and the Ernestine Bennett Memorial Sail Training Scholarship programs for trainees that sail aboard your vessel(s).**
- Eligibility for the ASTA Professional Crew Development Grant Program.
- Eligibility for the ASTA Crew Membership Program.**
- Eligibility for the ASTA Marine Health Insurance Program.**
- Eligibility for the ASTA Marine Insurance Program.**
- The opportunity to post help wanted ads in the very popular Billet Bank on the ASTA website. The Billet Bank is the most visited section of the ASTA website all year long and is the most effective service for matching professional sail trainers and open positions.
- 10 complimentary copies of Sail Tall Ships! for your staff and volunteers
- Subscription to e-Running Free, ASTA's monthly e-mail newsletter covering tall ships news and events.
- Discounts for staff to attend ASTA's Annual Conference on Sail Training and Tall Ships.
- Discounts for staff to attend ASTA Regional Meetings, educational and safety forums.
- Invitations to attend ASTA special events and friendraisers
- Complimentary ASTA Flag (new members only)
- 15% discount on sponsorship displays in Sail Tall Ships!*
- Additional copies of Sail Tall Ships! at production cost (plus shipping) for resale.***
* In those membership years when a printed directory is produced.
**Some restrictions apply
***We anticipate production cost to be less than $6.00 per book. Therefore, when you sell them at the suggested retail price of $14.95 you will not only be raising revenue for your program but equally important, you will be assisting us in spreading the word about the power of sail training.

Crew Membership

ASTA's Crew Membership Program

ASTA Sail Training Organization members may purchase blocks of 10 individual crew membership vouchers at a reduced rate, for distribution to their staff, crew, volunteers and trainees.

Crew memberships must be purchased by the member Sail Training Organization and are sold in blocks of 10 for US $250. Membership application forms are sent to the member STO who then distributes them to staff and crew. The individual crew memberships are valid for one year from the time ASTA receives the completed individual crew member application form and carry all the same benefits as an individual membership (US $50) plus some added benefits.

Benefits per individual crew membership:
• Complimentary copy of Sail Tall Ships! A Directory of Sail Training and Adventure at Sea
• Subscription to e-Running Free, our monthly e-mail newsletter
• Discounts to attend ASTA's annual conference
• Discounts to attend ASTA's regional meetings, education and safety forums and other special events
• Individual health insurance plans available to eligible crew members
• Professional Crew Development Grants available to eligible crew members

In addition to the above direct benefits, ASTA works on a regular basis with the Coast Guard, Customs and Immigration and other government agencies on behalf of the sail training industry.

We look forward to having you come aboard and join the ASTA Crew with the membership that best suits your interest and budget! Not only will you become a member of the largest sail training association in the world, but you will be supporting the youth education and leadership development programs that can help shape young people's lives!

To become a member please mail or fax the form on the following page to:

ASTA
PO Box 1459
Newport, RI 02840 USA
Fax: +1 401.849.5400

Organizational Crew Membership Application

Please sign us up in the Crew Membership Program!
(Available to ASTA Sail Training Organization Members only.)

Package of ten (10) Individual Crew Memberships   US $250.00

Benefits per individual crew membership:
• Complimentary copy of Sail Tall Ships! A Directory of Sail Training and Adventure at Sea
• Subscription to e-Running Free, our monthly e-mail newsletter
• Discounts to attend ASTA's annual conference
• Discounts to attend ASTA's regional meetings, education and safety forums and other special events
• Individual health insurance plans available to eligible crew members
• Professional Crew Development Grants available to eligible crew members

(Individual Crew Memberships are activated when the crew member submits to ASTA the membership form issued to them through the participating Sail Training Organization member. Membership is good for one year from the activation date.)

Member Organization: _____

Vessel(s): _____

Contact Name: _____

Mailing Address: _____

City:_____   State/Province: _____   Postal/Zip: _____

Country: _____

Phone: _____   Fax: _____

E-Mail: _____

Payment of dues:

___Check or money order enclosed (US dollars please)

___Visa or MasterCard (We do not accept AMEX)

Card number:_____   Expires:_____   CCV#:_____

NOC: _____   Signature: _____